Paleoenvironmental and Tectonic Controls in Coal-Forming Basins of the United States

Edited by

Paul C. Lyons
Charles L. Rice
U.S. Geological Survey
Reston, Virginia 22092

SPECIAL PAPER
210

Published by The Geological Society of America, Inc.
3300 Penrose Place, P.O. Box 9140, Boulder, Colorado 80301

GSA Books Science Editor Campbell Craddock

Printed in U.S.A.

Library of Congress Cataloging-in-Publication Data

Paleoenvironmental and tectonic controls in coal-
    forming basins of the United States.

    (Special paper / Geological Society of America ;
210)
    Bibliography: p.
    1. Coal—Geology—United States.   I. Lyons, Paul C.
II. Rice, Charles L.   III. Series: Special paper
(Geological Society of America) ; 210.
TN805.A5P35   1986   553.2'4'0973   86-25716
ISBN 0-8137-2210-1

Contents

Gordon H. Wood, Jr., retired in 1986 after a distinguished career of more than 40 years with the U.S. Geological Survey. For almost his entire Survey career he was concerned with fossil fuels, principally coal, both in western and eastern coal basins of the United States. The studies by him and his colleagues beginning in the 1950s on the Anthracite coal fields of eastern Pennsylvania are classic contributions to Appalachian geology. As Chief of the Branch of Coal Resources during the 1970s, he pioneered the installation of the computerized data base, the National Coal Resources Data System of the U.S. Geological Survey. Gordon, in the late 1970s and early 1980s, was a founding member and chairman of the Executive Committee of the World Coal Resources and reserves Data Bank Services of the International Energy Agency. He was the author of more than 100 publications and senior author of "Coal resource classification system of the U.S. Geological Survey" (U.S. Geological Survey Circular 891, 1983) which testifies to his international stature in coal resource classification and analysis. His final contributions to coal geology were the U.S. Geological Survey's "Coal map of North America" (in press; a simplified version is on the cover of this volume) and the paper on the Anthracite coal fields in this volume.

For his outstanding contributions to coal geology and coal resource classification and analysis, he received in 1985 the prestigious GSA Gilbert H. Cady Award and in 1986 the Distinguished Service Award, the highest award of the Department of the Interior.

We dedicate this volume to our colleague Gordon H. Wood, Jr., for his many contributions to coal science, for his encouragement of world-wide coal research, and for his dedication to the coal program of the U.S. Geological Survey.

Paul C. Lyons
Charles L. Rice
Editors
May 1986

Acknowledgment

The following geologists served as reviewers of Symposium abstracts or manuscripts appearing in this volume: E. S. Belt, M. P. Billings, T. C., Buschbach, V. V. Cavaroc, W. A. Cobban, A. Donaldson, W. E. Edmunds, G. S. Fraser, G. B. Glass, J. C. Horne, R. Jones, B. S. Kelso, E. F. Koppe, F. E. Kottlowski, J. D. Love, J. O. Maberry, J. H. Medlin, W. J. Nelson, W. W. Olive, C. L. Pillmore, M. W. Presley, J. Reinhardt, E. G. Sable, G. D. Stricker, and P. W. Whaley. These reviewers are greatfully acknowledged for their timely and thorough reviews.

Geological Society of America
Special Paper 210
1986

Introduction and Summary

Paul C. Lyons
U.S. Geological Survey
Reston, Virginia 22092

INTRODUCTION

In the last 20 years, geologists have had increased interest in modeling various paleoenvironments of peat deposition in order to predict the distribution of thick, low-sulfur coal beds in the United States. This interest was spurred by the Arab oil embargo of 1973–74 and by national environmental and health concerns for maintaining clean air and water.

Geologists active in such modeling participated in a symposium entitled "Paleoenvironmental and tectonic controls in coal-forming basins of the United States," which was held at the annual meeting of the Geological Society of America in Reno, Nevada, on November 4, 1984. Most of the papers in this volume were presented at that symposium. The papers are primarily summaries or syntheses of work in various coal basins of the United States, from New England to Alaska. A wealth of recent coal data and references to important literature on the field of coal-basin modeling in the United States are contained in this volume, which should be a valuable guide for the coal geologist as well as those interested in the evolution of coal basins, the origin of thick, high-quality coal beds, and the influence of paleoenvironment and paleotectonism on the geologic, paleogeographic, and spatial distribution of coal beds.

The coal basins of the United States have different ages, paleoenvironments, and tectonic settings and contain coal beds of different rank, thickness, and sulfur content. Western basins are characterized by thick Upper Cretaceous and lower Tertiary lignite, subbituminous, and bituminous coal beds, some more than 61 m (200 ft) thick. Most of the western coal beds are low in sulfur (less than 1 percent sulfur, Wood and others, 1983). Anthracite also occurs locally, but it is economically and volumetrically of minor significance. Eastern economic coal beds are Mississippian and Pennsylvanian in age and are typically less than 3 m (10 ft) thick; locally, they have been tectonically thickened to 15 m (50 ft) or more. They are of bituminous or anthracite rank and vary in sulfur content from low in the Pocahontas and Narragansett coal fields to medium (1.0–3.0 percent sulfur) and high (greater than 3 percent sulfur) in the Illinois basin.

The papers in this volume vary in depth and breadth mainly because we know more about some coal basins than others. The Illinois and Appalachian basins are well known because their respective geologies were investigated early due to historic mining. The coal basins of Alaska are not well known because of inaccessibility and lack of coal mining.

Many of the papers in this volume share four themes. The first is that many of the major coal-forming swamps developed near epeiric seaways such as the Late Cretaceous and Appalachian. Some swamps were close to a sea and developed in lagoons behind barrier-bar systems, while others were tens or hundreds of miles inland like the Narragansett basin. Nearness to a sea (an important source of sulfate) probably affected the sulfur content of the near-shore swamps, as is convincingly demonstrated by Englund and others (this volume). Although nearness to a sea influenced other paralic coal basins, such as the Illinois basin (Trask and Palmer, this volume), high sulfur coal can also be due to other factors.

The second theme is that swamp conditions were maintained by stability of the shoreline position and the tendency of fluvial or deltaic systems to geographically maintain themselves. These factors limited detrital influx into the swamps, favored peat development, and limited the ash content of the peats. In near-shore swamps, shoreline and deltaic stability also played an important part in controlling sulfur content of the peats by influencing the influx of marine sulfate as suggested by Englund and others (this volume).

The third theme is the association of thick sandstone bodies with thick coal beds. In backshore swamp environments, thick peats (coals) are found adjacent to thick shoreface marine sandstone bodies (Fassett, Roehler, this volume) or on top of thick marine deltaic sandstones (Englund and others, this volume). In more inland basins such as the Powder River Basin, thick fluvial sandstones are commonly stratigraphically equivalent to thick coal beds (Flores, this volume).

The fourth theme in these papers is the critical role of tectonism in many coal basins of the United States. Some original inland basins, such as the Powder River Basin (Kent, this volume) and the Narragansett basin (Skehan and others, this volume) were formed by tectonic forces. In these basins, tectonism continued to play the major role during swamp development. After a basin was formed, tectonic factors provided stability or instability for peat accumulation and triggered detrital influxes like the ones that interrupted plant growth in the swamps that became part of the Anthracite coal fields of Pennsylvania (Wood and others, this volume). Plate tectonic activity played a major role in the Anthracite coal fields as well as a more minor role in some of the coal basins of Alaska (Merritt, this volume). Kent (this volume) envisions that tectonic equilibrium was the major factor in the development of thick coal beds in the Powder River Basin, whereas Skehan and others (this volume) consider that extensional tectonism played the major role in basin dynamics and swamp development in the Narraganett basin.

EASTERN COAL BASINS

The coal basins of the Eastern United States belong to the Gulf, Interior, and Eastern Coal Provinces (Trumbull, 1960; U.S. Department of the Interior, 1975). The Gulf Coal Province contains lignite almost exclusively, except for local amounts of subbituminous and high-volatile bituminous coal, and is not discussed in this volume. The Interior Province includes the Michigan basin, Illinois basin (Illinois, Indiana, western Kentucky), Western Interior basin (Iowa, Missouri, Nebraska, Kansas, Oklahoma, and Arkansas), and southwestern region of Oklahoma and Texas. Of these, only the Illinois basin is discussed in this volume (Trask and Palmer). The coal beds of this province are almost exclusively of high-volatile bituminous rank, except for some low-volatile bituminous coal in Arkansas and Oklahoma and some semianthracite in Arkansas. Coal beds in the Illinois basin typically contain moderate to high amounts of sulfur because of a strong marine influence during or after their deposition.

The Eastern Coal Province includes the Appalachian basin, the Pennsylvania Anthracite region, the Atlantic Coast region (some isolated basins in Virginia, North Carolina, and South Carolina), and the New England coal basins, principally the Narragansett basin. Three of these basins are treated in this volume, the Appalachian basin, the Pennsylvania Anthracite region, and the Narragansett basin. Strata in the Eastern Coal Province range from gently deformed in the Appalachian basin to complexly deformed in the Pennsylvania Anthracite region and in the Narragansett basin. The province contains both the largest resource of anthracite and one of the richest sources of metallurgical-grade bituminous coal in the United States. Coal quality in the Appalachian basin ranges from low sulfur, low ash to high sulfur, high ash.

There is a voluminous literature on models of coal formation and on paleoenvironments of the coal basins of Pennsylvanian age in the Eastern United States. Principal summaries are by Branson (1962), Merriam (1964), Duff and others (1967), Wanless and others (1969), Briggs (1974), McKee and Crosby (1975), Ferm and Horne (1979), Englund and others (1979), and the U.S. Geological Survey (1979). Only some highlights will be presented here along with a summary of the four papers on eastern coal basins in this volume (Trask and Palmer; Englund and others; Wood and others; Skehan and others).

Interpretation of paleoenvironments of peat accumulation in eastern basins began in the early 1930s (Weller, 1930; Wanless and Weller, 1932; White, 1932). The cyclothem concept of cyclic Pennsylvanian sedimentation (Weller, 1930; Wanless and

Weller, 1932) was the first comprehensive model for coal deposition in these basins. It was based on the idea that marine transgressions and regressions during Pennsylvanian time caused cyclic episodes of marine and continental deposition, resulting in predictable groups of typical lithologies. Peat was deposited at the end of the regressive sequence.

The cyclothem of Wanless and Weller (1932) typically contained eight members and was assumed to be widely extensive. Nearly all cyclothems were envisioned to have certain unique characteristics and, therefore, could be recognized not only in distant localities within the same basin but also between basins, including the Eastern Interior, Western Interior, and northern Appalachian basins. Marine seaways were assumed to have periodically connected these basins, and widespread diastrophic movements were thought to have caused the cyclic transgressions and regressions.

The cyclothem concept was tested by Ferm and his colleagues in the Appalachian basin (discussed in Ferm, 1979) in a study of the Allegheny Formation (Middle Pennsylvanian) in western Pennsylvania. Application of this model to these deposits proved difficult and forced them to abandon the cyclothem model. A new model, popularly called the Allegheny duck model (so called because its cross-sectional form resembled a duck in flight), was substituted to explain the origin of these Allegheny deposits (Ferm and Williams, 1963). Their model shows marine limestone near the tail of the duck that grades laterally into delta plain detrital sequences associated with coal. The detrital sequences, in turn, grade into alluvial plain detrital sediments near the head of the duck. This model was based on the notion of pulsating influxes of terrigenous detrital deposits punctuated by marine nondetrital deposits (Ferm, 1979). Unlike Weller's (1930) model, this concept was not dependent on marine transgressions and regressions (Ferm, 1979). The Allegheny duck model shows that peat formed mainly in a deltaic paleoenvironment and that the mechanism of change was associated with delta dynamics (progradation, retreat, and lateral shifting).

Other problems attendant with the use of the cyclothem model in the Appalachian basin included lateral facies changes, abrupt changes in lithology, and local lack of marine conditions. Cross (1954) described "cyclothems" associated with the Pittsburgh coal bed, which consisted entirely of continental deposits. Cross' interpretation of deposits near the base of the Monongahela Formation (Upper Pennsylvanian) are consistent with peat deposition on a broad coastal plain several tens or more miles from the sea, where fluvial, lacustrine, and paludal conditions prevailed. A vast, presumably tree-fern dominated Pittsburgh swamp existed almost without interuption over this area.

Illinois Basin

The Illinois basin (Trask and Palmer, this volume), where the cyclothem model of Pennsylvanian sedimentation was developed by Weller (1930) and Wanless and Weller (1932), is a paralic coal basin in which coal is associated with marine strata.

The Pennsylvanian sequence in the Illinois basin consists of about 975 m (3,200 ft) of nonmarine and marine strata belonging to seven formations. Trask and Palmer characterize events during the deposition of these formations as follows:

```
A. Late          Mattoon Formation      extensive marine
   Pennsylvanian Bond Formation            invasions

B. Middle        Modesto Formation      extensive peat
   Pennsylvanian Carbondale Formation      swamps

C. Early         Spoon Formation        early clastic
   Pennsylvanian Abbott Formation          infilling
                 Caseyville Formation
```

Tectonic events controlled peat and clastic-sediment deposition during the Pennsylvanian Period in the Illinois basin. Major fluvial systems from the central and northern Appalachians and from the Canadian Shield brought sediment into the basin where fluvial, deltaic, and marine processes prevailed. Contemporaneous extensive swamps developed on a broad coastal plain. According to Trask and Palmer (this volume), some of the active tectonic features of the Illinois basin were below sea level at times during the Pennsylvanian Period, which allowed virtually uninterrupted sedimentation from Kansas to Pennsylvania. At other times, active anticlinal and monoclinal structures deflected stream flow and also limited the extent of swamps.

The paleoslope in the Illinois basin was generally southward, and clastic sediment carried by large river systems entered the basin from the east, northeast, and north and was deposited in a coastal-plain paleoenvironment. Paleovalleys trending southwest were cut as much as 137 m (450 ft) into the underlying Mississippian deposits during Early Pennsylvanian time.

The extensive peat swamps of Middle Pennsylvanian time were on broad coastal-plain deltas (Trask and Palmer). Wanless and Wright (1978) suggested that the delta complexes provided platforms for the thick, extensive coals of the Carbondale Formation. Proximity of the swamps to the sea is indicated by marine roof rocks over many coal beds and occurrences of coal balls (Phillips, 1980). Major contemporaneous paleostreams such as the Walshville, Galatia, and Oraville paleochannels partly controlled the thickness and sulfur content of the coal. Coal thins, thickens, and splits along the margins of these paleochannels, and coal having relatively low sulfur contents (less than 2.5 percent sulfur) is found closest to the paleochannels.

Appalachian Basin

The Appalachian basin is an extensive coal-bearing region of bituminous and anthracite coal that extends from northeastern Pennsylvania to Alabama, a distance of about 1300 km (806 mi). High-sulfur coal is associated with marine roof rocks of some coal beds (Williams and Keith, 1963), but other high-sulfur coal beds do not show this relationship. In the Appalachian basin, the rank of the coal ranges from high-volatile bituminous in the west and south to low-volatile bituminous on the east near the Allegheny Front, where the strata are gently folded into separate subbasins

or coal fields. Farther east, in the Pennsylvania Anthracite region, the coals are extensively folded and faulted and are of semianthracite and anthracite rank.

Englund and others (this volume) present a barrier bardeltaic model of peat development associated with terrestrial clastic sedimentation in the Pocahontas basin of southern West Virginia and southwestern Virginia. The authors postulate that during Early Pennsylvanian time, deltaic sediments derived from landmasses to the southeast were reworked and segregated into texturally mature quartz sand by coastal processes that formed a segmented, curvilinear barrier-bar system. According to the authors, peat developed in coastal lagoons on top of abandoned stacked delta lobes and shoreward of the protective barrier system during periodic stillstands of a regressing sea.

An isosulfur map of the Pocahontas No. 3 coal bed, based on 270 chemical analyses, shows that the total sulfur content increases from east to west (Englund and others, this volume). The authors suggest that the highest sulfur values are nearest the paleoshoreline, and that the ash content and number of partings in the coal also increase in a seaward direction and toward the periphery of each delta lobe. They conclude that their Pocahontas coal model "demonstrates that the geometry, thickness, and orientation of underlying delta lobes provide a feasible model for predicting the occurrence of thick, low-sulfur coal in the Pocahontas Formation."

Pennsylvania Anthracite Region

The Anthracite region of northeastern Pennsylvania consists of five coal fields. The region contains about 96 percent of the identified anthracite resources of the United States (Averitt, 1975). Anthracite occurs in all of the fields except the Western Northern field, which contains only semianthracite. Coal rank in the region increases from semianthracite in the west to anthracite in the east, reflecting either increasing depth of burial, according to Levine and Davis (1983), or increasing structural complexity, according to Wood and others (this volume). Anthracite and semianthracite also occur in Mississippian strata south of the Anthracite region, but these deposits are of little economic importance.

Coal occurs in the Pottsville Formation of Early and Middle Pennsylvanian age and the Llewellyn Formation of Middle and Late Pennsylvanian age (Wood and others, this volume). The thickest Pottsville coal beds have average thicknesses of a few meters (up to 3 m [10 ft]). About 40 anthracite beds have been mined in the Llewellyn Formation. These beds are found in the lower part of the Llewellyn and average from about .6 to 2.7 m (2 to 9 ft) in thickness. In the Llewellyn Formation, the Mammoth coal bed is as much as 15 m (50 ft) thick and the Buck Mountain (No. 5) coal bed is as much as 29 m (96 ft) thick because of tectonic folding and faulting.

Sedimentation in the Anthracite region was controlled by plate tectonism (Wood and others, this volume). Continental collisions produced major décollements, and uplift in the southeast provided clastic sediments to the Anthracite region. According to Wood and others, widespread swamps developed on an alluvial plain after Pottsville sediments were deposited, beginning with the deposition of the Buck Mountain (No. 5) peat at the base of the Llewellyn Formation. Peat evidently developed in broad interfluve swamps that received clastic influx periodically from the streams.

Coal-quality data for anthracite samples in the Anthracite region (Swanson and others, 1976) indicate that these coals average about 13 percent ash, 0.8 percent total sulfur (mainly organic sulfur), and have heating values of 12,800 Btu on an as-received basis. Maps showing the percentage of sulfur, from Deasy and Griess (1963), indicate that the coal beds having the highest sulfur contents occur principally in the Northern field. Wood and others (this volume) attribute this higher sulfur to influence by marine waters as indicated by the existence of the Mill Creek Limestone in the Northern field and its absence from the other coal fields of the Anthracite region.

Narragansett Basin

The Narragansett basin is in southeastern Massachusetts and eastern Rhode Island and structurally is one of the most complex coal basins in the United States. The coal ranges from anthracite to meta-anthracite (Lyons and Chase, 1981) and was affected by Early Permian plutonism, which converted some of the coal into graphite and natural coke (Gray and others, 1978). Coal mining began in the early nineteenth century, but is virtually nonexistent at present (Chase, 1978). Coal beds in the Narragansett basin range in thickness from a few centimeters to 12 m (an inch to 40 ft) where the coal has been tectonically thickened. Some of the coal at Portsmouth, Rhode Island, was used to smelt copper imported from Cuba during the mid-nineteenth century. More than 1 million tons of Portsmouth coal was mined from three beds, 0.8 m to 1.8 m (2 ft 7 in to 6 ft) thick (Shaler and others, 1899). The geology of the coal-bearing Narragansett basin and the adjacent Norfolk basin, which does not contain minable coal, is well summarized by Shaler and others (1899) and Skehan and others (this volume).

Coal beds in the Narragansett basin range in age from Middle to Late Pennsylvanian. All the minable coal beds are in the Rhode Island Formation, a graywacke sequence containing as many as 100 coal beds. Correlation of the beds from place to place is difficult because of faulting and other structural deformation. Plant megafossils, common in the roof rocks of the coal beds, have been used to determine the relative age of the beds and to correlate them with beds in the Appalachian basin and with those of western Europe (Lyons, 1984). Marine beds are absent from the Narragansett basin.

Skehan and others (this volume) propose a model of graben faulting beginning in Early Pennsylvanian time, which first affected the northern region (Norfolk basin and northern Narragansett basin) where early sedimentation took place. Late Pennsylvanian faulting (dated by megafloras) affected sedimentation in

the southern part of the Narragansett basin. A model of the Narragansett basin incorporating two sub-basins was previously proposed by Mosher (1983) and is further amplified by Skehan and others. This model postulates that there were two pull-apart grabens, one in the northern part and another in the southern part of the Narragansett basin, and that horsts associated with extension and block faulting provided marginal conglomerates for the intermontane basins that received different types of sediments from basement rocks uplifted during horst formation. Peat developed in interfluve swampy lowlands, and detrital influx into the swamps from fluvial sources produced partings in the peat. Severson and Boothroyd (1981) suggested that these fluvial clastic deposits were associated with alluvial-fan environments nearer the source of the sediments. They suggested that peats developed in between the alluvial fans on top of abandoned alluvial fans and also in backswamp environments far from stream channels.

There is some suggestion that the Narragansett basin may have opened to the sea toward the south. Shaler and others (1899, p. 381) reported the presence of *Aviculopecten,* a molluscan genus known from marine strata, in strata at the Portsmouth mine.

WESTERN COAL BASINS EXCLUSIVE OF ALASKAN BASINS

The coal basins of the Western United States exclusive of Alaska belong to the Rocky Mountain, Northern Great Plains, and Pacific Coast coal provinces (Trumbull, 1960; U.S. Department of Interior, 1975). Papers in this volume by Roehler, Fassett, and Windolph and others, on the Green River, San Juan, and Wind River Basins, respectively, deal with the Rocky Mountain coal province; the papers by Kent and Flores on the Powder River Basin describe, from different perspectives, parts of the Northern Great Plains coal province. The Alaskan coal basins of the Pacific Coast province are discussed in the next section.

Powder River Basin

A recent estimate of nonleased federal coal resources in the Powder River Basin indicates that 775 billion tons of coal are present in beds more than 152 cm (60 in) thick and at depths less than 914 m (3000 ft); this includes about 200 billion tons of surface minable coal at depths less than 152 m (500 ft) (Trent, 1985). Commercial coal deposits in the Powder River Basin are contained in the Tongue River Member of the Fort Union Formation of Paleocene age and the overlying Wasatch Formation of Eocene age (U.S. Department of Interior, 1975; Trent, 1985). About 98 percent of the coal in the Powder River Basin is subbituminous, but lignite occurs along the northeastern margin and bituminous coal occurs along the western and southwestern parts of the basin where folding is more pronounced (Trent, 1985). Most of the thickest coal beds occur in the northern and eastern parts of the basin, and some of these beds alone contain coal resources of tens of billions of tons. Kent (this volume) states that the Big George, Wyodak, and Felix coal deposits of the Fort Union and Wasatch Formations in northeastern Wyoming account for a total of 172 billion tons of coal resources in the Powder River Basin. Individual beds in each deposit may be as thick as 69 m (225 ft) (Mapel, 1959) and commonly are very persistent areally.

Chemical data presented by Kent (this volume) show that Big George is a low-ash (less than 8 percent ash, Wood and others, 1983), very low sulfur coal. In one carefully sampled core ash content averaged about 3 percent; total sulfur in that core averaged close to 0.2 percent. In order to explain such unusual quantities of low-ash, low-sulfur subbituminous coal, Kent envisions paleotectonic control resulting from Laramide orogenic movements during early Tertiary time. He proposes that fulcrum areas provided stability for swamp development between western (basin) subsidence and eastern uplift in the Black Hills. Kent shows a series of sections of both the Wyodak and Big Goerge coal deposits that indicate regional splitting and merging of coal beds. He gives an approximation of the amount of peat required to produce such thick coal deposits. Kent believes that such low ash content is consistent with an autochthonous origin of the peat.

An inland-basin alluvial model is presented by Flores (this volume) to explain the lithofacies relationships and occurrence of thick lower Tertiary coal deposits in the Powder River Basin. His model is based on 1,160 cross-bedding measurements and data from several hundred drill holes and measured sections. His paper synthesizes data for all the major economic coal zones in the Powder River Basin. These coal zones belong to both the Fort Union Formation of Paleocene age and the overlying Eocene Wasatch Formation.

Flores' model is that of a major meandering trunk stream that flowed northeastward toward the lignite-bearing Williston basin of eastern Montana and western North Dakota. According to this model, the thickest peats formed in poorly drained raised backswamps flanking the meandering streams and split laterally into individual beds due to channel levee deposits. According to Flores, the raised position of these swamps prevented detrital influx and, presumably, gave rise to very low ash peats (coals) in the Powder River Basin. This model differs in concept from an alternate model of the Powder River Basin in which a Moorhead delta prograded westward from the Black Hills area into a large lake in the central Powder River Basin area (Ayers and Kaiser, 1984).

Flores bases his paleofluvial model for Powder River coals on modern fluvial environments. He suggests that the fluvial setting of the meandering Mahakatan River in the Kutai basin of Borneo is probably the best modern analog for the Powder River Basin in terms of tectonic setting, size, the presence of a trunk-tributary meandering system, and extensive, poorly drained back swamps.

Wind River Basin

The Wind River Basin of central Wyoming is a large, faulted northwest-trending asymmetrical syncline. It contains mainly subbituminous coal, but lignite and high volatile C or B bituminous coal also occur (Windolph and others, this volume). Coal-bearing formations are of Late Cretaceous and Paleocene age. The major coal resources are in the Mesaverde and Meeteetse Formations, which contain coal beds as thick as 3 m (10 ft). The steep dips along the flanks of the basin have created unfavorable coal mining conditions.

Windolph and others (this volume) add a wealth of new data on the sequence of Upper Cretaceous and lower Tertiary strata. Their work includes 12,802 m (42,000 ft) of measured section, geologic mapping in twelve 7½ minute quadrangles, and lithologic and geophysical data from 61 coal exploratory drill holes.

According to Windolph and others (this volume), differences in ash, total sulfur, ash-silica, and trace-element contents of the various coal beds indicate contrasting geochemical influences during peat deposition in Late Cretaceous time. The Welton coal bed of the Meeteetse Formation is contrasted by the authors with the Signor coal bed of the Mesaverde Formation to illustrate, respectively, intermontane and paralic geochemical controls on coal quality.

Green River Basin

The Green River basin is north of the Uinta basin and is mainly in the southwestern part of Wyoming, extending into Utah and Colorado. The strata in the Green River basin are generally gently dipping except around the flanks and around the Rock Springs anticline, where dips as steep as 45° are known (Roehler, this volume).

Coals in the Green River basin are mainly of subbituminous rank and are as much as 13 m (42 ft) thick. Coal ranks higher than high-volatile C bituminous coal are locally associated with igneous intrusions (U.S. Department of Interior, 1975). The highest quality coal occurs in the Mesaverde Group of Late Cretaceous age. In the Rock Springs coal field (Roehler, this volume), the most important coal-bearing formation is the Rock Springs Formation of the Mesaverde Group.

Roehler presents lithologic, mineralogic, and sedimentologic data on strand-plain facies associated with the low-sulfur Glades coal bed of the Rock Springs Formation. He shows paleoenvironment reconstructions based partly on measured sections.

A lagoonal origin of the Glades coal bed, which is associated with the McCourt Sandstone Tongue of the Rock Springs Formation, is hypothesized by Roehler. Four imbricated quartzose sandstone units of the McCourt Sandstone Tongue are delineated and assigned to lower and middle shoreface, surf, and forebeach environments of deposition by Roehler. He considers Snuggedy Swamp, on the lower coastal plain of South Carolina, to be a good modern analog of this strand-plain paleoenvironment.

San Juan Basin

The San Juan Basin (Fassett and Hinds, 1971; Shomaker and others, 1971; Shomaker and Whyte, 1978) is in the southern part of the Rocky Mountain Province in northwestern New Mexico and southwestern Colorado. Structurally it is a northwest-trending asymmetric feature. Dips as steep as 40° are known for the Fruitland Formation in the northern and eastern parts of the basin; dips average less than 1° on the west and south sides (Fassett, this volume). Older coal-bearing strata are vertical to overturned in places on the east side of the basin. The coal resources in the basin are contained, in approximate order of decreasing coal-resource content, in the Fruitland (youngest), Menefee, Crevasse Canyon, and Dakota (oldest) Formations of Late Cretaceous age. Fassett and Hinds (1971) estimated the coal resources in the Fruitland to be about 200 billion tons in beds more than 0.6 m (2 ft) thick that are as deep as 1372 m (4500 ft).

Sulfur content of these coals is generally less than 1 percent, and ash content ranges from about 5 percent to more than 30 percent on an as-received basis. Ash content appears to be significantly higher in the Fruitland coals, which are commonly high-ash (more than 15 percent ash) coals, than that in the Menefee coals, which are low- to medium-ash coals (8 to 15 percent ash, Wood and others, 1983) (Shomaker and Whyte, 1978).

Coal beds in the Fruitland generally are low sulfur and high ash, range in rank from subbituminous to low-volatile bituminous, and are as much as 12 m (40 ft) thick (Fassett and Hinds, 1971; Fassett, this volume). The rank of Fruitland coal increases from southwest to northeast in the direction of the structural axis, indicating that rank there is related to depth of burial. The bands of thickest coal in the Fruitland trend northwest, apparently controlled by the depositional strike of the underlying Pictured Cliffs Sandstone. The highest quality coal is found in the northern part of the basin. Coal in the underlying Menefee Formation of the Mesaverde Group is of higher quality than coal in the Fruitland (Fassett and Hinds, 1971). Coals in the Menefee are generally lenticular and range in thickness from less than 3 m (10 ft) to as much as 5.5 m (18 ft).

Fassett and Hinds (1971) showed that Fruitland peat developed landward of thickly stacked, strandline sandstone beds that form the Pictured Cliffs Sandstone. The Pictured Cliffs Sandstone was deposited during the final northward regression of the Late Cretaceous epeiric seaway from the San Juan Basin.

To test whether this model could be used to predict thick coals deposited in similar paleoenvironments in the San Juan Basin, Fassett (this volume) applies his Fruitland Formation model to underlying coals of the basal Menefee Formation and the associated strandline sandstone, the Point Lookout Sandstone. However, there are no thick coals behind comparable stratigraphic rises of the Point Lookout even though Menefee coals were deposited in a paleoenvironment similar to that of the Fruitland coals. On the basis of this example, he suggests that coal models may only apply where they are developed and have little or no transferability because of the large number of variables that control peat accumulation and preservation.

ALASKAN COAL BASINS

By far the most significant coal resources in the Pacific Coast coal province are in Alaska. The rank of Alaskan coal generally ranges from lignite to anthracite. High-rank coal is also found in highly folded and faulted rocks along the Coastal Ranges (Landis, 1966; U.S. Department of Interior, 1975) but these are not discussed in this volume.

Merritt (this volume) shows that the major coal deposits of Alaska are found in the Interior Plains on the north coast and in the Pacific Mountain System in the south (see back cover). Most of these coal beds are of Late Cretaceous and Tertiary age. Folded Upper Cretaceous rocks underlie about 70,000 sq km (27,000 sq mi) in northern Alaska and contain numerous bituminous coal beds as much as 5 m (15 ft) thick, making this area one of the richest coal regions in the United States. Higher rank coals of Paleozoic age are found in structurally complex terranes along the northwest coast but their economic value is uncertain (U.S. Department of Interior, 1975).

According to Merritt (this volume), Alaska's coal is divided by rank as follows: 57 percent bituminous, 42 percent subbituminous, and 2 percent lignite and anthracite. Lignite beds as much as 30 m (85 ft) thick and subbituminous Tertiary coal as much as 18 m (60 ft) thick are present. Also, there are Paleozoic anthracite beds of unreported thickness (Barnes, 1967) along the northwest coast.

Semianthracite and anthracite are found in a highly deformed area of sheared and brecciated rocks in the Bering River field of southeastern Alaska (U.S. Department of Interior, 1975). These coals are Tertiary in age, are as much as 18 m (60 ft) thick and contrast significantly in age with anthracites of the Eastern United States (Wood and others, this volume), which are of Late Paleozoic (Mississippian and Pennsylvanian) age.

Merritt (this volume) summarizes the geology of six major coal basins in Alaska. These are the Susitna, Matanuska, Bering River, Nenana, Chignik Bay–Herendeen Bay, and Northern Alaska basins. These coal deposits are mainly Cretaceous bituminous and Tertiary subbituminous coal, which, according to Merritt, may underlie as much as 8.5 percent of Alaska's land area.

Chemical data presented by Merritt show the range of quality of Alaskan coal. Total sulfur content is generally less than 1 percent, but coals having total sulfur contents as high as 2.8 percent occur in the Chignik Formation (Chignik Bay–Herendeen Bay). Ash content of Alaskan coals ranges from 2 to 30 percent in the various Alaskan basins. Low-volatile bituminous coal in the Bering River basin has total sulfur contents ranging from 0.2 to 1.0 percent and ash contents as high as 30 percent.

Merritt shows that Alaska's coal resources range in age from Mississippian to Pliocene. Most of the important coal resources are of Late Cretaceous age or younger. Coal of Mississippian age is known in the Lisburne coal field on the northwest coast. Alaska's coal resources are distributed in seven coal-resource regions: Northern, Western, Eastern Interior, Southwestern, South Central, Southeastern, and Alaska Peninsula (and Kodiak). The largest basins are the Northern; the Susitna and Kenai in the South Central region; and the Nenanda and Eagle-Circle in the Eastern Interior region. The total area of Alaska's Northern basin exceeds the total area of all the other known Alaskan coal basins by at least twofold. Thus, the Northern basin is one of the largest in the United States and rivals in area the Appalachian, combined Powder River-Williston, and Gulf Coast basins.

Susitna Lowland

The Susitna lowland is in the South Central region of Alaska and contains coal beds up to almost 15 m (50 ft) thick. The major coal resources are found in subbituminous coal beds of the Kenai Group of Tertiary age. According to Merritt, peat developed in backswamps of a meandering fluvial intermontane paleoenvironment during late Oligocene and Miocene time.

Matanuska Coal Basin

The Matanuska coal basin in the South Central region of Alaska contains coal beds as much as 12 m (38 ft) thick. All the known coal resources in this basin are of Paleocene and Eocene age and have been subjected to intense folding and faulting. Coal rank ranges from subbituminous to anthracite. Anthracite is found in the upper Mantanuska Valley where, according to Merritt, there has been extensive contact metamorphism and regional deformation associated with subduction of the Pacific plate.

Bering River Basin

The Bering River basin coal deposits in the South Central region of Alaska are of late Eocene and early Miocene age. The western part of the basin contains mainly medium-volatile bituminous coal and there is a progressive increase in metamorphism to the east where anthracite occurs. The coal-bearing rocks are intruded by basaltic rocks, particularly on the east side of the basin. At least 22 coal beds greater than 1 m (3 ft) thick to as much as 18 m (60 ft) thick are known, but the latter are lenticular and high in ash, presumably due to squeezing and mineralization associated with plate tectonics. According to Merritt, these coals were formed from peat developed in a coastal plain or marginal-fluvial paleoenvironment.

Nenana Basin

Most of the coal resources in the Nenana basin of the Eastern Interior region of Alaska are in Tertiary subbituminous coal beds ranging from 3 to 18 m (10 to 60 ft) in thickness. Tonsteins occur at several horizons in the coal-bearing units. Some of the peats developed in a fluvial paleoenvironment with paleodrain-

age from the north and the greatest subsidence to the south where the thickest coal occurs.

Chignik Bay and Herendeen Bay Basins

The Chignik Bay and Herendeen Bay coal fields of the Alaska Peninsula cover more than 200 km^2(77 mi^2) of coal-bearing strata of Late Cretaceous age that were deposited in a marine deltaic paleoenvironment. The coal beds are of high-volatile bituminous rank. A distinctive arkosic to quartzose platform sandstone as much as 12 m (40 ft) thick provided a stable base for the thick peats, a paleoenvironment very similar to that proposed by Englund and others (this volume) for the Pocahontas coals of the Appalachian basin.

Northern Alaska Basin

Most of the coal resources of Alaska are found in strata of the Nanushuk Group (Cretaceous) in the Arctic Foothills and in the Arctic Coastal Plain of the Northern region of Alaska (Merritt, this volume). Coal resources are found in the Nanushuk Group in subbituminous and high-volatile bituminous coal beds ranging from 1.5 to 7 m (5 to 23 ft) in thickness. According to Merritt, the coal beds are more deformed towards the Brooks Range where the Arctic Alaskan Plate was obducted by oceanic crust. This peat accumulated in a marginal marine to inland basin paleoenvironment, and the coal shows a decrease in total sulfur content upward in the most terrestrial part of the section. Some of the peat developed in abandoned channels and on splay deposits. Higher sulfur contents and thinner coal may have developed in interdistributary bays; the thickest coal occurs in the transition zone from lower to upper delta plain.

Economic Potential of Alaskan Coal

Merritt feels that the Susitna lowland offers the greatest potential for large surface coal mines because of nearness to water transport via the Cook Inlet. Bituminous coal in the Matanuska coal basin is accessible by railroad, but complex geology will limit development of mining there as it will in the Bering River and Nenana basins. The Chignik Bay and Herendeen Bay basins will be limited for development by the small size of the resource base and lack of continuous coal beds. The coal beds of the Nanushuk Group in the northern Alaska basins are potentially minable, but development will be slow because of remoteness and problems with mining in a permafrost region (Merritt, this volume).

REFERENCES CITED

Averitt, Paul, 1975, Coal resources of the United States, January 1, 1974: U.S. Geological Survey Bulletin 1412, 131 p.

Ayers, W. B., Jr., and Kaiser, W. R., 1984, Lacustrine-interdeltaic coal in the Fort Union Formation (Paleocene), Powder River Basin, Wyoming and Montana, *in* Rahamani, R. W., and Flores, R. M., eds., Sedimentology of coal and coal-bearing sequences: International Association of Sedimentologists Special Publication 7, p. 61–84.

Barnes, F. F., 1967, Coal resources of Alaska: U.S. Geological Survey Bulletin 1242-B, 36 p.

Branson, C. C., ed., 1962, Pennsylvanian System in the United States—A symposium: Tulsa, Oklahoma, American Association of Petroleum Geologists, 508 p.

Briggs, Garrett, ed., 1974, Carboniferous of the southeastern United States: Geological Society of America Special Paper 148, 361 p.

Chase, H. B., Jr., 1978, Coal and graphite mines and prospects of Massachusetts, Rhode Island, *in* Skehan, J. W., and Murray, D. P., eds., The coal-bearing Narragansett basin of Massachusetts and Rhode Island, v. 1: Weston, Massachusetts, Boston College, Department of Geology and Geophysics, Appendix B, 31 p.

Cross, A. T., 1954, The geology of the Pittsburgh coal—stratigraphy, petrology, origin and composition, and geologic interpretation of mining problems: West Virginia Geological and Economic Survey Report of Investigations No. 10, p. 32–99.

Deasy, G. F., and Griess, P. R., 1963, Atlas of Pennsylvania coal and coal mining, Part II, Anthracite: Pennsylvania State University, Mineral-Industries Experiment Station, Bull. 80, 123 p.

Duff, P.M.D., Hallan, A., and Walton, E. K., 1967, Cyclic sedimentation: New York, Elsevier, 280 p.

Englund, K. J., Arndt, H. H., and Henry, T. W., eds., 1979, Proposed Pennsylvanian System Stratotype, Virginia and West Virginia: American Geological Institute Selected Guidebook Series 1, 138 p.

Fassett, J. E., and Hinds, J. S., 1971, Geology and fuel resources of the Fruitland Formation and Kirtland Shale of the San Juan Basin, New Mexico and Colorado: U.S. Geological Survey Professional Paper 676, 76 p.

Ferm, J. C., 1979, Pennsylvanian cyclothems of the Appalachian Plateau, a retrospective view, *in* Ferm, J. C., and Horne, J. C., 1979, Carboniferous depositional environments in the Appalachian region: Columbia, South Carolina, privately printed, p. 284–290.

Ferm, J. C., and Horne, J. C., 1979, Carboniferous depositional environments in the Appalachian region: Columbia, South Carolina, privately printed, 760 p.

Ferm, J. C., and Williams, E. G., 1963, A model for cyclic sedimentation in the Appalachian Pennsylvanian [abs.]: American Association of Petroleum Geologists Bulletin, v. 47, no. 2, p. 356–357.

Gray, Ralph, Raben, J. D., and Murray, D. P., 1978, Unusual anthracites from the Narragansett basin, southern New England: Geological Society of America Abstracts with Programs, v. 10, no. 7, p. 412.

Landis, E. R., 1966, Coal, *in* Mineral and water resources of California, Pt. 1, Mineral resources: U.S. 89th Congress, Second Session, Committee on Interior and Insular Affairs, Committee print, p. 134–139.

Levine, J. R., and Davis, A., 1983, Tectonic history of coal-bearing sediments in eastern Pennsylvania using coal reflectance anisotropy: Pennsylvania State University Special Report SR—118, 314 p.

Lyons, P. C., 1984, Carboniferous megafloral zonation of New England, *in* Sutherland, P. K., and Manger, W. L., eds., Ninth International Congress on Carboniferous Stratigraphy and Geology, Proceedings, Compte Rendu, v. 2, Biostratigraphy: Carbondale, Ill., Southern Illinois University Press, p. 503–514.

Lyons, P. C., and Chase, H. B., Jr., 1981, Rank of coal beds of the Narragansett basin, Massachusetts and Rhode Island: International Journal of Coal Geology, v. 1, p. 155–168.

Mapel, W. J., 1959, Geology and coal resources of the Buffalo-Lake de Smet area, Johnson and Sheridan Counties, Wyoming: U.S. Geological Survey Bulletin 1078, 148 p.

McKee, E. D., and Crosby, E. J., coordinators, 1975, Paleotectonic investigations of the Pennsylvanian System in the United States: U.S. Geological Survey Professional Paper 853, v. 1, 349 p., v. 2, 192 p.

Merriam, D. F., ed., 1964, Symposium on cyclic sedimentation: Kansas Geological Survey Bulletin 169, v. 1, 2, 636 p.

Mosher, Sharon, 1983, Kinematic history of the Narragansett basin, Massachusetts and Rhode Island—Constraints on late Paleozoic plate reconstructions: Tectonics, v. 2, no. 4, p. 327–344.

Phillips, T. L., 1980, Stratigraphic and geographic occurrences of permineralized coal-swamp plants—Upper Carboniferous of North America and Europe, *in* Dilcher, D. L., and Taylor, T. N., eds., Biostratigraphy of fossil plants: Stroudsburg, Pennsylvania, Dowden, Hutchinson, and Ross, Inc., p. 25–92.

Severson, R. H., and Boothroyd, J. C., 1981, Depositional environments, facies associations, and coal occurrence in Carboniferous sediments of the Narragansett basin: Geological Society of America Abstracts with Programs, v. 13, no. 3, p. 176.

Shaler, N. S., Woodworth, J. B., and Foerste, A. F., 1899, Geology of the Narragansett basin: U.S. Geological Survey Monograph 33, 402 p.

Shomaker, J. W. Beaumont, E. C., and Kottlowski, F. E., 1971, Strippable low-sulfur coal resources of the San Juan Basin in New Mexico and Colorado: New Mexico Bureau of Mines and Mineral Resources Memoir No. 25, 189 p.

Shomaker, J. W., and Whyte, M. R., 1978, Geologic appraisal of deep coals, San Juan Basin, New Mexico: New Mexico Bureau of Mines and Mineral Resources Circular 155, 39 p.

Swanson, V. E., Medlin, J. H., Hatch, J. R., Coleman, S. L., Wood, G. H., Jr., Woodruff, S. D., and Hildebrand, R. T., 1976, Collection, chemical analysis, and evaluation of coal samples in 1975: U.S. Geological Survey Open-File Report 76-468, 503 p.

Trent, V. A., 1985, Summary of results of the coal resource occurrence and coal development potential mapping program in part of the Powder River Basin, Montana and Wyoming: U.S. Geological Survey Open-File Report 85-621, 49 p., 1 sheet, scale 1:1,000,000.

Trumbull, J.V.A., 1960, Coal fields of the United States, exclusive of Alaska, Sheet 1 of Coal fields of the United States: Washington, D.C., U.S. Geological Survey, scale, 1:5,000,000.

U.S. Department of the Interior, 1975, Final environmental impact statement, Proposed Federal Coal Leasing Program: Washington, D.C., U.S. Department of Interior, variously paged.

U.S. Geological Survey, 1979, The Mississippian and Pennsylvanian (Carboniferous) Systems in the United States: U.S. Geological Survey Professional Paper 1110A-L, variously paged.

Wanless, H. R., Baroffio, J. R., and Trescott, P. C., 1969, Conditions of deposition of Pennsylvanian coal beds, *in* Dapples, E. C. and Hopkins, M. E., eds., Environments of coal deposition: Geological Society of America Special Paper 114, p. 105–142.

Wanless, H. R., and Weller, J. M., 1932, Correlation and extent of Pennsylvanian cyclothems: Geological Society of America Bulletin, v. 43, p. 1003–1016.

Wanless, H. R., and Wright, C. R., 1978, Paleoenvironmental maps of Pennsylvanian rocks, Illinois basin and northern Midcontinent region: Geological Society of America Map and Chart Serires MC-23, 32 p.

Weller, J. M., 1930, Cyclical sedimentation of the Pennsylvanian period and its significance: Journal of Geology, v. 38, p. 97–135.

White, C. D., 1932, The carbonaceous sediments, *in* Twenhofel, W. H., Treatise on sedimentation, 2d ed.: Baltimore, The Williams and Wilkins Co., p. 351–430.

Williams, E. G., and Keith, M. L., 1963, Relationship between sulfur in coals and the occurrence of marine roof beds: Economic Geology, v. 58, p. 720–729.

Wood, G. H., Jr., Kehn, T. M., Carter, M. D., and Culbertson, W. C., 1983, Coal resource classification system of the U.S. Geological Survey: U.S. Geological Survey Circular 891, 65 p.

MANUSCRIPT ACCEPTED BY THE SOCIETY APRIL 16, 1986

Geological Society of America
Special Paper 210
1986

Paleoenvironmental and tectonic controls of sedimentation in coal-forming basins of southeastern New England

J. W. Skehan, S. J.
Weston Observatory
Department of Geology and Geophysics
Boston College
Weston, Massachusetts 02193

Nicholas Rast
Department of Geology
University of Kentucky
Lexington, Kentucky 40506

Sharon Mosher
Department of Geological Sciences
University of Texas
Austin, Texas 78712

ABSTRACT

An erosional hiatus over almost the entire area between Pennsylvania and western New Brunswick suggests that the region was mountainous from the Middle Devonian Acadian orogeny through Pennsylvanian time. Of seven basins or deposits of southeastern New England, the ages of three (Narragansett, Norfolk, and Worcester) are florally determined as Westphalian B (Middle Pennsylvanian) to Stephanian B or C (Late Pennsylvanian); three lack flora but are of inferred Carboniferous age (North Scituate, Woonsocket, and Pin Hill), and one is of possibly Carboniferous age (Sturbridge). The first three are characterized by flora suggesting a tropical or subtropical climate and by alluvial fan facies deposited in an intermontane basin. Four of these basins or deposits lie in the Avalon Terrane, three just west of the Nashoba Terrane, but none has been recognized in the intermediate Nashoba Terrane. These basin deposits can be correlated with similar deposits in Atlantic Canada.

Tectonic effects of the Alleghanian orogeny are many and diverse, resulting in important tectonic controls on the formation and evolution of the coal basins. Grabens surrounded by uplands were formed by extension or strike-slip fault-related extension and were filled with Carboniferous sediments during the earliest Alleghanian orogenic episode. These sediments along with the basement complex, were multiply deformed during Permo-Carboniferous Alleghanian orogenic episodes, which involved folding, thrust faulting, plutonism, regional metamorphism, and strike-slip faulting. Metamorphism throughout the outcrop areas ranges from anchizone to K-spar zone in the Narragansett Basin; anchizone to possibly lower greenschist in the Norfolk Basin; and below the almandine zone in the "Worcester Coal Mine" deposit. Important effects of the tectonism are the widespread anthracitization and tectonic thickening of the low-sulfur and high-ash coals.

INTRODUCTION

The existence of coal-bearing Carboniferous rocks surrounded by Precambrian and Paleozoic metamorphic and plutonic rocks of Rhode Island and Massachusetts has been known for a long time (Jackson, 1840; Hitchcock, 1841, 1861; Shaler and others, 1899; Emerson, 1917; Quinn and Oliver, 1962; Quinn and Moore, 1968; Quinn, 1971). For an equally long time the existence of other non-coal-bearing rocks of similar age has been inferred (Emerson, 1917; LaForge, 1932; Billings, 1929, 1976, 1979a, 1979b). Recently, a renewal of interest in the coal

deposits of southeastern New England led to a series of descriptive studies and interpretations of the geology of some seven dated or inferred Carboniferous basins or deposits. Those include deposits in the Narragansett, Norfolk, North Scituate and Woonsocket basins, and at the Worcester coal mine, Pin Hill in Harvard, and the Sturbridge graphite mine (Fig. 1).

The Boston Basin is no longer considered Carboniferous in age. It has now been established as Precambrian (Lenk and others, 1982; Billings, 1982) and, therefore, will not be discussed in

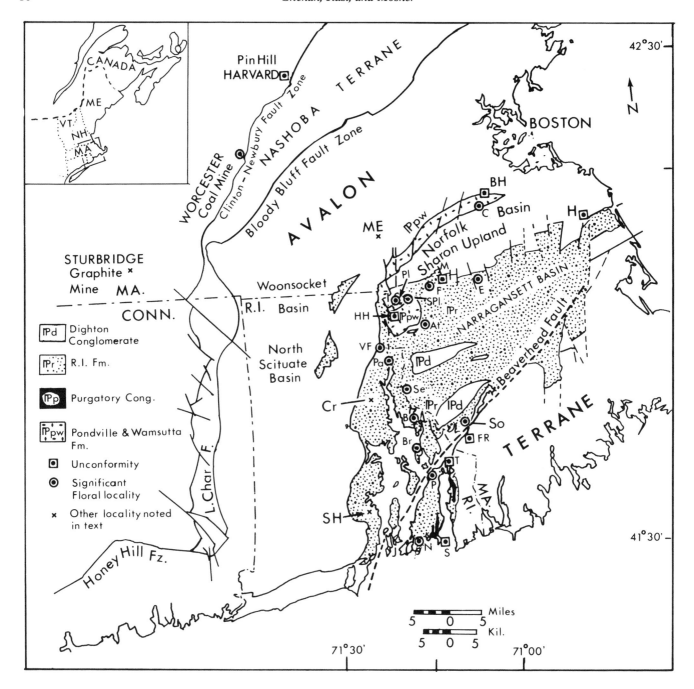

Figure 1. Map of southeastern New England showing the Narragansett, Norfolk, Woonsocket, and North Scituate Basins in the Avalon Terrane; the Nashoba Terrane; the Pin Hill locality of Harvard, Massachusetts, the Worcester coal mine and the Sturbridge graphite mine west of the Clinton-Newbury fault zone. A generalized geological map of the Norfolk and Narragansett Basins is presented showing localities where profound nonconformities between Pennsylvanian strata and upper Proterozoic plutonic rocks are exposed or interpreted: FR—Fall River; H—Hanover; M—Foolish Hill, Mansfield; Pl—Masslite Quarry, Plainville; and J—Mackeral Cove, Jamestown, Rhode Island; between lower Paleozoic igneous rocks and Pennsylvanian sedimentary rocks at BH. The contact of basal Sachuest Arkose (formerly called Pondville Formation, Quinn, 1971) is probably a fault at S—Sachuest Point, the type locality, but an unconformity is exposed at T—Tiverton. Other named localities on Figure 2 or in the text are as follows: At—Attleboro; C—Canton; Cr—Cranston; E—Easton; F—Foxboro; Se— Seekonk, Massachusetts; B—Barrington; Br—Bristol; N—Newport; Pa—Pawtucket; P—Portsmouth; So—Somerset; VF—Valley Falls; SH—Stook Hill, Rhode Island; ME—Wamsutta volcanic outlier in Medway, Massachusetts.

this report. The North Scituate and Woonsocket basins have been interpreted as possibly of Proterozoic Z age (Skehan and Murray, 1979b; Zen, 1983). Of the aforementioned seven basins or outlier deposits, four of the largest lie in the area of the Avalon Platform (Skehan, 1983) and the other three (Fig. 1) in the Kearsarge and Merrimack structural complex west of the Nashoba Terrane (see Hepburn, 1976, 1979 for Pin Hill and Worcester coal-mine; Emerson, 1917, p. 71 for Sturbridge graphite mine). The Narragansett Basin has yielded a rich Carboniferous macroflora and minor macrofauna (Lyons, 1979) that recently have been extensively analyzed by Darrah (1969), Lyons, (1976, 1979, 1984), Lyons and Chase (1976), and Oleksyshyn (1976). The flora is entirely terrestrial.

Doyle (1979) describes unfossiliferous sedimentary rocks in parts of Hancock and Washington Counties, Maine, that he infers to be of Carboniferous age. These deposits are fault-bounded blocks situated along the southeastern margin of the Kearsarge-Central Maine synclinorium, locally called the Central Maine Flysch Belt (Ludman, 1986). Osberg and others (1985) widen the possible age range of these rocks from Carboniferous to Devonian on the basis that they are similar to the post-tectonic Perry Formation of nearby eastern Maine. On the other hand, in New Brunswick, along the trace of the Norumbega fault where it becomes known as the Fredricton fault, there are slices of steeply inclined deformed redbeds that locally resemble the known Mississippian rocks. The age of these rocks may thus be in the range of Devonian to Mississippian since the Fredericton fault is probably overlain by Pennsylvanian strata in southwestern New Brunswick.

STRUCTURAL SETTING IN THE AVALON PLATFORM

Narragansett and Norfolk Basins

In the Avalon Platform the two main basins, Narragansett and Norfolk, involve deformed successions of Pennsylvanian strata that rest unconformably on the Precambrian basement or on Cambrian metasedimentary rocks. The unconformity is exposed or inferred in several localities including the following (shown on Figure 1): Sachuest Point (Mutch, 1968), Mackeral Cove, Jamestown (Skehan and others, 1981a), Tiverton (Mutch, 1968; Quinn, 1971), near Hanover, Massachusetts (Shaw and Petersen, 1967), the south slope of Foolish Hill just east of Route I-95, Mansfield (Mutch, 1968), at Hoppin Hill, North Attleboro, Massachusetts, in addition to the Precambrian unconformity (Dowse, 1950; Anstey, 1979, Locality H), and in a borehole in Plainville, Massachusetts where the Carboniferous rests nonconformably on granite (Skehan and others, 1979b, 1981b). At Sachuest Point the contact is unexposed, and structural relationships between the adjacent Precambrian and Carboniferous are ambiguous; the contact is probably a fault but may be an angular unconformity. Elsewhere the unconformities have been confirmed by one or more of the authors of this paper.

Thus the Carboniferous succession of the Narragansett Basin is, in general, autochthonous. Internally, however, the succession is strongly deformed and involves local overthrusts, as on Mackeral Cove, Jamestown, where the basement rocks are overthrust onto Cambrian strata as well as onto unconformably overlying Pennsylvanian beds, a reinterpretation of structural relationships previously reported by Skehan and others (1981a). The sequence is strongly deformed elsewhere, as at Foolish Hill, Mansfield (Locality M), where the unconformity is overturned. In general, the sediments experienced polyphase deformation (Skehan and others, 1976; Murray and Skehan, 1979; Mosher, 1981, 1983; Mosher and Rast, 1984; Burks and others, 1981; Thomas, 1981; Farrens and Mosher, 1982; Berryhill and Mosher, 1983) and Barrovian metamorphism (Skehan and others, 1977; Murray and Skehan, 1979; Murray and Raben, 1980; Murray and others, 1979).

The Norfolk Basin is mapped as a narrow strip to the north of the Narragansett Basin (Fig. 1). Chute (1964) and Cazier (1984a, 1984b) mapped and described the Norfolk Basin and it was further described by Cameron and Murray (1979). There are several localities where the basal unconformity between the Carboniferous and Lower Paleozoic rocks has been recorded (e.g. Fig. 1, Loc. BH; Lyons, 1977; Lyons and Chase, 1976; Lyons and others, 1976), especially on the northwestern side of the Norfolk Basin (Stanley, 1968; Mutch, 1968). The southeastern and northwestern margins of the Basin are largely governed by thrusts and high-angle reverse faults, respectively, (Chute, 1964; Cazier, 1984a, 1984b) and the rocks have undergone polyphase deformation (Cazier, 1984a, 1984b). Locally a small outlier of inferred Carboniferous rocks is known at a locality two and a half miles to the northwest of the Norfolk Basin at Medway, Massachusetts (Fig. 1, Loc. ME; Zen, 1983).

WOONSOCKET AND NORTH SCITUATE BASINS

The Woonsocket and North Scituate basins to the west of the Narragansett Basin (Fig. 1) form limited outcrops of dark gray to black micaceous schists and conglomeratic schists that have experienced low to middle-grade regional metamorphism. In the absence of reported fossils, the age of these rocks is somewhat uncertain, but, as is mentioned by Quinn (1971), the obvious mapped discordance with the older rocks indicates a presumed unconformity, and the polyphase deformation is very similar to that in the Narragansett Basin. Rose and Murray (1984), however, indicate that the basement rocks have younger fabrics superimposed on older fabrics, thus implying that the strata of these basins were deformed along with the underlying basement. They "cautiously conclude" that at least the Woonsocket Basin is younger than 370 Ma but imply that its deformation and that of the North Scituate Basin is related to Alleghanian orogenesis. However, the similarity of deformational styles and sequence is not a conclusive criterion for establishing the age of these basins. In summary, therefore, the status of the North Scituate and Woonsocket basins remains somewhat unresolved, although the similarity of lithologies to known Pennsylvanian rocks in the Narragansett basin favors a late Carboniferous age.

Outliers in the Kearsarge-Merrimack Complex

The Pin Hill and Worcester deposits both lie to the northwest of the Nashoba Terrane and its western boundary, the Clinton-Newbury fault system (Fig. 1). In Worcester, Pennsylvanian plants have been identified (Grew and others, 1970; Lyons, cited in Grew, 1976) from a coal bed in garnetiferous black phyllite. The deposit at the Worcester Coal Mine is a faulted inlier with uncertain tectonic relationships. Competent observers from the early 19th century onward commented on the similarity of these deposits to those of the Narragansett Basin (Grew, 1976).

The Pin Hill deposit is a meta-conglomerate overlying, apparently unconformably, the metamorphic equivalents of the Ordovician Ayer Granite. The deposit is cut off from high grade gneisses to the east by a post-metamorphic fault. Most workers assume that the conglomerate is Carboniferous (Thompson and Robinson, 1976).

The Sturbridge graphite deposit occurs in a series of flat lensoid bodies. Emerson (1917) correlated the Brimfield Schist, in which the graphite lenses lie, with the Worcester Phyllite and although at present the schist is considered to be pre-Acadian (?) (Peper and Pease, 1976; Zen, 1983), it still may be a part of the Carboniferous as Emerson (1917) had originally suggested.

The Devono-Carboniferous sedimentary rock units of eastern Maine that occur along the Norumbega fault occupy a tectonic position along the faulted eastern margin of the Central Maine Flysch Belt where it abuts a terrane that may be approximately the equivalent of the Nashoba belt.

BIOSTRATIGRAPHY

Narragansett and Norfolk Basins

Of the Carboniferous outcrops in New England, only the Narragansett and Norfolk basins have strong paleontological controls, hence the following discussion will be limited to these and to the Worcester Coal Mine, which also has diagnostic flora. It has been generally accepted that the Carboniferous sedimentation pattern in the Norfolk and the northern part of the Narragansett Basins has been similar. However, the biostratigraphy of these Basins provides us with useful information for determining comparative dates of sedimentation not only to the north and south of the Sharon Upland (Fig. 1) but also for comparisons between the northern and southern parts of the Narragansett Basin.

A rich and varied literature on the megaflora of the Norfolk and Narragansett Basins has been summarized, and the biostratigraphy, analyzed by Lyons and others (1976) and Lyons (1979, 1984). Figure 2 is based on these summaries and interpretations. The megaflora consists of about 300 nominal species, nearly all of which are from the Rhode Island Formation (Lyons, 1979).

In the Norfolk Basin (Fig. 1) a florule found at Canton, Massachusetts in the upper member of the Pondville Conglomerate (Lyons, 1979, 1984), indicates that these Pennsylvanian rocks are Westphalian A or B (Early to Middle Pennsylvanian) in age (Fig. 2). These strata probably contain the oldest known Carboniferous flora from New England. Lyons and others (1976) considered the assemblage to be generally similar to that of the Upper Pottsville rocks of the Southern Anthracite coal field except for the presence of *Lonchopteris*, a genus not known west of the Narragansett Basin (Lyons, 1979, 1984). Only one outcrop of graphitic black slate, characteristically associated with the Rhode Island Formation, has been recognized in the Norfolk Basin (Cazier, 1984b).

In the northern Narragansett Basin, a florule in the upper part of the Wamsutta Formation in Attleboro ranges up to at least early Westphalian C in age and is approximately equivalent to those in the lower part of the Rhode Island Formation at Valley Falls, Pawtucket, Rhode Island, and three other localities shown in Figure 2. Thus the Wamsutta Formation is probably equivalent to the early Alleghenian strata of the central Appalachians. The floral evidence also indicates that the lower part of the Rhode Island Formation is Westphalian C (Middle Pennsylvanian) in age (Fig. 2). The oldest known flora from the Rhode Island Formation of the northwestern part of the Narragansett Basin is from Plainville, Massachusetts. Oleksyshyn (1976) reported 28 species or genera from this locality (Fig. 2). Recent drilling in the basin (Skehan and others, 1979b, 1981b, 1982) shows that the coal bed associated with this flora is about 253 stratigraphic meters above the granitic basement. This coal bed is lenticular and is as much as 10 m thick. It is probably the oldest mineable coal bed in the Narragansett Basin. The age of the Plainville flora is probably Westphalian C or perhaps a little older. Thus the lowermost part of the Rhode Island Formation is about the same age as the top of the Wamsutta Formation (Lyons, 1984). On the basis of floral evidence, the Rhode Island Formation in Mansfield and Foxboro (Fig. 2) is also assigned to Westphalian C age (Lyons, 1984).

A Westphalian D floral locality (Figs. 1 and 2) near North Attleboro, in what is now South Plainville, Massachusetts, reported by Hitchcock (1861), is one of the first biostratigraphic studies published in the United States. Lyons (1979) correlated that assemblage of species and genera, identified by Lesquereux (1889) for Hitchcock's study, with the Upper Freeport coal bed of the Appalachian Basin (Darrah, 1969).

The upper part of the Rhode Island Formation, as evidenced by floras from Easton, Massachusetts and Seekonk (Fig. 2), Rhode Island, ranges upward from about the Westphalian D-Cantabrian boundary (Lyons, 1984) (about the transition from the lower to upper Conemaugh). The flora at Easton was earlier assigned to the Westphalian D but, on the basis of further study, is now interpreted by Lyons (1984) as Stephanian. Thus the rich flora (40 species) from Easton (Lyons, 1979) is now correlated with the Cantabrian to Stephanian A stages of Europe.

The youngest known flora from the Rhode Island Forma-

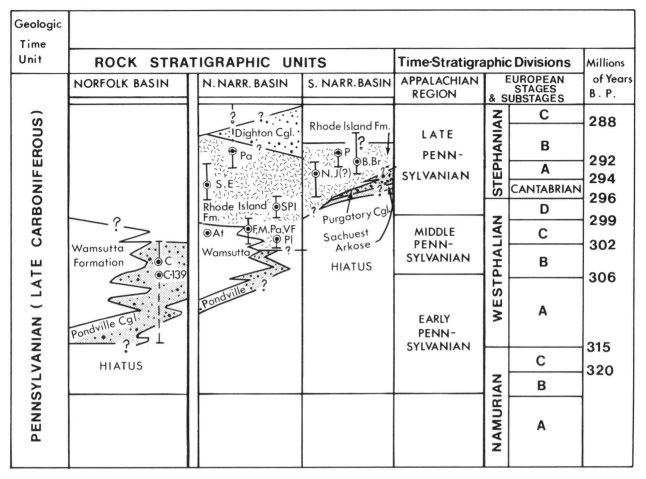

Figure 2. Rock-stratigraphic relationships for the Norfolk Basin, the northern part and the southern part of the Narragansett Basin, respectively, and their relationships to the time-stratigraphic divisions in the Appalachian and European regions (based mainly on Lyons, 1984; in part based on Lyons, 1979, and Palmer, 1983, and modified from Skehan and Murray, 1979). Floral locality abbreviations are: At—Attleboro, MA; B—Barrington, R.I.: Br—Bristol, R.I.; C—Canton, MA; E—Easton, MA; F—Foxboro, MA; J—Jamestown (Conanicut Island), R.I.; M—Mansfield, MA; N—Newport, R.I.; P—Portsmouth, R.I.; Pa—Pawtucket, R.I.; Pl—Plainville, MA; Se—Seekonk, MA (Perrin's Crossing); SP1—South Plainville, MA; VF—Valley Falls, R.I. Their locations are shown on Figure 1.

tion in the northern Narragansett Basin was found in Pawtucket, Rhode Island (Figs. 1 and 2) where there is a distinctive florule approximately equivalent to that of Newport and Portsmouth and, therefore, ranges into Stephanian B, which is equivalent to the upper Conemaugh to Monongahela. A flora of 31 species (Darrah, 1969), closely related to that of Pawtucket, is found at the Portsmouth Coal Mine in Rhode Island. The absence of several species found in the Middle Stephanian of France, but not at Pawtucket or Portsmouth, has been interpreted by Lyons (1984) as possibly suggesting a slightly older age for these two latter localities, possibly late Stephanian A to early Stephanian B. Lesquereux (1889) noted that the Pawtucket flora contained elements of the Permian of Europe (Lyons, 1984). Here the Rhode Island Formation is overlain by the 427-m-thick Dighton Conglomerate but the latter contains no florule. On the basis of

stratigraphic position, however, Lyons (1984) considers the Dighton to be Stephanian B to C in age. Skehan and Rast (1986), on the other hand, correlating the Dighton Conglomerate with the Purgatory Conglomerate, suggest that the Dighton may be overthrust on the Rhode Island Formation.

In the southern Narragansett Basin, florules from Newport, and possibly those from Jamestown (Conanicut Island), provide the oldest dates in that part of the Basin with ages of Cantabrian or Stephanian A (Lyons, 1984). On the other hand, florules from Portsmouth provide the youngest dates so far of Stephanian B (middle Late Pennsylvanian) (Fig. 2). Those of Bristol and Barrington, Rhode Island, provide intermediate ages, probably Stephanian A or B. The flora discussed above are indicative of subtropical to tropical environments.

On the northwestern margin of the Narragansett Basin, the

lower part of the Wamsutta Formation and the lower member of the Pondville Conglomerate do not have known florules (Fig. 2). Lyons (1979, 1984), however, concludes that they are probably assignable, respectively, to floral zones 4 or 5 (Westphalian A or B) of Read and Mamay (1964). The Dighton Conglomerate, although having as yet no identified florule, is, on the basis of stratigraphic position (Lyons, 1984), probably assignable to the floral zone 11 or 12 (Stephanian B or C). Thus the maximum time range of rocks in the Norfolk and Narragansett Basins is probably from Namurian C or Westphalian A to Stephanian B or C. There is no evidence to indicate that the Permian is represented in the Narragansett Basin. Although there is an overlap in ages from north to south, a general absence of documented older floras from the southeastern part of the Basin has led Mosher (1983) to suggest that the Basin is younger in the south.

Worcester Coal Mine

On the basis of work by Grew and others (1970), the florule from the Worcester Coal Mine (Fig. 1) was assigned to floral zone 4, which would be equivalent to Namurian B (Early Pennsylvanian). However, Lyons (1979) has identified a probable *Neuropteris scheuchzeri* in the Worcester assemblage and has referred it to floral zone 9, or late Westphalian C (late Middle Pennsylvanian).

Insect Fauna

An insect fauna, found chiefly in the northern Narragansett Basin, consists of a number of wings, a spider, more than a dozen species of cockroaches (ten of them new), two other species of insects, *Spirorbis,* a tube of an annelid worm, and a probable track of a gastropod (Packard, 1889; Scudder, 1893, 1895). The fauna is derived chiefly from the lower part of the Rhode Island Formation. Several amphibian footprints (six new species) were reported by Willard and Cleaves (1930) from the northern part of the Narragansett Basin, mainly from the Rhode Island Formation, and one from the Wamsutta Formation. Lyons and Chase (1976) noted a possible amphibian skin and a burrow. Thus faunal evidence provides some paleoenvironmental control inasmuch as it suggests that the climate was wet, the water table high, and the water was probably not saline. The fauna discussed above is indicative of subtropical environments.

STRATIGRAPHY AND SEDIMENTARY ENVIRONMENT

Pondville and Wamsutta Formations

In both the Norfolk and the northern Narragansett basins, the basal Pondville Formation grades laterally into and is overlain by the Wamsutta Formation (Fig. 2 and Table 1). The Pondville rests unconformably on igneous rocks in each of these basins. Florules are known from the upper part of the Wamsutta Forma-

tion of the Narragansett Basin (Knox, 1944) and the upper member of the Pondville Conglomerate in the Norfolk Basin, but not from the Wamsutta of the Norfolk Basin or from the Pondville of the Narragansett Basin (Lyons and others, 1976; Lyons, 1979, 1984). Thus floral controls on the age of the earliest deposited sediments in the Norfolk and Narragansett basins are lacking. However, the upper member of the Pondville of the Norfolk Basin may be as old as Westphalian A, although a Westphalian B age is more likely (Lyons, 1979, 1984). The older age of the upper member of the Pondville suggests that similar rocks were being deposited sequentially in the originally proximate but separate small basins (Mosher, 1983). If so, the rocks mapped as Pondville and Wamsutta Formations in the Norfolk Basin may be somewhat older than their counterparts in the northern Narragansett Basin.

The Pondville Conglomerate is a variable formation, first named for a locality in the Norfolk Basin (Pondville Group of Shaler and others, 1899; redefined by Emerson, 1917), and is of a limited but variable thickness (up to 1600–2300 m) (Table 1). Here most of the rocks in the formation represent a proximal alluvial fan facies depositional environment (Cazier, 1984a, 1984b). Chute (1966) recognized the lower conglomeratic and the upper sandstone members. The lower member crops out at the northern end of the Norfolk Basin (Stanley, 1968) and there represents very proximal alluvial fan facies suggestive of a fan head canyon (Cazier, 1984a). Lithologically, Pondville sediments include polymictic conglomerates (some very coarse), graywackes, and shales. The clasts in the Pondville Conglomerate of the Norfolk Basin are mainly of quartzite, quartz porphyry, and granite and in the northern Narragansett Basin, of granite and quartzite (Towe, 1959). Lyons and others (1976) maintain that the conglomerate is partly interdigitated with the overlying Wamsutta Formation, and Cazier (1984a) does not separate the two units, considering them as part of one principal depositional system. Local derivation of pebbles and boulders is remarked upon by many (e.g. Chute, 1966; Mutch, 1968). In the Norfolk Basin, provenance was from the north (Cazier, 1984a) and in the northern Narragansett Basin, northerly and westerly (Mutch, 1968). Paleocurrent indicators in the Norfolk Basin indicate a predominantly southward paleoflow (Cazier, 1984a, 1984b). In the northern Narragansett Basin, paleoflow was probably southward and eastward on the basis of provenance and a similar depositional environment to that of the Norfolk Basin.

The Wamsutta Formation of the Norfolk and northern part of the Narragansett basins is a fairly thick sequence of red conglomerates, arkosic sandstones and shales, arranged in both upward-fining and upward-coarsening sequences (Cazier, 1984b; Lyons, 1979). Quinn and Oliver (1962), Hepburn and Rehmer (1981) and Cazier (1984a) described a series of cycles in it. Some members in the formation are graded graywackes with flute casts, which Stanley (1968) attributes to deposition by flood waters. The abundance of mud cracks, rain pits, and terrestrial plant remains show that the rocks were deposited on land and subjected periodically to dry conditions. Cazier (1984a, 1984b) points out that the facies is that of a wet alluvial fan composed primarily of braided stream deposits with related crevasse splay and floodplain deposits and dewatering structures. In the Narragansett Basin, Shaler and others (1899) and Warren and Powers (1914) described contemporaneous felsic volcanics, the boulders and pebbles of which are abundant in Wamsutta conglomerates. In general, volcanic fragments are common throughout the formation. There are also intruded diabases as well as apparent flows of basalt, and a bed of fresh-water limestone (Towe, 1959). The conglomerates, in addition to the volcanic debris, have abundant quartzites, some granite, vein quartz, and metamorphic rock fragments. Although the conglomerates in the Norfolk Basin again show a predominant southward paleoflow, the more distal deposits in that basin show a subordinate southward paleoflow indicative of either secondary flow or a trend toward axial drainage as the basin developed (Cazier, 1984a). The 900-m-thick Wamsutta interfingers with the generally overlying Rhode Island Formation.

Sachuest Arkose

A totally different type of sediment has been referred to as the "Pondville" in the southern part of the Narragansett Basin (Quinn, 1971) from Tiverton to Jamestown, on Conanicut Island (Fig. 1, Localities T and J, respectively). The sediment is a pebbly arkosic, bedded sandstone with intercalations of dark shale. The quartz grains are very dark (smoky) to almost black and the white to gray weathered and altered feldspar is commonly converted completely into mica or kaolin (Mutch, 1968); detrital fragments of granite are recorded. Because of its differences from the type Pondville Conglomerate in the Norfolk Basin, we suggest the name be changed to Sachuest Arkose for this deposit, named for its occurrence at the easily accessible locality at Sachuest Point (Fig. 1, Locality S).

Rhode Island Formation

The Rhode Island Formation is present at only one locality in the Norfolk Basin (Cazier, 1984a), but is widespread in the Narragansett Basin. Its extent is matched by the apparent great thickness, estimated by Shaler and others (1899) to be as much as 3 km, and by Lyons (1977), as approximately 6 km thick. It consists mainly of gray sandstones, siltstones, shales, anthracitic coals, and also lenticular conglomerates, although in southeastern Rhode Island, the very coarse Purgatory-type of conglomerates form an important constituent (Mosher and Wood, 1976). Many fragments are of fossiliferous Cambrian quartzite but some granite boulders and vein quartz are also present. Sediments of the Rhode Island Formation are fluvial, associated with medial to distal alluvial fan environments (Severson, 1979; Severson and Boothroyd, 1981), with the exception of the Purgatory Conglomerate facies, which is associated with a very proximal to proximal fan environment (Houle and Mosher, unpublished data). The shale and coal represent low energy areas fringing distal fans or

between active fans, vegetated areas on inactive portions of the alluvial fans, and back-levee swamps on abandoned bar and channel complexes (Severson, 1979). Coals deposited in such environments should be lenticular, areally restricted, and of variable thickness. Additionally, such coals should be low in sulfur as they are not in contact with brackish water and should have variable and high ash contents because they are intercalated with muds (A. J. Scott, personal communication). The thickness depends on the rate of subsidence and the position of the water table.

Purgatory and Dighton Conglomerates

The presence of coarse conglomerates in the southeast suggests a Late Pennsylvanian rapid subsidence. The absence of Purgatory-like conglomerates from the western side of the Basin in the south and the distribution of sediments suggests an easterly provenance. A possible eastward source for the predominantly quartzite clasts of the Purgatory Conglomerate and quartz-rich sandstone of the Rhode Island Formation in the southern part of the Narragansett Basin, is indicated by quartzite xenoliths and screens in the adjacent Bulgarmarsh Granite, which may represent the remnants of almost completely eroded thick quartzite units (Mosher, 1983). In the northwestern part of the Narragansett Basin, (East Mansfield) conglomerates in the lower part of the Rhode Island Formation are 90 percent quartzite (Lyons, 1969). This observation suggests that the provenance of conglomerates of the Rhode Island Formation in the northwestern Narragansett Basin should be sought to the north of the Basin. One possible source would be the adjacent Blackstone Series. In the Attleboro syncline abundant muscovite-biotite granite and micaceous pegmatite pebbles and cobbles, similar to Andover Granite, suggest possible provenance from the north to northwest. The sandstones in the northern Narragansett Basin are partly arkosic, mainly feldspathic sandstones, and paleocurrent indicators suggest a NNE to SSW direction of sediment transport (Towe, 1959).

The apparently highest unit in the succession is the Dighton Conglomerate (Shaler and others, 1899) (Figs. 1 and 2), whose type locality is in the township of the same name in the southeasternmost syncline (Fig. 1, NW of Fall River [FR]) of the Narragansett Basin. It comprises the cores of three synclines within the Rhode Island Formation and is partly interbedded with it. The maximum estimated thickness is about 450 m. Severson (1979) and Severson and Boothroyd (1981) interpret this formation as a proximal alluvial fan with braided stream deposits. The conglomerate may be confused with the Purgatory Conglomerate since it contains Cambrian quartzite pebbles and boulders. One of these quartzite pebbles contains brachiopods of Late Cambrian age (Shaler and others, 1899). Mutch (1968) has suggested that quartzite conprises 90 percent of pebbles in the southeast but the percentage decreases to 30 percent in the northwest. This observation suggests that the provenance of the quartzite in the Dighton should be sought to the southeast of the northern Basin, perhaps, in large part from the same source as for the Purgatory

TABLE 1. DESCRIPTION OF LITHOLOGIC, STRATIGRAPHIC, AND SEDIMENTATIONAL FEATURES OF THE
PENNSYLVANIAN STRATIFIED ROCKS IN THE NORFOLK BASIN AND THE NORTHERN AND SOUTHERN PARTS OF
THE NARRAGANSETT BASIN, RESPECTIVELY

	Lithology	Age	Sedimentary features and environment
Norfolk Basin			
Wamsutta Formation– 900 m thick	Predominantly fine-grained red rocks and interbedded red shale; some gray granule and pebble conglomerate; interbedded purple and green shale and sandstone; 3 zones (0.3-2.6 m) of lenses of light gray carbonate and carbonate nodules in red shale (Chute, 1966).	Lower Wamsutta has no known florules, but is believed to be in floral zone 6, Westphalian B or C (Lyons, 1984).	Cyclic or rhythmic sedimentation in graded beds; features characteristic of floodplain strata and crevasse splay deposits with features similar to turbidites, overbank, and lateral accretion deposits. Plane bedding and coarse sediments indicate that initial waters were turbulent with high velocity (Stanley, 1968). "Upward-fining succession of wet alluvial fan facies and braided stream subfacies with associated overbank/floodplain deposits. Formed in medial to distal alluvial fan environment" (Cazier, 1984a). Wamsutta is conformable and gradational with the underlying Pondville. Contact placed where gray beds typical of Pondville or red beds typical of Wamsutta predominate.
Pondville Formation: Upper member– 600-900 m thick	At type locality (Pondville Station, MA): interbedded red and green slate, siltstone, arkose, and quartzite-pebble conglomerate; gray coarse sandstone, gray granule conglomerate, and pebble conglomerate.	High Westphalian B, (upper Pottsvillian); oldest Pennsylvanian of New England (Lyons, 1976, p. 192)	Pebbles and cobbles consist of quartzite, felsite porphyry, and granite; local source (Blue Hills quartz-porphyry). Pondville includes basal arkose beds, graywacke, and conglomerates beneath Wamsutta and above the basement rocks. "Massive bedded, clast-supported conglomerate with infiltrated sandstone and siltstone" (Cazier, 1984a). Type section of Pondville belongs to the upper member; general absence of basal conglomerate; the first deposited beds are commonly mudstone, sandstone and conglomerate of the upper member and may lie directly on older rocks; clasts 15-60 cm in diameter; thickens westward. Formed in proximal to very proximal alluvial fan environment (Cazier, 1984a).
Lower member– 1000-1700 m thick	Cobble and boulder conglomerate; lower member grades into upper member through interval of 25-100 ft (Chute, 1966).	Lower member has no known florules, but is believed to be in floral zone 4, Namurian B or C (Lyons, 1984).	The description of the upper member applies also to the lower member, but contains cobble to boulder conglomerate (Chute, 1966).
Northern Narragansett Basin			
Dighton Conglomerate– 300-450 m thick	Gray conglomerate consisting primarily of rounded quartzite cobbles to boulders and containing subordinate rounded granite cobbles and slate; very little sand matrix, lenses of medium sandstone form less than 20% of the unit.	Small amounts of allocthonous, non-diagnostic plant debris, probably floral zone 11 or 12, i.e., Stephanian B(?) or C(?) (Quinn, 1971; Lyons, 1979, 1984; Skehan and others, 1976).	The sandstone lenses are faintly cross-bedded and coarser both upward and downward into the adjacent conglomerate. Formed in proximal alluvial fan environment with facies representing longitudinal bar and top bar deposition (Severson and Boothroyd, 1981).
Rhode Island Formation– 3000-6000 m thick	Gray sandstone and siltstone and lesser amounts of gray to black shale, gray conglomerate, and coal up to 12 m (40 ft) thick. Sandstone is arkosic to feldspathic (Mutch, 1968) and conglomerate contains a majority of quartzite clasts (Lyons, 1979).	Westphalian C to D and Stephanian. (Skehan and Murray, 1978; Lyons and Chase, 1976; Lyons, 1984).	Both fining- and coarsening-upward sequences are present; paleocurrents have been defined locally; conglomerate is relatively less abundant than in the Dighton. Formed in medial to distal alluvial fan environments. Two cyclic sequences represent bed-load deposition in bar and channel complexes and vertical accretion in previously abandoned bar and channel complexes (Severson and Boothroyd, 1981).

TABLE 1. (CONTINUED)

	Lithology	Age	Sedimentary features and environment

Northern Narragansett Basin (continued)

Wamsutta Formation- 595 m thick	Thin, interbedded felsites, melaphyres, and a thin, discontinuous fresh water limestone. A large mass of red rocks mainly in North Attleboro, and Attleboro, MA, extends into R.I. but only in NW part of basin. Interbedded red coarse-grained conglomerate, some felsite, lithic graywacke, sandstone and shale; a few lenses of limestone, one flow of red rhyolite, and several sheets of basalt in MA.	Westphalian C	Amphibian footprint (Willard and Cleaves, 1930; Lyons, 1979, 1984); flora and fauna suggest wet humid climate and high water table. Cross bedding and interfingering of layers is characteristic; ripple marks and mudcracks present. Environment same as for Norfolk Basin; in addition, local mud flows and possible lahars (Mutch, 1968).
Pondville Conglomerate- 100 m thick	A discontinuous unit of gray to greenish coarse conglomerate with sandy matrix, interbedded with sandstone and lithic graywacke.	Westphalian A(?) to B(?).	Wamsutta Formation is partly equivalent to Pondville as it locally lies directly on Pre-Pennsylvanian rocks and is also partly equivalent to the Rhode Island Formation. Most pebbles are quartzite with some granite and schist derived locally. Environment similar to that of Norfolk Basin.

Southern Narragansett Basin

Rhode Island Formation- 3000 m thick	Gray sandstone and green siltstone with lesser amounts of gray and black shale, pebble conglomerates and coal. Quartz forms the major component of the sandstone and conglomerate (Mutch, 1968).	Westphalian B or C to Stephanian B.	Both fining- and coarsening-upward sequences; cross stratification, planar beds, pebble lag deposits, and scours are present. Formed in a medial to distal alluvial fan environment.
Purgatory Conglomerate- 30 m thick	Coarse-grained to very coarse-grained conglomerate, interbedded with thin sandstone and magnetite-rich sandstone lenses; clasts in conglomerate are almost entirely quartzite, and vein quartz, but several varieties of quartzite are present.	No Pennsylvanian floras yet known; several distinctive lower Paleozoic faunas are present in quartzite clasts. (Mosher and Wood, 1976).	Some cross stratification in thin sand layers; both coarsening- and fining-upward sequences. Contacts with Rhode Island Formation gradational, marked by decrease in thickness and number of pebble layers. Scours and pebble lag deposits common near contacts. Formed in proximal to very proximal alluvial fan environment.
Sachuest Arkose- 500 m thick	A discontinuous unit consisting dominantly of light-gray to dark-gray granule conglomerate and sandstone, containing pebbles of smoky quartz up to 5 mm, and feldspars and weathered feldspars, interbedded black carbonaceous phyllite, thin beds of pebble conglomerate, and isolated cobbles of granite.	May be younger than Pondville Conglomerate of northern basins and interfingers with Rhode Island Formation.	Derived from in situ weathering of granite with, in places, minor fluvial transport.

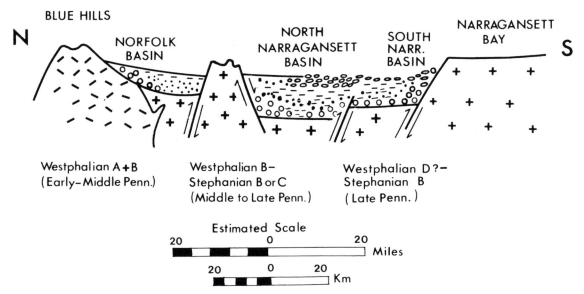

Figure 3. Schematic profile through the Norfolk, the northern, and southern Narragansett basins, graphically illustrating a possible model for their sequential structural and sedimentological development.

Conglomerate and related southern Basin sediments. Although quartzite is abundant, granite and slate clasts are common in the northwestern part of the Dighton Conglomerate outcrop. Vein quartz is also found in many parts of the conglomerate. The presence of such coarse conglomerate at the top of the succession suggests a rapid sinking of the basin at this time in comparison with the sides of the basin.

Schematic Model

A schematic profile through the Norfolk, northern and southern Narragansett basins is presented in Figure 3 to graphically illustrate a possible model for their structural and sedimentological development. To summarize the sedimentological review of the Norfolk and Narragansett Basin complex, the following points can be made:

1. Sedimentation probably started as early as Westphalian A or possibly Namurian C (Lyons, 1979) in the Norfolk Basin, which was at that time separated from the Narragansett Basin by a barrier of basement rocks. Since the Pondville Conglomerate on the north limb of the Norfolk Basin is paraconformable with the underlying subaerially weathered quartz porphyries, it is possible that the Norfolk Basin was a half-graben. The fault, presumably bounding the half-graben on its western margin, may have been a source of volcanicity in the Wamsutta Formation of the Narragansett Basin during the period Westphalian B and C and possibly as early as Westphalian A.

2. The northern side of the Narragansett Basin may have developed initially during Westphalian A or B time, while the southern was probably formed in the Westphalian D to Stephanian time. The possibility should be left open that the southern part

of the basin may have originated earlier since there are a number of floral localities that either have never been collected, studied, and/or described. An example can be found in Bristol where Lyons (personal communication, 1984) collected a florule containing *Odontopteris* (thus it may be Early Stephanian in age).

3. The termination of deposition and the final sinking of the Narragansett Basin occurred in Stephanian-Permian time and may have led to the deposition of the Dighton Conglomerate, though it may have formed earlier.

4. Differences in paleoflow directions and clast and sediment composition between the Norfolk and different parts of the Narragansett basins are the result of deposition on alluvial fans with flow away from uplifted margins and local derivation of sediment. The change in provenance and paleoflow directions between formations probably reflects a local change in tectonic activity. The active margins during deposition of the Pondville, Wamsutta, and lower Rhode Island Formation of the northern Narragansett Basin were the northern and northwestern margins. During deposition of the southern Narragansett Basin Purgatory and Rhode Island formations, the eastern margin was actively uplifted, and during deposition of the Dighton, the southeastern margin of the northern Narragansett Basin was active.

5. Throughout Pennsylvanian deposition, sedimentation took place in a warm, wet environment through the agency of fluvial activity (cf. Severson and Boothroyd, 1981; Cazier, 1984a, 1984b). The faunal record of amphibians and insects supports the interpretation of a high water table and a warm climate (Belt, 1984, written communication) and the floral record supports a subtropical to tropical climate. Coals present in the Rhode Island Formation (Narragansett Basin) suggest local swampy conditions where large amounts of peat accumulated.

6. The thickness of Pennsylvanian sediments, and especially of the Rhode Island Formation, is difficult to measure or to estimate, due to structural complexities and poor exposure. Nevertheless, Quinn (1971) estimated the total thicknesses of these sedimentary rocks to be of the order of 3 to 4 km, and Lyons (1977) considered that they probably reached a thickness of up to 6 to 7 km. In this regard it should be pointed out that Mosher (1983) and her students recognized two sub-basins—the northern and the southern—in the Narragansett Basin and suggested that the total preserved thickness in the southern sub-basin is considerably less than in the northern sub-basin.

COAL

Occurrence

Prospecting and mining of coal dates to 1736 at Leonard's Mine in Mansfield (then part of Norton) in the northern Narragansett Basin (Figs. 1, Locality M, and 2). The maximum amount extracted from any one district is an estimated 1.1 million tons, produced from several mines in Portsmouth, Rhode Island (southern part of Narragansett Basin) in the 19th and 20th centuries. The coal there was used mainly for copper smelting. Coal for raising steam and for household usage was mined in lesser amounts in Massachusetts and Rhode Island, and "graphite" or natural carbon was mined chiefly in the southwestern part of the Narragansett Basin, and mainly used for foundry and crucible facings. Currently carbonaceous shale and shaly meta-anthracite is being quarried together with the enclosing siltstone and slate in Plainville, Massachusetts, for the production of lightweight aggregate (Lyons and Chase, 1976; Skehan and others, 1982). A summary of the history of prospecting, mining, and production in the Narragansett Basin of Massachusetts and Rhode Island is presented in Skehan and others (1982).

Known coal occurrences, restricted to the Rhode Island Formation, are concentrated along or near the western, northwestern, and southeastern margins of the basin, the former two being located in the northern and the last being in the southern Narragansett Basin (Fig. 1). This pattern probably reflects the representative distribution of coal in the Basin rather than merely the relative abundance of fortuitous near-surface coal discoveries.

Structurally the Narragansett Basin is characterized by relatively gently folded and faulted rocks in its northern part. The southern part, however, is more intensely and complexly deformed (Skehan and Murray, 1979; Murray and Skehan, 1979; Mosher, 1983). The rocks, including coal, have been regionally metamorphosed, the grade of metamorphism ranging from anchizone in the northwestern part of the Basin to K-spar-sillimanite zone in the southwestern part of the Basin (Fig. 4) where the metasedimentary rocks are cut by the Permian Narragansett Pier Granite (ca. 275 m.y., Kocis and others, 1978). On the basis of oral and written communication, it appears that combustible coaly material (burned as a fuel in the Budlong Greenhouses) was derived from the Budlong Mine, Cranston, Rhode Island (Charles

Doll, son of the owner of the greenhouses and former State Geologist of Vermont, personal communication). "Graphite" was mined in the southern Narragansett Basin in rocks metamorphosed to the chloritoid zone and higher (Skehan and others, 1982).

Coal Characteristics

The coals of the Narragansett Basin are highly variable in quality and in thickness from one part of the basin to another, and even between coal samples within a specific part of the basin. Table 2 illustrates the range of such variability by comparison with Pennsylvania anthracite. Quantifying the coals in terms of standard parameters is insufficient to characterize the coal in a fully meaningful manner. However, routine chemical analyses of volatile matter and dry, ash-free carbon or H/C atomic data for vitrains would probably be adequate for establishing coal rank. Lyons and Chase (1981) have correctly stated that "an absolutely reliable way of distinguishing anthracite from meta-anthracite has *not* been reported for coal beds of the Narragansett Basin." For further discussions of the petrography of the coals, meta-anthracites, and carbonaceous shales, the reader is referred to Raben (1979), Raben and Gray (1979a, 1979b, 1979c, and 1979d), Murray and Raben (1980), Raben and others (1978), and Murray and others (1981). Compared to Pennsylvania anthracites, Narragansett Basin coals are generally characterized by the following features (Skehan and others, 1982; Skehan and others, 1981b):

● Generally higher ash content both as regards the sedimentary or syngenetic ash, and the epigenetic ash, chiefly as quartz veins. High ash content is consistent with deposition on alluvial fan complexes.

● Lower sulfur values, generally less than 0.5 percent, and very low hydrogen content. These low sulphur values may be the result of the depositional environment.

● Unusual petrographic features, e.g. features due to coals having been coked in the metamorphic processes, including nucleation of graphitic carbon in the anthracitic groundmass (Raben and Gray, 1979c; and Murray and Raben, 1980).

● Coals in thick seams (up to 30–40 ft in Cranston, Portsmouth, and Bristol, Rhode Island (Fig. 1), complexly folded and faulted, and laterally discontinuous. Thickness variations are, in part, tectonic but may also represent fast subsidence and a high water table. The shape and areal extent of the coal bodies is both tectonically and depositionally controlled.

● Ignition temperatures range from a low of 1200°F to 1600°F compared to 970°F for Pennsylvania anthracite.

Petrographic and X-ray methods may give some results that are consistent with those from chemical methods, but commonly these results are ambiguous. Most of the complicating factors are related to the complex thermal and structural history of the coals, which have been heated and then reheated locally to produce graphite, natural coke (Gray and others, 1978), and meta-anthracite. Additionally the coals and enclosing rocks have a

Skehan, Rast, and Mosher

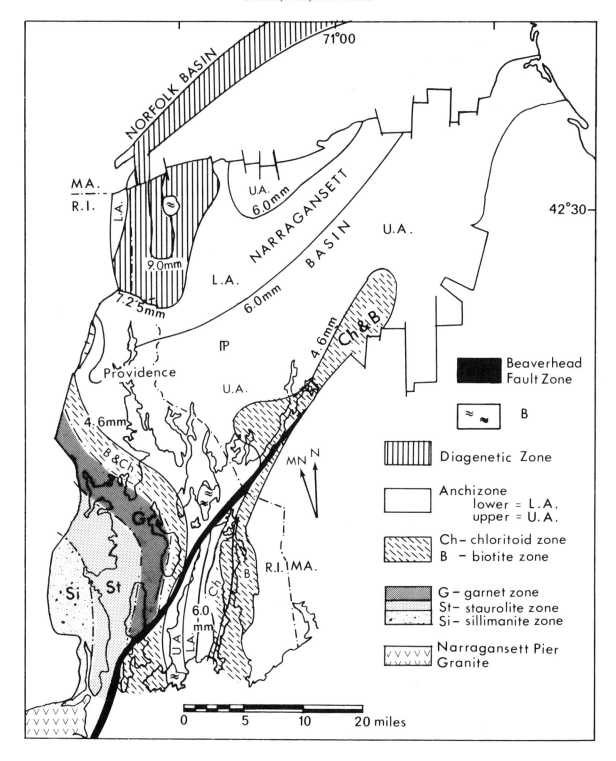

Figure 4. Map of the Norfolk and Narragansett basins showing illite crystallinity contours based on peak
width at one-half height in millimeters with instrumentation correlated to Kubler's (1964) standards
(Hepburn and Rehmer, 1981) and metamorphic isograds (modified from Mosher, 1983, in southern
Narragansett Bay and from Murray and others, 1979). The boundary of the upper anchizone with the
greenschist facies is approximately at the chloritoid isograd, and the boundary of the lower anchizone
with the upper anchizone is taken to be the chlorite isograd (J. Rehmer, personal communication).

TABLE 2. ULTIMATE AND PROXIMATE ANALYSES AND REFLECTANCE
OF SELECTED COAL BEDS OF THE NARRAGANSETT BASIN
AS COMPARED WITH PENNSYLVANIA ANTHRACITE

	1 Pennsylvania anthracite southern field		2 Mansfield, MA. drillhole # 8		3 Somerset, MA. drillhole # 33		4 Portsmouth, R.I. drillhole # 2		5 Bristol, R.I. drillhole # 51		6 Cranston, R.I. Budlong mine
	as rec'd	dry basis	as rec'd	dry basis	as rec'd	dry basis	as rec'd	dry basis	as rec'd	dry basis	dry basis
Ultimate analyses											
carbon	78.84	81.41	53.27	55.27	77.52	78.89	60.99	68.79	63.87	64.03	
hydrogen	3.05	2.89	.91	.51	.86	.68	1.40	.15	.53	.50	
nitrogen	.75	.76	.21	.22	.28	.28	.23	.26	.16	.16	
oxygen		1.17		.58		1.27		.00		.33	
sulphur	2.98	3.04	1.02	1.06	.30	.31	.050	.06	.05	.05	.002
ash	10.52	10.73	40.82	42.36	18.25	18.57	27.26	30.75	34.84	34.93	
moisture	1.93		3.64		1.74		11.34		.25		
Proximate analyses											
volatile matter				4.9		4.6		3.1		3.6	2.4
fixed carbon				51.8		77.7		64.1		61.8	78.1
ash				43.3		17.7		32.8		34.6	19.5
Vitrinite reflectance											
mean maximum	3.52		6.48		7.19		4.47		5.98		
mean minimum	2.61		3.93		3.70		2.75		2.64		
mean bireflectance	.91		2.55		3.49		1.72		3.34		
HGI*			94.5		50		47.5		38		

*HGI = Hardgrove Grindability Index

complex structural history involving primary folding and refolding, microfolding related to faulting, and brecciation and secondary mineralization (Skehan and Murray, 1978; Skehan and others, 1979b; Lyons and Chase, 1981).

Metamorphic Effects

The Narragansett and Norfolk basins record the best example of Alleghanian metamorphism in New England and display a complete sequence of Barrovian metamorphic zones, ranging from anchizone (unmetamorphosed) to upper amphibolite facies (K-spar-sillimanite zone). Illite crystallinity studies by Hepburn and Rehmer (1981) have provided controls in the lower grades of metamorphism (Fig. 4), for both the Narragansett Basin and Norfolk Basin. The Norfolk Basin (Fig. 4) is shown almost entirely in the diagenetic zone because Hepburn and Rehmer's (1981) values were obtained on slates and are thus comparable with results from the Narragansett Basin. Cazier's (1984a) values of 3.1 to 3.8 mm on sandstones from the Norfolk Basin are noted but are difficult to compare with the Narragansett Basin results. Mosher (1983) has provided controls for isograds in the higher zones of metamorphism in the southern Narragansett Basin (Fig. 4). Figure 4 indicates that the northwestern part of the Narragansett Basin is in the diagenetic zone of metamorphism; the rest of the northern and central part of the northern, and the medial portion of the southern Narragansett Basin are in the anchizone. The remainder of the Narragansett Basin is in the greenschist or amphibolite zones, with the highest metamorphic effects being in the southwestern part of the Narragansett Basin.

In the past, coal from the Narragansett Basin has been variously ranked as semi-anthracite, anthracite, and meta-anthracite, with somewhat ambiguous and conflicting results. Most of the coals for which there are useful chemical and other data come from the areas of diagenetic and anchizone metamorphism that comprise the bulk of the Basin. According to most recent compilations, these have an apparent rank of anthracite and meta-anthracite. However, petrographic analysis by Gray and others (1978) and Raben and Gray (1979a, b, c, d) shows that the Narragansett Basin coals have undergone a very complex thermal and structural history that can explain many of the previously confusing chemical and physical analyses of the coal and shaly coals. As a result of these studies, only the coals in the northwestern part of the Basin may be considered normal anthracite and even these have higher than usual reflectance values.

The bulk of the coal deposits of the Narragansett Basin are primarily the products of thermal alteration and coking of coals

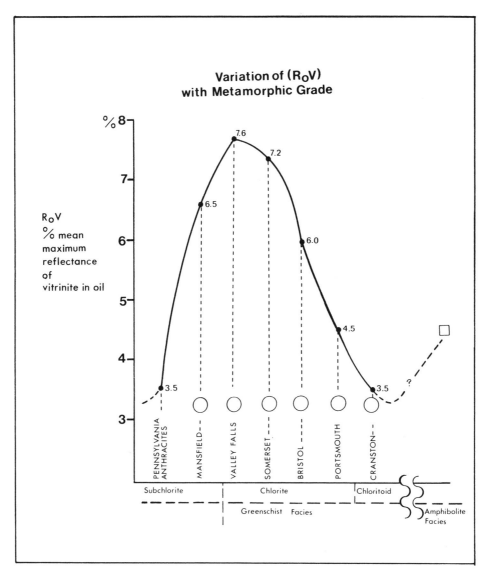

Figure 5. Graph of variations in mean maximum reflectance values of coals from the Narragansett Basin with variations in metamorphic intensity (based on Raben, 1979; and Gray and Raben, unpublished data 1979).

that were already at least bituminous rank prior to coking (Hepburn and Rehmer, 1981; Murray and others, 1981). Figure 5 shows reflectance values for several Narragansett Basin coals in various metamorphic zones by comparison with Pennsylvania anthracites. The chart indicates that the coals from Mansfield are true anthracites with, however, a reflectance value substantially higher than that for Pennsylvania anthracite. The highest such value is on coal from Valley Falls, with progressively decreasing values on other samples from the greenschist zone. The lowest value, 3.5, comparable with that of Pennsylvania anthracite, is on a coal from Cranston, Rhode Island. Figure 5 thus suggests that with increasing metamorphic grade and accompanying metamorphic growth of graphitic carbon, reflectance values continue

to decline to levels comparable to values of Pennsylvania anthracite. Thus, on the basis of reflectance values alone, metaanthracites might be erroneously classified as anthracite coals. However, there appears to be a generally systematic pattern for the mean bireflectances that may prove useful in classifying these coals (Fig. 5).

Evidence for four major phases of deformation occurs widely in the southern Narraganset Basin. Figure 6 indicates that the regional Barrovian metamorphism to sillimanite grade took place after D_1 and before D_2; that the intrusion of the 276-Ma Narragansett Pier Granite was emplaced during D_3 (Reck, 1984); and that D_4 was followed by an episode of metamorphism that reached chlorite grade.

Summary of Paleoenvironmental Controls

The fossil and sedimentary records, discussed in previous sections, indicate that the paleoenvironment was wet, non-marine, subtropical to tropical, with early periods of drier conditions. The coal was deposited in discontinuous swampy lowlands adjacent to fluvial systems in the upper alluvial fan environment. Consequently, the coals derived from this environment are low in sulfur, have high and variable ash contents, are lenticular, areally restricted, and of variable thickness. The water table was generally high and if the rate of subsidence was also fast at times, the thick coal beds may be primarily the result of the sedimentary environment.

TECTONIC CONTROLS OF SEDIMENTATION

Coarse conglomerates in the Narragansett and Norfolk basins suggest fault movements contemporaneous with deposition. The wet alluvial fan sedimentation and early bimodal volcanism are indicative of continental rifting, but do not constrain the driving mechanism for rifting. Mosher (1983) and Mosher and Rast (1984) proposed that the sediments as a whole were deposited in a series of pull-apart grabens. In the Narragansett Basin, a northern graben and later southern grabens have been recognized by Mosher (1983) on the basis of generally younger floral ages in the south and various stratigraphic relationships within the two basins. The Norfolk and the northern Narragansett basins are at present separated by a barrier of basement rocks known as the Sharon Uplands (LaForge, 1932). The same barrier, the Sharon horst, may have been an ENE-WSW–trending uplift in Late Carboniferous time separating the two basins as they developed sequentially.

To the west, both the Norfolk and Narragansett basins (Fig. 1) are cut off by either N-S faults or by a possible unconformity of approximately the same trend. To the east at Tiverton, Rhode Island, an unconformity (Fig. 1, Locality T) between the Carbon-

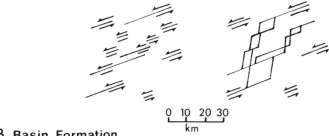

A. Intra-Basin Graben Formation: Namurian C (?)

B. Basin Formation

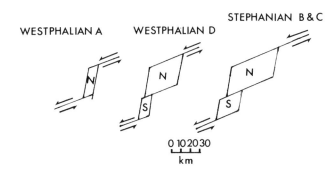

Figure 7. Schematic model involving sinistral strike-slip faulting. Two possible stages in the evolution of the Norfolk and Narragansett basins, (A) small pull-apart grabens formed between closely spaced parallel strike-slip faults early in the basins' history. Coalescence of some of these formed the Norfolk Basin and others interacted with younger grabens to form the northern graben. (B) Evolution with time of the northern and southern composite grabens. Intrabasinal horsts and grabens have been omitted for clarity (modified from Mosher, 1983).

iferous and Precambrian forms an edge to the southern Narragansett Basin. The unconformity continues northeastward, but is interrupted by an apparently faulted junction along the Beaverhead fault zone composed of NE-SW and N-S segments (Lyons, 1977; Zen, 1983). Additionally, west of the Narragansett Basin in the Avalonian Terrane, the North Scituate and Woonsocket basins, and in the Merrimack synclinorium, there are Pennsylvanian deposits that are farther north and/or in higher zones of metamorphism than one might expect from the trend of the higher metamorphic isograds in the southwestern part of the Narragansett Basin. All of these situations require an explanation.

Hypotheses for Basin Formation

Three basic hypotheses can be advanced to interpret these relationships:

1. Sinistral Strike-slip. Mosher (1983) makes a strong case for the pull-apart grabens to be activated by an NE-SW system (Fig. 7) of sinistral strike-slip faults on the basis of distribution and geometry of alluvial fans, sedimentation processes, transport directions, and geometric and spatial relationships of intrabasinal horsts and grabens and of the two sub-grabens. This system im-

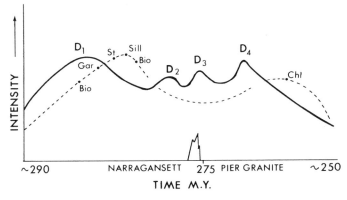

Figure 6. Variation of intensity of metamorphism and deformation phases with time (Murray and others, 1981, p. 175; Mosher, 1983; Reck, 1984), and in relation to the time of intrusion of the Narragansett Pier Granite (Kocis and others, 1978). Symbols: chl—chlorite; bio—biotite; st—staurolite; sill—sillimanite zones of metamorphism; D₁ through D₄-sequential phases of deformation.

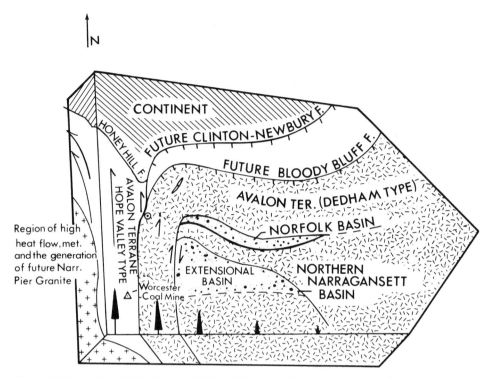

Figure 8. Schematic model by Rast and Skehan (this paper) for the development of southeastern New England in late Devonian to Carboniferous time period related to continental collision. Coarse arrows indicate the relative magnitude of motion; fine arrows indicate the motion along North-South right-lateral ductile shear faults and branching splay faults. Relations between the Dedham and Hope Valley terranes adapted from O'Hara and Gromet (1986).

plies an E-W Late Carboniferous extension. One of the implications is that the faults bounding the Sharon horst might be strike-slip faults. The other presumed Carboniferous deposits would be the result of very minor sinistral strike-slip movements on adjacent faults producing small grabens.

2. Tensile or Dextral Wrench Faults. A second hypothesis implying N-S extension to cause a graben has been advanced by Skehan and Rast (this paper) on the general basis expounded by Bradley (1982, 1984). This hypothesis considers the ENE-WSW faults (Fig. 8) as essentially tensile or dextral wrenches (Rast and Skehan, 1986). It is suggested that the almost straight N-S western boundary of the Narragansett Basin is a large dextral fault that northward passes into a series of large fractures known as the Mount Hope fault, the Neponset fault and Ponkapoag fault that border the southern part of the Boston Basin (Billings, 1979a, b) and Norfolk Basin. The implication of this hypothesis (Fig. 8) is that the initial displacement on faults such as the Bloody Bluff, Clinton-Newbury, and the Lake Char was dextral, and, during subsequent compression, displacement was converted into reverse fault motions.

The present-day shape of the Clinton-Newbury, Bloody Bluff, and Honey Hill faults is sinuous, but originally they were probably traces of large, straight tensional or wrench faults. At the end of the Devonian and the beginning of Carboniferous

time, a major thermal dome originated to the southeast of the Honey Hill fault, resulting in the northward movement of the by-then assembled Avalon plate, which in the process was partially subducted under the North American craton, converting the above-mentioned faults into thrust features. At the commencement of this movement, extensional basins opened to give rise to sedimentary troughs that became the Narragansett and Norfolk basins.

The approximate parallelism of trends of major faults and of the Narragansett-Norfolk basins themselves implies that the extensional motions in the southern part of the region and the compression to the north and west were coeval. As a hypothetical model, the growth of a major thermal dome (Fig. 8) is proposed as an explanation. The Gromet and O'Hara (1984), O'Hara and Gromet (1984, 1985) hypothesis of the separate nature of two Avalonian terranes in New England accords well with our model, implying that the Hope Valley Terrane was adjacent to the thermal dome. Our model could also explain the northerly position of the Worcester coal mine and the conglomerate at Pin Hill, as having been moved northward by dextral faulting. The Worcester coal mine, it should be recalled, has been widely compared with the Narragansett Basin lithology (Grew, 1976).

The second model outlined above in terms of large scale plate tectonics is compatible with the evolutionary schemes of the

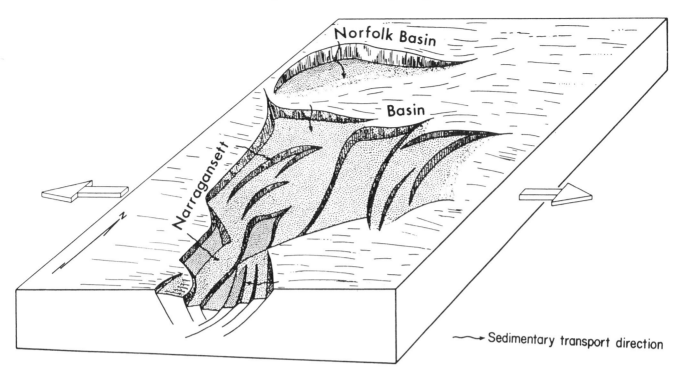

Figure 9. Schematic model for basin development, involving extension without major strike-slip motion. Dominant tectonic regime affecting sedimentation, therefore, is extensional with alluvial fans forming off uplifted margins (Cazier and Mosher, unpublished data).

Variscan-Hercynian orogen outlined by Dewey (1982) and Rast (1986).

3. Extension. A third hypothesis proposed by Cazier (1986) and Cazier and Mosher (unpublished data) is that the basins are caused by extension, with any associated sinistral or dextral strike-slip motion being minor or non-existent (Fig. 9). Recent work in the Norfolk Basin by Cazier (1984a, b) coupled with the sedimentary evidence of Mosher (1983), shows that the dominant tectonic regime affecting sedimentation was extensional with alluvial fans forming from uplifted margins. The extension directions compatible with known sediment transport directions are approximately north-south in the Norfolk Basin and east-west in the southern Narragansett Basin. No evidence of strike-slip motion related to basin formation has been found, and some faults bounding the basins, most notably the northern boundary fault for the Norfolk Basin, show no offset of source areas. Thus, there is currently no sedimentary evidence for strike-slip origin of the basins. Cazier (1984a, b) has shown that either sinistral or dextral faulting could have caused the Norfolk Basin, but of the two, regional sinistral motion fits the data best.

The strike-slip reactivation of these faults in the Permian makes it difficult to determine which of these hypotheses is valid. It should be noted that the detailed analysis for the subsequent post-rifting Permian deformation constructed by Mosher (1983) and her students is independent of the mechanism driving basin formation as long as intrabasinal horst and graben were formed.

Regardless of which of these three models is preferred, it seems almost certain that the Norfolk and Narragansett basins started as grabens or pull-apart basins and were surrounded by uplands producing conglomerates. Thus, from a paleogeographic standpoint, they can be considered as intermontane basins characterized by braided streams flowing on wet alluvial fans, similar to basins formed in Early Carboniferous times in the Atlantic provinces of Canada.

POST-SEDIMENTATION DEFORMATION AND METAMORPHISM

Deformation

The Pennsylvanian sedimentation was succeeded by a strong episode of deformation, metamorphism, and granite emplacement of Late Pennsylvanian-Permian age during the Alleghanian orogeny recognized by Lahee (1912) and Quinn and Moore (1968). The deformation was polyphase (Skehan and others, 1976; Rast and others, 1978; Skehan and Murray, 1979; Mosher, 1981, 1983; Mosher and Rast, 1984). In the Narragansett Basin, two major events were compressional with tectonic transport of F_1 being to W, and F_2 to E. In the adjacent Norfolk Basin, however, tectonic transport of both F_1 and F_2 was to SE.

In the northern Narragansett Basin, the dominant folding and cleavage is F_2 and S_2, the latter dipping toward N, NW and NE, thus indicating tectonic transport toward S. Preliminary data on D_1, on the other hand, indicates that tectonic transport is

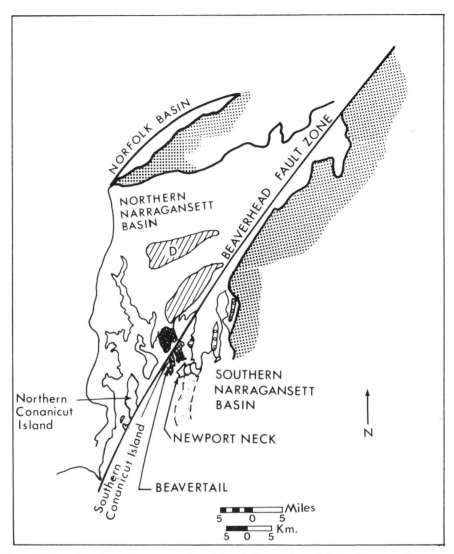

Figure 10. Tentative schematic reconstruction of the relative positions of Carboniferous rocks preserved in the northern and southern parts of the Narragansett Basin prior to late dextral offset (8 km) on the Beaverhead fault zone. Dotted pattern along the Beaverhead fault zone represents Precambrian and Cambrian inliers in restored positions prior to strike-slip movement along the Beaverhead fault zone based on metamorphic isograds determined by Mosher (1983). D—Dighton Conglomerate.

toward N. The Worcester Coal Mine, the third fossiliferous deposit in addition to the Norfolk and Narragansett basins, shows an F_1 schistosity affected by S_2 crenulation cleavage. In the Norfolk and Narragansett basins these early-formed ductile deformation features were cut by later-formed brittle normal and strike-slip faults; movement on the latter also caused multiple generations of folds, crenulation cleavages, and boudins in the adjacent rocks. Mosher (1983) associated the deformation with stages of closure of the basin, involving the interaction of basement and cover.

Metamorphism and Tectono-Metamorphic Correlations

The main high-grade metamorphism of the Narragansett Basin is syntectonic to post-tectonic (Fig. 6) (Skehan and Murray,

1979; Farrens and Mosher, 1982; Thomas, 1981), and by virtue of the local presence of kyanite, must be attributed to the middle to high pressure (Barrovian) type of regional metamorphism. On the other hand the mineralogy of Narragansett Pier Granite suggests that it was generated high in the crust. Thus it appears that the main regional metamorphism of the Narragansett Basin and the formation of the granite are not related and were produced by two contrasting mechanisms.

The combined effects of pressure and temperature have strongly affected the coals of the Rhode Island Formation, leading to their structural discontinuity, local thickening, and anthracitization (Skehan and Murray, 1978). The original lenticular shapes of these discontinuous upper alluvial fan coals were accentuated by structural effects.

Correlations of tectono-metamorphic Alleghanian events along the Appalachian orogen have been made by Rast and Grant (1973), Murray and others (1978), and lately by Rast (1984), and Mosher and Rast (1984); these indicate a considerable parallelism of events. However, Skehan and Rast (1984) and Rast and Skehan (1986) have suggested correlations of tectono-stratigraphic zones of Europe with North America, while Skehan and Murray (1980) suggested along-strike correlations of tectonic phases from New Brunswick, Canada, to South Carolina, U.S.A. Most early correlations (pre-1980) were concerned with ductile events, including phases of folding and foliation. The consideration of brittle events became significant in the aftermath of the paper by Arthaud and Matte (1977) and by Lefort and Van der Voo (1981) who suggested a system of Late Paleozoic strike-slip faults. Mosher (1983) suggests that some faulting in southeastern New England may be postmetamorphic, thus producing faulted isograds (Fig. 10). Late dextral faults are very widely claimed both in Canada, where they have ENE to WSW or NE-SW trends, (Webb, 1969) and in the United States. In the Narragansett Basin, one such fault zone, the Beaverhead (Fig. 10), can be used to restore roughly the pre-faulting relationships if one assumes that the biotite isograd, as indicated by Quinn (1971), as well as Precambrian inliers of granite in Newport and Bristol were originally continuous. A tentative restoration implies 9 km of dextral displacement. Thus on a smaller scale the fault is analogous to the Minas geofracture (Keppie, 1982) of Nova Scotia.

CONCLUSIONS

The Norfolk Basin and the northern and southern parts of the Narragansett Basin are nonmarine intermontane basins that probably formed sequentially in an active tectonic environment dominated by extension and block faulting from early Westphalian through Stephanian times. Sediments represent large alluvial fans that contain floras suggestive of tropical to subtropical environments and having affinities closer to Europe than to North America. During the Carboniferous, present-day southeastern New England was most likely located near the equator, as suggested by paleomagnetic studies summarized by Irving (1979). The coals of the Narragansett Basin were formed from peat that accumulated in discontinuous swampy lowlands adjacent to fluvial systems in the upper alluvial fan environment, mainly during Middle and Late Pennsylvanian times.

ACKNOWLEDGMENTS

We thank Frances Ahearn, Elizabeth Bergenheim, R. Duff Collins, Catherine I. Gabis, Dorothy M. Sheehan, Patricia Tassia and Janet L. Titsworth for assistance in the process of preparing the text and illustrations. J. W. Skehan acknowledges Boston College and NSF Grant No. EAR-82-00047 for partial support in the writing of this paper. We are grateful to Edward S. Belt and Marland P. Billings for review of an earlier version of the manuscript and to Paul C. Lyons for painstaking review of each revision. Their suggestions have materially improved the resulting paper.

REFERENCES CITED

Anstey, R., 1979, Stratigraphy and Depositional Environment of Early Cambrian Hoppin Slate of southern New England and its Acado-Baltic Fauna: Northeastern Geology, v. 1, p. 9–17.

Arthaud, F., and Matte, P., 1977, Late Paleozoic strike-slip faulting in southern Europe and northern Africa, Results of a right-lateral shear zone between the Appalachians and the Urals: Geological Society of America Bulletin, v. 88, p. 1305–1320.

Berryhill, A. W., and Mosher, S., 1983, Fault-related polyphase deformation of Dutch Island, Rhode Island: Geological Society of America Abstracts with Programs, v. 15, no. 3, p. 129.

Billings, M. P., 1929, Structural geology of the eastern part of the Boston Basin: American Journal of Science, 5th series, v. 18, p. 97–137.

——, 1976, Geology of the Boston Basin, *in* Lyons, P. C., and Brownlow, A. H., eds., Studies in New England geology: Geological Society of America Memoir 146, p. 5–30.

——, 1979a, Boston Basin, Massachusetts, *in* Skehan, J. W., S. J., Murray, D. P., Hepburn, J. C., Billings, M. P., Lyons, P. C., and Doyle, R. O., eds., The Mississippian and Pennsylvanian (Carboniferous) systems in the United States-Massachusetts, Rhode Island, and Maine: U.S. Geological Survey Professional Paper 1110-A-L, p. A15–A20.

—— 1979b, Bedrock geology of the Boston Basin, *in* Cameron, B., ed., Carboniferous Basins of Southeastern New England, Guidebook for field trip No. 5, Ninth International Congress of Carboniferous Stratigraphy and Geology: Falls Church, Virginia, American Geological Institute, p. 47–74.

——, 1982, Ordovician cauldron subsidence of the Blue Hills Complex, eastern Massachusetts: Geological Society of America Bulletin, v. 93, p. 909–920.

Bradley, D. C., 1982, Subsidence in Late Paleozoic Basins in the Northern Appalachians: Tectonics, v. 1, p. 91–105.

——, 1984, Late Paleozoic strike-slip tectonics of the Northern Appalachians, [Ph.D. thesis]: Albany, State University of New York, 205 p.

Burks, R. J., Mosher, S., and Murray, D. P., 1981, Alleghanian Deformation and Metamorphism of Southern Narragansett Basin, *in* Hermes, O. D., and Boothroyd, J. C., eds., Guidebook to Geologic Field Studies in Rhode Island and Adjacent Areas: New England Intercollegiate Geological Conference, 73rd Annual Meeting, University of Rhode Island, Kingston, Rhode Island, p. 265–275.

Cameron, B., and Murray, D. P., 1979, Geology of the Norfolk Basin, Massachusetts, *in* Cameron, B., ed., Field Guidebook for trip No. 5, IX International Congress of Carboniferous Stratigraphy and Geology: Falls Church, Virginia, American Geological Institute, p. 36–40.

Cazier, E. C., 1984a, Late Paleozoic tectonic evolution of the Norfolk Basin, Southeastern Massachusetts [M.A. thesis]: Austin, University of Texas, 147 p.

——, 1984b, Tectonic Evolution of the Norfolk Basin, Massachusetts, Fluvial Sedimentation and polyphase deformation: Geological Society of America Abstracts with Programs, v. 16, no. 1, p. 8.

——, 1986, Late Paleozoic tectonic evolution of the Norfolk Basin, Southeastern Massachusetts: Journal of Geology (in press).

Chute, N. E., 1964, Geology of the Norfolk Basin Carboniferous, sedimentary, and the various igneous rocks of the Norwood and Blue Hills quadrangle, *in* Skehan, J. W., S. J., ed., New England Intercollegiate Geological Conference Guidebook, 56th Annual Meeting, Boston College, p. 91–114.

——, 1966, Geology of the Norwood quadrangle, Norfolk and Suffolk Counties, Massachusetts: U.S. Geological Survey Bulletin 1163-B, 78 p.

Darrah, W. C., 1969, A critical review of the Upper Pennsylvanian floras of eastern United States, with notes on the Mazon Creek flora of Illinois: Gettysburg, Pennsylvania, privately published, 220 p.

Dewey, J. F., 1982, Plate tectonics and the evolution of the British Isles: Journal of the Geological Society of London, v. 139, no. 4, p. 371–412.

Dowse, A. M., 1950, New evidence on the Cambrian contact at Hoppin Hill, North Attleboro, Massachusetts: American Journal of Science, v. 248, p. 95–99.

Doyle, R. G., 1979, Rocks of Maine inferred to be Carboniferous, *in* Skehan, J. W., S. J., Murray, D. P., Hepburn, J. C., Billings, M. P., Lyons, P. C., and Doyle, R. O., eds., The Mississippian and Pennsylvanian (Carboniferous) Systems in the United States-Massachusetts, Rhode Island and Maine: U.S. Geological Survey Professional Paper 1110-A-L, p. A24–A25.

Emerson, B. K., 1917, Geology of Massachusetts and Rhode Island: U.S. Geological Survey Bulletin, v. 289, 597 p.

Farrens, C., and Mosher, S., 1982, Alleghenian deformation in Southeastern Narragansett Basin, Rhode Island: Geological Society of America Abstracts with Programs, v. 14, no. 1, p. 17.

Gray, R. J., Raben, J. D., and Murray, D. P., 1978, Unusual anthracites from the Narragansett basin, southeastern New England: Geological Society of America Abstracts with Programs, v. 10, no. 7, p. 412.

Grew, E. S., 1976, Pennsylvanian Rocks of east-central Massachusetts, *in* Cameron, B., ed., Geology of Southeastern New England: New England Intercollegiate Geological Conference, 68th Annual Meeting, p. 383–404.

Grew, E. S., Mamay, S. H., and Barghoorn, E. S., 1970, Age of plant fossils from the Worcester coal mine, Worcester, Massachusetts: American Journal of Science, v. 268, no. 2, p. 113–126.

Gromet, L. P., and O'Hara, K. D., 1984, Two Distinct Late Precambrian Terranes within the "Avalon Zone," southeastern New England, and their late Paleozoic Juxtaposition: Geological Society of America Abstracts with Programs, 16, no. 1, p. 20.

Hepburn, J. C., 1976, Lower Paleozoic rocks west of the Clinton-Newbury fault zone, Worcester area, Massachusetts, *in* Cameron, B., ed., Geology of southeastern New England: New England Intercollegiate Geological Conference, 68th Annual Meeting, p. 366–382.

——, 1979, Carboniferous Deposits near Worcester, Massachusetts, *in* Skehan, J. W., S. J., Murray, D. P., Hepburn, J. C., Billings, M. P., Lyons, P. C., and Doyle, R. O., eds., The Mississippian and Pennsylvanian (Carboniferous) systems in the United States-Massachusetts, Rhode Island, and Maine: U.S. Geological Survey Professional Paper 1110-A-L, p. A15.

Hepburn, J. C., and Rehmer, J. A., 1981, The Diagenetic to Metamorphic transition in the Narragansett and Norfolk Basins, Massachusetts and Rhode Island, *in* Hermes, O. D., and Boothroyd, J. C., eds., Guidebook to Geologic Field Studies in Rhode Island and adjacent areas, 73rd Annual Meeting of New England Intercollegiate Geological Conference, University of Rhode Island: Kingston, Rhode Island, p. 47–65.

Hitchcock, C. H., 1861, Synchronism of coal beds in the New England and western United States coal basins: American Association Advancement Science Proceedings, v. 14, p. 138–143.

Hitchcock, E. H., 1841, Final Report on the geology of Massachusetts: Amherst and Northampton, Massachusetts, v. 2, p. 831.

Irving, E., 1979, Paleopoles and paleolatitudes of North America and speculations about displaced terranes: Canadian Journal of Earth Science, v. 16, p. 669–694.

Jackson, C. T., 1840, Report on the geological and agricultural survey of the State of Rhode Island: Providence, Rhode Island, 312 p.

Keppie, J. D., 1982, The Minas Geofracture, *in* St-Julien, P., and Beland, J., eds., Major structural zones and faults of the northern Appalachians: Geological Association of Canada, Special Paper no. 24, p. 263–280.

Knox, A. S., 1944, A Carboniferous flora from the Wamsutta formation of southeastern Massachusetts: American Journal of Science, v. 242, no. 3, p. 130–138.

Kocis, D. E., Hermes, O. D., and Cain, J. A., 1978, Petrologic comparison of the pink and white facies of the Narragansett Pier Granite, Rhode Island: Geological Society of America Abstracts with Programs, v. 10, no. 7, p. 71.

Kubler, B., 1964, Les argiles, indicateurs de métamorphisme: Rev. Inst. Franc. Petrole, v. 19, p. 1093–1112.

LaForge, L., 1932, Geology of the Boston area, Massachusetts: U.S. Geological Survey Bulletin, v. 839, 105 p.

Lahee, F. H., 1912, Relations of the degree of metamorphism to geological structure and to acid igneous intrusion in the Narragansett Basin, Rhode Island: American Journal of Science, 4th series, v. 33, p. 249–262, 354–372,

447–469.

Lefort, J. P., and Van der Voo, R., 1981, A kinematic model for the collision and complete suturing between Gondwanaland and Laurasia in the Carboniferous: Journal of Geology, v. 89, no. 5, p. 537–550.

Lenk, C., Strother, P. K., Kaye, C. A., and Barghoorn, E. S., 1982, Precambrian age of the Boston Basin: new evidence from microfossils: Science, v. 216, p. 619–620.

Lesquereux, L., 1889, Fossil plants of the coal-measures of Rhode Island: American Journal of Science, 3rd series, v. 37, no. 219, p. 229–230.

Ludman, A., 1986, Timing of terrane accretion in eastern and east-central Maine: Geology, v. 14, no. 5, p. 411–414.

Lyons, P. C., 1969, Bedrock geology of the Mansfield quadrangle, Massachusetts [Ph.D. thesis]: Boston, Massachusetts, Boston University, 283 p.

——, 1976, Implications of coal flora and stratigraphy of the Narragansett Basin, New England on plate tectonic models: Geological Society of America Abstracts with Programs, v. 8, no. 6, p. 989–990.

——, 1977, Report on the bedrock geology of the Narragansett Basin, Massachusetts: U.S. Geological Survey Open-File Rept. 77-816, 39 p., 24 pls., scale 1:24,000.

——, 1979, Biostratigraphy in the Pennsylvanian of Massachusetts and Rhode Island *in* Skehan, J. W., S. J., Murray, D. P., Hepburn, J. C., Billings, M. P., Lyons, P. C., and Doyle, R. G., eds., The Mississippian and Pennsylvanian (Carboniferous) Systems in the United States-Massachusetts, Rhode Island and Maine: U.S. Geological Survey Professional Paper, 1110-A-L, p. A20–A24.

——, 1984, Carboniferous Megafloral Zonation of New England, *in* Sutherland, P. K., and Manger, W. L., eds., Neuvieme Congres International de Stratigraphie et de Geologie du Carbonifere, Compte Rendu, v. 2, Biostratigraphy: Carbondale, Illinois, Southern Illinois University Press, v. 2, p. 503–514.

Lyons, P. C., and Chase, H. B., Jr., 1976, Coal flora and stratigraphy of the northwestern Narragansett Basin, *in* Cameron, B., ed., New England Intercollegiate Conference, 68th Annual Meeting, Boston, Mass., Oct. 8-10, 1976, Geology of southeastern New England; a guidebook for field trips to the Boston area and vicinity: Princeton, New Jersey, Science Press, p. 405–427.

——, 1981, Rank of Coal Beds of the Narragansett Basin, Massachusetts and Rhode Island: International Journal of Coal Geology, v. 1, p. 155–168.

Lyons, P. C., Tiffney, B., and Cameron, B., 1976, Early Pennsylvanian age of the Norfolk Basin, southeastern Massachusetts, based on plant megafossils, *in* Lyons, P. C., and Brownlow, A. H., eds., Studies in New England Geology: Geological Society of America Memoir 146, p. 181–197.

Mosher, S., 1981, Late Paleozoic deformation of the Narragansett Basin, Rhode Island: Geological Society of America Abstracts with Programs, v. 13, p. 515.

——, 1983, Kinematic history of the Narragansett Basin, Massachusetts and Rhode Island: constraints on Late Paleozoic plate Reconstructions: Tectonics, v. 2, no. 4, p. 327–344.

Mosher, S., and Wood, D. S., 1976, Mechanisms of Alleghanian deformation in the Pennsylvanian of Rhode Island, *in* Cameron, B., ed., New England Intercollegiate Geological Conference, 68th Annual Meeting, Boston, Massachusetts, Oct. 8-9, 1976, Geology of southeastern New England; a guidebook for field trips to the Boston area and vicinity: Princeton, New Jersey, Science Press, p. 472–490.

Mosher, S., and Rast, N., 1984, The deformation and metamorphism of Carboniferous rocks in Maritime Canada and New England, *in* Hutton, D.H.W., and Sanderson, D. J., eds., Variscan tectonics of the North Atlantic region: Geological Society Special Publication 14, Blackwell Scientific Publications, Oxford, p. 233–243.

Murray, D. P., and Raben, J. D., 1980, The metamorphism of carbonaceous material, Narragansett Basin, southeastern New England, USA: Industrie Minerale les Techniques, p. 315–325.

Murray, D. P., and Skehan, J. W., S. J., 1979, A Traverse across the eastern margin of the Appalachian-Caledonide orogen, southeastern New England, *in* Skehan, J. W., S. J., and Osberg, P. H., eds., The Caledonides in the USA:

Geological Excursions in the Northeast Appalachians, International Geological Correlation Program (I.G.C.P.) Project 27: Weston, Massachusetts, Weston Observatory, p. 1–35.

Murray, D. P., Skehan, J. W., S. J., and Rast, N., 1978, The Convergence of the Caledonian and Variscan (Alleghanian) Episodes in the Northern Appalachians: Abstracts with Program (IGCP) Project Caledonide Orogen, Trinity College, Dublin, 51–52.

Murray, D. P., Hepburn, J. C., and Rehmer, J. A., 1979, Metamorphism of the Narragansett Basin, *in* Skehan, J. W., S. J., Murray, D. P., and Rider, T. H., eds., Evaluation of coal deposits in the Narragansett Basin, Massachusetts and Rhode Island: U.S. Bureau of Mines, Contract No. J0188022, Final Report, p. 39–47.

Murray, D. P., Raben, J. D., Lyons, P. C., and Chase, H. B., Jr., 1981, The geologic setting of coal and carbonaceous material, Narragansett Basin, southeastern New England, *in* Boothroyd, J. C., and Hermes, O. D., eds., Guidebook to Geologic Field Studies in Rhode Island and Adjacent areas: 73rd Annual Meeting, p. 175–200.

Mutch, T. A., 1968, Pennsylvanian non-marine sediments of the Narragansett Basin, Massachusetts-Rhode Island, *in* Klein, G., deV., ed., Late Paleozoic and Mesozoic continental sedimentation, northeastern North America: Geological Society of America Special Paper 106, p. 177–209.

O'Hara, K., and Gromet, L. P., 1984, Identification, characterization and age of a ductile shear zone separating two Late Precambrian terranes, southeastern New England: Geological Society of America Abstracts with Programs, v. 16, no. 1, p. 54.

—— , 1985, Two distinct Late Precambrian (Avalonian) Terranes in Southeastern New England and their Late Paleozoic juxtaposition: American Journal of Science, v. 285, no. 10, p. 673–709.

Oleksyshyn, J., 1976, Fossil plants of Pennsylvanian age from northwestern Narragansett basin, *in* Lyons, P. C., and Brownlow, A. H., eds., Studies in New England Geology: Geological Society of America Memoir 146, p. 143–180.

Osberg, P. H., Hussey, A. M., and Boone, G. M., eds., 1985, Bedrock Geologic Map of Maine: Maine Geological Survey, scale 1:500,000.

Packard, A. S., 1889, Recent discoveries in the Carboniferous flora and fauna of Rhode Island: American Journal of Science, 3rd series, v. 37, no. 221, p. 411.

Palmer, A. R., 1983, The Decade of North American Geology 1983 Time Scale: Geology, v. 11, no. 9, p. 503–504.

Peper, J. D., and Pease, M. H., 1976, Summary of stratigraphy in the Brimfield area, Connecticut and Massachusetts, *in* Page, L. R., ed., Contributions to the stratigraphy of New England: Geological Society of America Memoir 148, p. 253–270.

Quinn, A. W., 1971, Bedrock geology of Rhode Island: U.S. Geological Survey Bulletin 1295, 68 p.

Quinn, A. W., and Moore, G. E., 1968, Sedimentation, tectonism, and plutonism in the Narragansett Basin region, *in* Zen, E-an, White, W. C., Hadley, J. B., and Thompson, J. B., eds., Studies of Appalachian Geology, Northern and Maritime: New York, Interscience Publishers, p. 269–280.

Quinn, A. W., and Oliver, W. A., Jr., 1962, Pennsylvanian rocks of New England, *in* Branson, C. C., ed., Pennsylvanian System in the United States—A symposium: Tulsa, Oklahoma: American Association of Petroleum Geologists, p. 60–73.

Raben, J. D., 1979, Coal: chemistry, petrography, rank and stratigraphy, *in* Skehan, J. W., S. J., Murray, D. P., and Rider, T. H., eds., Evaluation of coal deposits in the Narragansett Basin, Massachusetts and Rhode Island: U.S. Bureau of Mines, Contract No. J0188022, Final Report, p. 48–64.

Raben, J. D., and Gray, R. J., 1979a, Deformational textures in Narragansett Basin coals and their implications for utilization: Geological Society of America Abstracts with Programs, v. 11, no. 1, p. 46.

—— , 1979b, The geology and petrology of anthracites and meta-anthracites in the Narragansett Basin, southeastern New England, *in* Cameron, B., ed., Geology of southeastern New England: Field Trip Guidebook, New England Intercollegiate Geological Conference, 68th Annual Meeting: Princeton, New Jersey, Science Press, p. 93–108.

—— 1979c, The nature of highly deformed anthracites and meta-anthracites in southeastern New England, Ninth International Congress of Carboniferous Stratigraphy and Geology: Urbana, Illinois, Abstracts with Programs, p. 169.

—— , 1979d, Simplified classification and optical characteristics of meta-coals in the Narragansett Basin, southeastern New England: Geological Society of America Abstracts with Programs, v. 11, no. 1, p. 49.

Raben, J. D., Rushworth, P. A., and Murray, D. P., 1978, Coal, *in* Skehan, J. W., S. J., and Murray, D. P., eds., The coal-bearing Narragansett Basin of Massachusetts and Rhode Island: Geology, v. 1, NSF Grant No. AER-76-02147, Final Report, p. 66–72.

Rast, N., 1984, The Alleghanian orogeny in eastern North America *in* Hutton, D.H.W., and Sanderson, D. J., eds., Variscan Tectonics of the North Atlantic Region: Geological Society London, Special Publication 14, Blackwell Scientific Publications, p. 197–217.

Rast, N., and Grant, R. H., 1973, Trans-Atlantic Correlation of the Variscan Appalachian Orogeny: American Journal of Science, v. 273, p. 572–579.

Rast, N., and Skehan, J. W., S. J., 1986, Avalon plate in North America, Europe and Africa, Notes & memoires service geologique du Maroc, Rabat, no. 335, *in* Destombes, Jacques, ed., L'Orogene Caledonien de Maroc et l'orogenie Paleozoique: Programme Internationale Conference Geologique Project no. 27, Symposium de Rabat, 22 aout- 3 septembre 1983, 470 p. (in press).

Rast, N., Skehan, J. W., S. J., and Murray, D. M., 1978, The correlation of the Avalonian Precambrian and Lower Paleozoic rocks of the eastern Maritimes (Canada) and southeastern New England: Geological Society of America Abstracts with Programs, v. 10, no. 2, p. 81.

Read, C. B., and Mamay, S. H., 1964, Upper Paleozoic floral zones and floral provinces of the United States: U.S. Geological Survey Professional Paper 454-K, p. 35.

Reck, B. H., 1984, Timing of Alleghanian Granite Intrusion Relative to Deformation, SW Narragansett Basin, RI: Geological Society of America Abstracts with Programs, v. 16, no. 1, p. 57.

Rose, S., and Murray, D. P., 1984, Age relations in the Woonsocket and Scituate Basin, southeastern New England: Geological Society of America Abstracts with Programs, v. 16, no. 1, p. 60.

Scudder, S. H., 1893, Insect fauna of the Rhode Island coal field: U.S. Geological Survey Bulletin 101, p. 27.

—— , 1895, Revision of the American fossil cockroaches with description of new forms: U.S. Geological Survey Bulletin 124, p. 176.

Severson, R. H., 1979, Depositional environments, facies associations and coal occurrence in Carboniferous sediments of the Narragansett Basin [M.S. thesis]: Kingston, Rhode Island, University of Rhode Island, 72 p.

Severson, R. H., and Boothroyd, J. C., 1981, Depositional environments, facies associations, and coal occurrence in Carboniferous sediments of the Narragansett Basin: Geological Society of America Abstracts with Programs, v. 13, p. 176.

Shaler, N. S., Woodworth, J. B., and Foerste, A., 1899, Geology of Narragansett Basin: U.S. Geological Survey Monograph 33, p. 410.

Shaw, C. E., Jr., and Petersen, R. G., 1967, Surficial geologic map of the Hanover quadrangle; Plymouth County, Massachusetts: U.S. Geological Survey map GQ-633.

Skehan, J. W., S. J., 1983, Geological profiles through the Avalonian Terrain of southeastern Massachsetts, Rhode Island, and eastern Connecticut, U.S.A., *in* Rast, N., and Delaney, F., eds., Profiles of orogenic belts, Geodynamics Series: American Geophysical Union and International Union of Geological Sciences, v. 10, p. 275–300.

Skehan, J. W., S. J., and Murray, D. P., eds., 1978, The coal-bearing Narragansett Basin of Massachusetts and Rhode Island: Volume 1-Geology: National Science Foundation Final Report, Grant No. AER 76-02147, 99 p. and 12 Appendices.

—— 1979a, Geology of the Narragansett Basin, southeastern Rhode Island, *in* Cameron, B., ed., Carboniferous basins of southeastern New England: Ninth International Congress of Carboniferous Stratigraphy and Geology, Field Trip Guidebook no. 5: Falls Church, Virginia, American Geological Institute, p. 7–35.

——, 1979b, General Geology of the Woonsocket and North Scituate Basins, *in* Cameron, B., ed., Carboniferous Basins of southeastern New England, Field Guidebook for Trip No. 5: Ninth International Congress of Carboniferous Stratigraphy and Geology, p. 45–46.

——, 1980, A geologic profile across southeastern New England: Tectonophysics, v. 69, p. 285–319.

Skehan, J. W., S. J., and Rast, N., 1984, Correlation of Carboniferous Tectonostratigraphic Zones in Europe and North America, *in* Geldsetzer, H.H.J., Neuvieme Congres International de Stratigraphie et de Geologie du Carbonifere, p. 5–12.

——, 1986, Preliminary Geological Map of Pennsylvanian Narragansett Basin, MA, and Pre-Pennsylvanian Rocks of Narragansett Bay, Rhode Island: Geological Society of America Abstracts with Programs, v. 18, no. 1, p. 66.

Skehan, J. W., S. J., Belt, E. S., and Rast, N., 1977, Late Paleozoic stratigraphic and structural evolution of the Narragansett Basin of Massachusetts and Rhode Island: Geological Society of America Abstracts with Programs, v. 9, no. 3, p. 318.

Skehan, J. W., S. J., Rast, N., and Logue, D. F., 1981, The Geology of Cambrian rocks of the Connanicut Island, Jamestown, Rhode Island, *in* Boothroyd, J. C., and Hermes, O. D., eds., Guidebook to Geologic Field Studies in Rhode Island and Adjacent areas: 73rd Annual Meeting, New England Intercollegiate Geological Conference, p. 237–264.

Skehan, J. W., S. J., Murray, D. P., Belt, E. S., Hermes, O. D., Rast, N., and Dewey, J. F., 1976, Alleghenian deformation, sedimentation, and metamorphism in southeastern Massachusetts and Rhode Island, *in* Cameron, B., ed., Geology of Southeastern New England, New England Intercollegiate Geologic Conference, p. 447–471.

Skehan, J. W., S. J., Murray, D. P., Hepburn, J. C., Billings, M. P., Lyons, P. C., and Doyle, R. G., eds., 1979a, The Mississippian and Pennsylvanian (Carboniferous) Systems in the United States-Massachusetts, Rhode Island and Maine: U.S. Geological Survey Professional Paper 1110-A, p. A1–A30.

Skehan, J. W., S. J., Murray, D. P., Raben, J. D., Ring, J. W., S. J., Bouchard, R., Rushworth, P. A., and Cutter, G., 1979b, The exploration problem, *in* Skehan, J. W., S. J., Murray, D. P., and Rider, T. H., eds., Evaluation of coal deposits in the Narragansett Basin, Massachusetts and Rhode Island: United States Department of the Interior Bureau of Mines final report, Weston Massachusetts, Weston Observatory, Department of Geology and Geophysics, Boston College, p. 140–159.

Skehan, J. W., S. J., Gill, G. E., Raben, J. D., Schapiro, Norman, and Murray, D. P., 1981, Exploration of coal and anthracite carbonaceous shale resources, Narragansett Basin, Massachusetts and Rhode Island: Final Report No. DOE/FE/20029-1, Contract DE-AC01-79RA20029, U.S. Department of Energy, Division of Anthracite, Washington, D.C. 20461, 44 p. and 26 p. of Appendices (Stratigraphic Logs and Glossary.)

Skehan, J. W., S. J., Murray, D. P., Raben, J. D., and Chase, H. B., Jr., 1982, Exploration and Exploitation of the Narragansett coal basin, Massachusetts and Rhode Island, *in* Farquhar, O. C., ed., Geotechnology in Massachusetts: Amherst, Massachusetts, University of Massachusetts, p. 381–399.

Stanley, D. J., 1968, Graded bedding-sole marking-greywacke assemblage and related sedimentary structures in some Carboniferous flood deposits, eastern Massachusetts, *in* Klein, G. deV, ed., Late Paleozoic and Mesozoic continental sedimentation, northeastern North America: Geological Society of America, Special Paper 106, p. 211–239.

Thomas, K., 1981, Structural Evolution of Prudence Island and vicinity, southern Narragansett Bay, Rhode Island [M.S. thesis]: Austin, Texas, University of Texas, 111 p.

Thompson, J. B., Jr., and Robinson, P., 1976, Geologic setting of the Harvard Conglomerate, Harvard, Massachusetts, *in* Cameron, B., New England Intercollegiate Geological Conference, 68th Annual Meeting, Boston, Mass.,

Oct. 8-10, 1976, Geology of southeastern New England; a guidebook for field trips to the Boston area and vicinity: Princeton, New Jersey, Science Press, p. 345–351.

Towe, K. M., 1959, Petrology and source of sediments in the Narragansett Basin of Rhode Island and Massachusetts: Journal of Sedimentary Petrology, v. 29, p. 503–512.

Warren, C. H., and Powers, S., 1914, Geology of Diamond Hill-Cumberland district in Rhode Island-Massachusetts: Geological Society of America Bulletin, v. 25, p. 435–476.

Webb, G. W., 1969, Paleozoic wrench faults in Canadian Appalachians, *in* Kay, M., ed., North Atlantic Geology and Continental Drift: American Association of Petroleum Geologists Memoir, v. 12, p. 754–786.

Willard, B., and Cleaves, A. B., 1930, Amphibian footprints from the Pennsylvanian of the Narragansett Basin: Geological Society of America Bulletin, v. 41, no. 2, p. 321–327.

Zen, E-an, ed., 1983, Bedrock geologic map of Massachusetts: U.S. Geological Survey, 3 map sheets, scale 1:250,000.

MANUSCRIPT ACCEPTED BY THE SOCIETY APRIL 16, 1986

Discussion of paper by Skehan, Rast, and Mosher. Responses by Skehan

Alison H. Jones (Consultant, Denver, CO)
Question: If these coal fields are considered North American analogs of the Variscan coal fields of the British Isles, how do the coals compare with regard to flora and degree of coking?
Response: The Narragansett Basin coals and sequences in which they occur are more comparable with those of western and central Europe and the Iberian Peninsula than with the British Isles. This is especially the case as regards intensity of deformation in the Variscan orogeny. As suggested by Skehan and Rast (1984), the Narragansett Basin probably lies considerably southeast of the Variscan front and more likely lies in one of the Variscan belts.

Paul C. Lyons
Comment: I would caution you on the age of the arkose at Sachuest Point and the Purgatory Conglomerate. We need new collections in that area.
Response: T. N. Dale has found floral fragments at Sachuest Point (Dale, 1885). Collections should be undertaken from black shales in which there are large boulders. Whether this is the basal unit of the Pennsylvanian is uncertain but may be in (thrust) fault contact with the basement volcaniclastic rocks. You are right on the need for more floral collections from the Purgatory as well as the Dighton which I believe are lithologically similar.

James E. Palmer (Sigma Consultants)
Question: Have you compared the New England coal fields with those of Jerada, Morocco? The structural framework is very similar.
Response: Only in one paper which described thin coal beds. It would not be surprising, however, to discover similar coals in Morocco deformed in the Variscan orogeny. Western Morocco, especially the Anti-Atlas Mountains, compare closely in stratigraphy and Precambrian plutonism and volcanism and Cambrian stratigraphy with the Avalonian of southeastern New England, on which the Naragansett Basin rests.

Geological Society of America
Special Paper 210
1986

Depositional and structural history of the Pennsylvania Anthracite region

Gordon H. Wood, Jr.*
6115 Ramsgate Rd.
Bethesda, Maryland 20816

Thomas M. Kehn
Jane R. Eggleston
U.S. Geological Survey
National Center, M.S. 956
Reston, Virginia 22092

ABSTRACT

The Pennsylvania Anthracite region contains numerous thick, extensive, low-sulfur coal beds of Pennsylvanian age. These coal beds are the result of the accumulation of swamp vegetation, and deposition of fine- to coarse-grained clastics in a terrestrial, rapidly sinking asymmetric basin, whose source area lay to the southeast of the Anthracite region. The beds in this basin were extensively folded and faulted in Permian-Triassic time as the strata above a basal décollement were thrust northwestward.

INTRODUCTION

The Pennsylvania Anthracite region consists of one small and four large coal fields within a parallelogram-shaped area of about 8,850 sq km (5,500 sq mi) in north-central Pennsylvania (Fig. 1). The region includes all or parts of 12 counties: Carbon, Columbia, Dauphin, Lackawanna, Luzerne, Lebanon, Northumberland, Schuylkill, Sullivan, Susquehanna, Wayne, and Wyoming. The region is in the Valley and Ridge and Appalachian Plateaus physiographic provinces (Fenneman, 1938). Coal within the four large fields and in the outliers is of anthracite and semianthracite rank. The region is drained by the Susquehanna, Delaware, and Schuylkill Rivers and their tributaries. The coal fields are the sites of a series of moderately to deeply downwarped synclinoria that are separated by complementary anticlinoria. Each of the synclinoria and anticlinoria are complexes of closely spaced anticlines and synclines broken by many reverse, thrust, and bedding plane faults that are rooted in one or more décollements underlying the coal-bearing rocks.

Coal-bearing strata in the region are Pennsylvanian in age. Between the coal fields, the underlying Devonian and Mississippian age rocks crop out. Resistant strata of the Pottsville Forma-

tion of Early and Middle Pennsylvanian age form high ridges around each field, and the overlying less resistant Llewellyn Formation of Middle and Late Pennsylvanian age underlies the valley (synclinal) floor within each field.

Although the Pottsville Formation contains some coal beds of economic value, the Llewellyn Formation is truly rich in the number and thickness of its coal beds. The depositional and structural history of the Pennsylvania Anthracite region and surrounding areas is responsible for the presence of these numerous, thick, low-sulfur coals. This paper presents a summary of our understanding of the geologic characteristics of the region and the development of the Pennsylvania Anthracite fields.

STRATIGRAPHY

Although the main coal-bearing strata of the region are the Pottsville and Llewellyn Formations, the Mauch Chunk Formation forms the basal part of the depositional sequence, and sets the depositional framework for subsequent coal-bearing sequences. The Mauch Chunk Formation is of Late Mississippian and Early Pennsylvanian age and overlies the Pocono Formation of Early Mississippian age (Fig. 2). The Mauch Chunk is overlain successively by the Pottsville Formation and the major coal-bearing

*Deceased May 22, 1986.

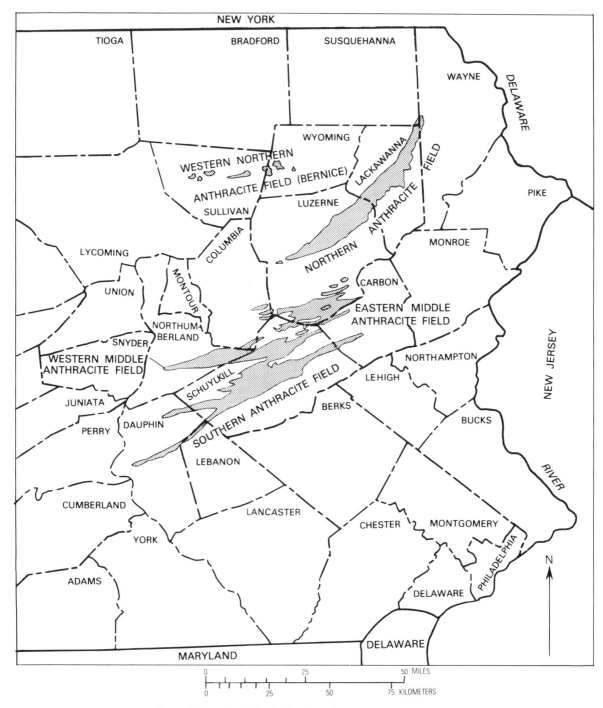

Figure 1. Location of the Anthracite region, eastern Pennsylvania.

formation, the Llewellyn. The Mauch Chunk and underlying Pocono Formation and the Spechty Kopf Formation of Late Devonian age are absent in the northeast half of the Northern Anthracite field, where the Pottsville Formation lies disconformably on the Catskill Formation.

The general stratigraphy of Upper Mississippian and Pennsylvanian rocks in the region is known, but the details and interrelations are not completely understood because of structural complexities and poor exposures. The rocks are almost entirely nonmarine except for the Mill Creek limestone member of Ashburner (1886). The biostratigraphy is based largely on plant fossils. Paleobotanical data combined with depositional interpretations were used to develop the stratigraphic framework for the region.

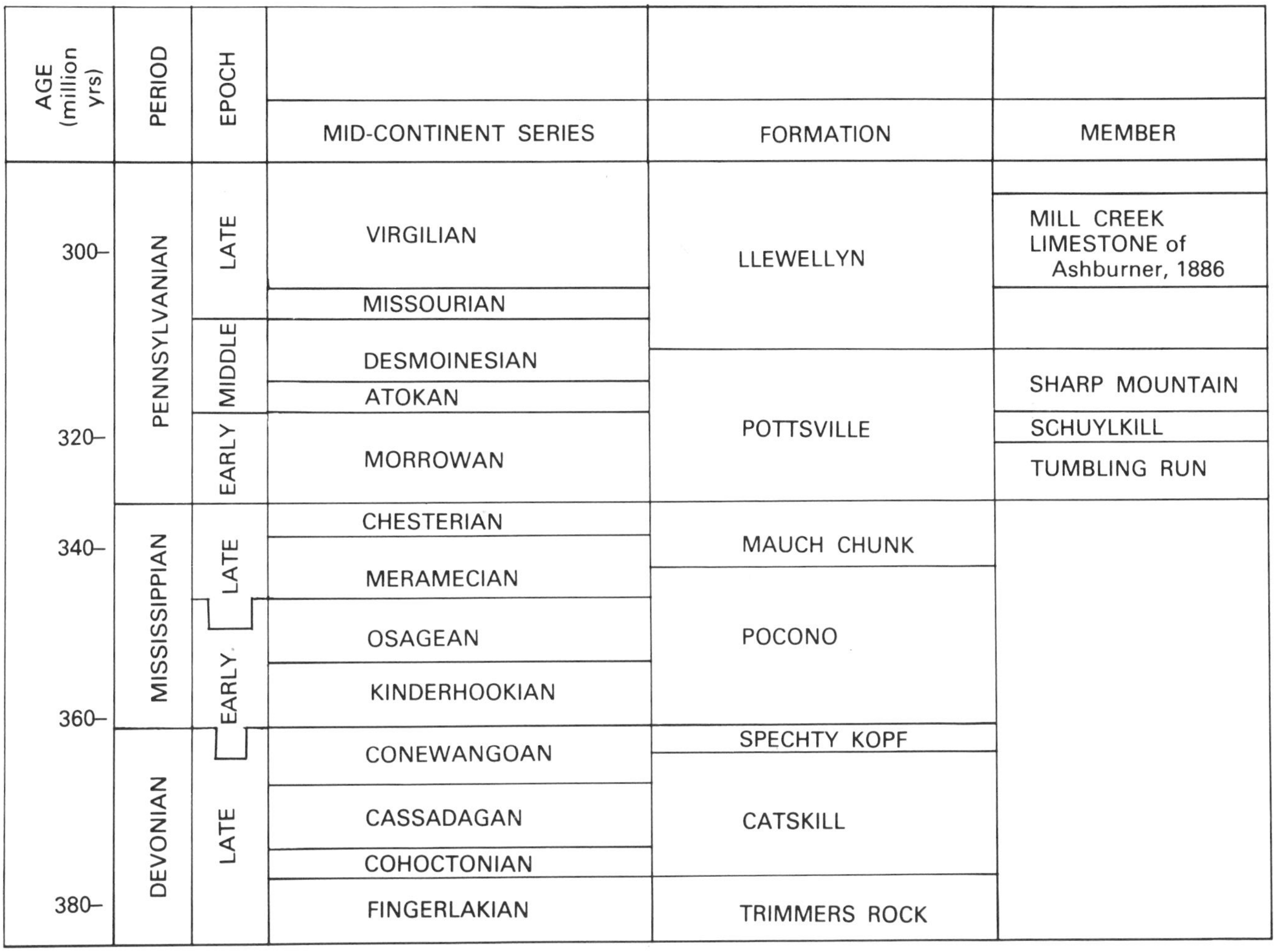

AGE (million yrs)	PERIOD	EPOCH	MID-CONTINENT SERIES	FORMATION	MEMBER
300–	PENNSYLVANIAN	LATE	VIRGILIAN	LLEWELLYN	MILL CREEK LIMESTONE of Ashburner, 1886
			MISSOURIAN		
		MIDDLE	DESMOINESIAN	POTTSVILLE	SHARP MOUNTAIN
			ATOKAN		SCHUYLKILL
320–		EARLY	MORROWAN		TUMBLING RUN
340–	MISSISSIPPIAN	LATE	CHESTERIAN	MAUCH CHUNK	
			MERAMECIAN		
		EARLY	OSAGEAN	POCONO	
			KINDERHOOKIAN		
360–	DEVONIAN	LATE	CONEWANGOAN	SPECHTY KOPF	
			CASSADAGAN	CATSKILL	
			COHOCTONIAN		
380–			FINGERLAKIAN	TRIMMERS ROCK	

Figure 2. Chart of strata of Late Devonian to Late Pennsylvanian age in the Pennsylvania Anthracite region (units not to scale).

Physical Stratigraphy

Mauch Chunk Formation. In the Anthracite region, the Mauch Chunk Formation includes all of the strata between the Pocono and Pottsville Formations (Fig. 2). Although the Mauch Chunk rocks are poorly exposed and are structurally complicated by faulting and folding, and lack stratigraphic markers, they have been subdivided into three informal members; lower, middle, and upper. The lower and upper members contain more sandstone and siltstone and underlie moderate to steep slopes adjacent to the underlying Pocono and the overlying Pottsville Formations; the middle member, which contains mostly fine-grained sandstone, siltstone, and shale, underlies valleys where the relief is generally less than 91 m (300 ft).

The contact between the Mauch Chunk and Pottsville Formations was defined at the type section of the Pottsville Formation in the Southern Anthracite field and at the boundary between the Mississippian and Pennsylvanian Systems (Moore and others, 1944, p. 665; Wood and others, 1956, p. 2670–2671). The type section of the Pottsville is at Schuylkill Gap in Sharp Mountain at the southern edge of the Southern Anthracite field. There, the upper member of the Mauch Chunk intertongues with the overlying Tumbling Run Member of the Pottsville Formation. Elsewhere in the Anthracite region, the time boundary lies within the upper member of the Mauch Chunk because of the intertonguing and northward rise of the contact.

The contact of the lower member of the Mauch Chunk Formation and the underlying Pocono is placed at the top of the gray beds of Pocono lithology and at the base of the lowest red beds of Mauch Chunk lithology. The lower member wedges out in the subsurface in the northern part of the Northern Anthracite field but is as much as 244 m (800 ft) thick on the south side of the western part of the Southern Anthracite field; commonly it is from 61 to 152 m (200 to 500 ft) thick. The lower member consists of grayish-red and pale brown shale, siltstone, sandstone, and sparse conglomerate. Gray rocks of the member are similar to those of the Pocono, except that mica is more abundant and rock fragments are less abundant than in the Pocono. The gray sandstone is mostly medium-grained, whereas the red sandstone is very fine to fine-grained. Beds are commonly tabular, ranging from thin- to thick-bedded. Small-scale and planar cross-beds are conspicuous in a few places, but generally are uncommon. The mineral assemblages of the rocks are assignable to the proto-quartzite and subgraywacke clans (Wood and others, 1969). Limonite and hematite occur as films around mineral grains, fillings in interstitial openings, and, along with silica and clay, form cement in the red rocks. However, hematite and limonite are rare in the gray rocks.

The basal contact of the middle member is at the top of the uppermost gray, light-brown, or orange sandstone or conglomer-ate bed of the lower member. Locally, the middle member inter-tongues with and elsewhere grades laterally upward into the upper member. The middle member is about 335 m (1,100 ft) thick in southwestern parts of the Southern and Western Middle fields. Largely grayish-red in color, the middle member is com-posed of sandstone, siltstone, shale, and clay gall conglomerate, which are commonly classified as graywackes, subgraywackes, and protoquartzite clans (Wood and others, 1969). The gray sandstone is predominantly medium- to coarse-grained, whereas the red sandstone is very fine grained. Some of the red sandstone beds in the upper part of the member contain as much as 20% andesine. In addition to limonite, hematite, silica, and clay miner-als, calcite and sericite are cementing minerals. Bedding thickness ranges from .33 cm to 5 m (0.13 in to 16 ft) and averages about 15 cm (6 in). Beds are commonly platy or massive and, in larger exposures, exhibit wedge-shaped or lenticular bedding. Ripple scale cross-laminations and laminations are very common and are in places contorted, suggesting syngenetic slumping.

The basal contact of the upper member is placed at the base of the oldest gray conglomerate, sandstone, siltstone, or shale of Pottsville-type lithology and is located commonly at a topo-graphic steepening. The upper contact is at the top of the uppermost red bed lithology. The upper member consists of al-ternating and intertonguing beds of red rocks typical of the Mauch Chunk Formation and gray rocks typical of the Pottsville Formation (Smith, 1895; White, 1900; Barrell, 1907). The thick-ness of the upper member is difficult to determine due to inter-tonguing with the underlying middle member and with the overlying Pottsville strata. The upper member is about 183 m (600 ft) thick in the south, thins to 15 m (50 ft) toward the northwest, and feathers out to the northeast. Rocks of this member include conglomerate, sandstone, siltstone, and shale, which are either grayish-red Mauch Chunk lithology or medium- to dark-gray Pottsville lithology facies. Bedding is tabular in finer grained rocks, and wedge or lenticular in coarser grained rocks; beds are generally less than 1.5 m (5 ft) thick and average about .6 m (2 ft). Cross-beds are common in the conglomerate and coarser sandstone. Fine-grained rocks are commonly ripple marked and may contain carbonized plant fragments. Rock com-position of both lithologies of the upper member is protoquartzite or subgraywacke. Clasts in the conglomerate are largely vein quartz; however, the basal parts of the conglomerates often con-tain granule to cobble-sized fragments of red shale, siltstone, and sandstone. The major constituents of rocks in the upper member are quartz and quartzite. Cements are similar to those in the middle member, except for a paucity of limonite and hematite in the gray Pottsville lithologies.

Pottsville Formation. The Pottsville Formation, which in-cludes all rocks between the underlying Mauch Chunk and over-lying Llewellyn Formation, ranges from 15 to 457 m (50 to 1500 ft) in thickness. It is divided, in ascending order, into three members in the Anthracite region: the Tumbling Run Member of early Early Pennsylvanian age, the Schuylkill Member of late Early Pennsylvanian age and the Sharp Mountain Member of Middle Pennsylvanian age (Wood and others, 1956). The Sharp Mountain Member is immediately overlain by the Buck Moun-tain (No. 5) coal bed of the Llewellyn Formation.

The Pottsville Formation was named by Lesley in 1876 (p. 221–227) for a sequence of rocks in the Boyds Hill well near Pittsburgh, Pennsylvania. It was defined by Lesley as a conglomerate overlying the Mauch Chunk Red Shale and under-lying the lower productive coal measures (Allegheny Formation of modern usage). In 1900, C. D. White (p. 755–756) redesig-nated the location of the type section as being in Schuylkill Gap, south of Pottsville, Pennsylvania rather than in the Boyds Hill well. The stratigraphic type section exposed in Schuylkill Gap was measured on the east side of the Gap along the tracks of the Pennsylvania Railroad. The stratigraphic sequence contains four recognized paleobotanical divisions (White, 1900, p. 733–775). A better exposed reference section was established about 46 m (150 ft) east of the type section on the east side of Pennsylvania State Highway 61 (Wood and others, 1956, p. 2671–2673). The reference section of the Pottsville is the type section of the Tumbling Run, Schuylkill, and Sharp Mountain Members.

Tumbling Run Member. The oldest member of the Potts-ville Formation in the Anthracite region, the Tumbling Run Member, was named after a small stream southeast of Schuylkill Gap (Wood and others, 1956, p. 2671). It underlies ridges sup-ported by the Pottsville throughout much of the southern part of the region, including all of the Southern and Western Middle Anthracite fields. The Tumbling Run Member may be missing along parts of the northernmost outcrop belt of the Pottsville in the Eastern Middle field in Luzerne County. It has not been recognized in the Northern field in Luzerne, Lackawanna, Wayne, and Susquehanna Counties or in the Western Northern (Bernice) field in Sullivan and Wyoming counties (Fig. 1). The thickness of the Tumbling Run Member ranges from very thin or absent in the Eastern Middle field to about 183 m (600 ft) thick on the south side of the Southern field.

The lower contact of the Tumbling Run Member is at the top of the uppermost red bed of the Mauch Chunk Formation. Conglomerate and conglomeratic sandstone comprise about 55 percent of the member and are concentrated mostly in the lower and middle parts of the unit. The conglomeratic rocks are gener-ally poorly sorted. Cobbles and pebbles are scattered in the matrix and show no apparent lineation, except that the more ovoid cobbles and pebbles are oriented parallel to bedding. Pebbles and cobbles in the lower and middle parts of the unit average about 2.5 cm (1 in), although some are as much as 20 cm (8 in) in diameter; the size generally decreases in a north-northwest direction. In the upper part of the unit, the pebbles average about 1.3 cm (0.5 in) in diameter but can be as much as 3.8 cm (1.5 in) in diameter. Most cobbles and pebbles are well-rounded, broken and fractured and, on weathering, separate easily from the matrix.

Fine- to coarse-grained sandstone comprises about 30 percent of the Tumbling Run and is largely concentrated in the upper part of the member. Generally, sandstone beds are .6 to 4.6 m (2 to 15 ft) thick, but in some zones they range from 2.5 cm to .5 m (1 in to 1.5 ft) in thickness. Although tabular bedding predominates, lenticular and wedge bedding are common. Small- to medium-planar cross-bedding is prevalent in all beds. Shale and siltstone comprise about 15 percent of the Tumbling Run. Although some beds reach 6 m (20 ft) in thickness, most are about 1.3 to 60 cm (0.5 in to 2 ft) thick. The beds are mostly tabular, though some are lenticular and wedge-shaped, and generally the beds are parallel laminated. Six beds of anthracite are present in the Tumbling Run and are exposed in the southeastern part of the region in the Southern and Western Middle Anthracite fields. Their stratigraphic positions are shown in Figure 3. Three of these beds—the Lykens Valley Nos. 4, 5, and 6—are fairly persistent and have been mined. The thicknesses of these beds vary greatly, but in many places they may be as much as 2.4 m (8 ft) thick.

Most clastic rocks of the Tumbling Run Member are compositionally subgraywacke but some are orthoquartzite. The constituents of these rocks are similar, regardless of grain size, and differ only in the percentages of the various minerals present. The mineral assemblage consists of quartz, ilmenite, magnetite, tourmaline, zircon, sphene, leucoxene, andesine, oligoclase, kyanite, staurolite, garnet, epidote, limonite, hematite, biotite, muscovite, chlorite, sericite, and unidentified clay minerals; rock fragments include chert, schist, phyllite, slate, shale, sandstone, and quartzite. Cements include silica, sericite, clay minerals, hematite, limonite, and a clastic binder of clay- and silt-sized quartz fragments. Very coarse grains are generally rounded to well-rounded; very fine to coarse grains average subangular to subrounded.

The upper contact of the Tumbling Run Member is at the base of the lowermost pebble conglomerate of the Schuylkill Member, and the lithologies of the two members can be distinguished by several specific characteristics. Rocks of the Tumbling Run are generally finer grained than the basal pebble conglomerate and their color includes more green, yellow, and orange tints than the overlying light- to dark-gray conglomerate. In addition, pebbles in the upper part of the Tumbling Run are sparsely scattered in a sandstone matrix. They are generally less than 3.8 cm (1.5 in) in diameter, commonly fractured, and generally well-rounded. They are polymictic and consist of vein quartz, quartzite, chert, schist, gneiss, sandstone, siltstone, and shale. In contrast, pebbles in the conglomerate of the Schuylkill are oligomictic,

more abundant, evenly distributed in a sandstone or granule matrix, as much as 7.6 cm (3 in) in diameter, generally not fractured, mostly well-rounded, and composed chiefly of vein quartz and quartzite.

Schuylkill Member. The Schuylkill Member, the middle member of the Pottsville Formation in the Anthracite region, was named by Wood and others (1956, p. 2671) for the Schuylkill River, which drains through a gap of the same name on the south edge of the Southern Anthracite field. The member is widely exposed along the margins and crests of the Southern, Western Middle, and Eastern Middle Anthracite fields. It has not been identified in the Northern or Western Northern (Bernice) fields and appears to be missing due to nondeposition. Generally, belts of outcrop are very steep and smooth compared to those of the Tumbling Run and Sharp Mountain Members. Locally, the belt is mantled by talus and is almost everywhere covered by a heavy forest. Throughout the Southern and Western Middle Anthracite fields, the basal conglomerate of the Schuylkill rests conformably on the finer-grained rocks of the Tumbling Run Member. Stratigraphic studies in these fields indicate that the Schuylkill Member intertongues on a regional scale with the Tumbling Run Member. The basal conglomerate of the Schuylkill Member gradually rises in the stratigraphic section from south to north and has not been recognized north of the Eastern Middle field. Where the Tumbling Run Member is absent due to the onlap or stratigraphic rise of the Pottsville strata, the Schuylkill Member locally may rest unconformably on the middle or lower members of the Mauch Chunk Formation.

Thickness of the Schuylkill Member ranges from about 15 m (50 ft) in the Eastern Middle Anthracite field to about 213 m (700 ft) in the southeastern part of the Southern Anthracite field. Weathered and fresh rocks of the member range from light- to dark-gray, but commonly are medium-gray. Fresh outcrops are commonly stained lightly with limonite; weathering gradually removes the staining. Tabular bedding predominates, but wedge-shaped and irregular bedding are common. Parallel laminated beds predominate over cross-laminated beds. Most cross-stratifications are simple and planar, and range from small to large. The thickness of most conglomerate and sandstone beds range from .6 to 7.6 m (2 to 25 ft), whereas most shale and siltstone beds are 1.2 cm to .5 m (0.5 in to 1.8 ft) thick. Graded and reverse graded beds are common in the coarse-grained rocks. Coalified plant fragments are abundant in many shale beds and are common on bedding planes in the coarser-grained rocks. Conglomerate and conglomeratic sandstone comprise about 50 percent of the Schuylkill Member. The pebbles in these rocks are largely composed of vein quartz and quartzite. Chert is also common. Other constituents are schist, phyllite, gneiss, sandstone, shale, siltstone, and granite. Most clastic rock fragments are well-rounded and equidimensional to ovoid. Generally, the chert is scattered evenly in a dark- to light-gray matrix consisting of very fine to very coarse grains of quartz, quartzite, rock fragments, and accessory mineral grains. The larger clasts, which are locally as much as 7.6 cm (3 in) in diameter, are generally concentrated in

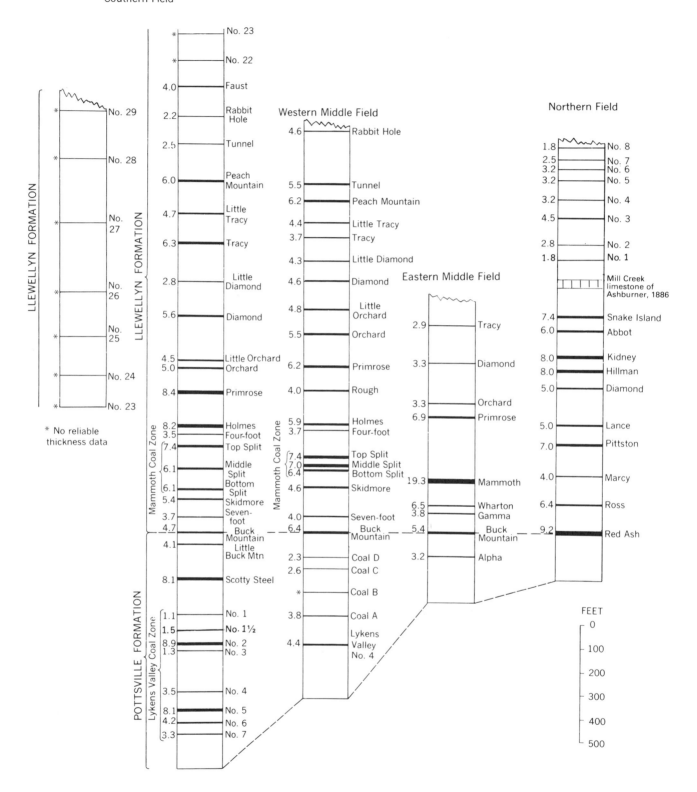

Figure 3. Generalized columnar sections showing names, average thickness of coals (in feet), and intervals between coal beds in the Pennsylvania Anthracite fields (modified from Arndt and others, 1968).

the basal conglomerates of the member. Pebbles above the basal conglomerate are mostly less than 2.5 cm (1 in) in diameter and average .6 to 1.2 cm (0.25 to 0.5 in) in diameter. The conglomerate and conglomeratic sandstone in the Schuylkill generally weathers into pebble gravels that are distinctive because of the small average diameter of the well-rounded pebbles, which are in an unfractured condition. Sorting is poor to moderate; the long axes of clasts are mostly parallel to the bedding. The rock is generally well cemented. Rocks of the Schuylkill are, compositionally, protoquartzite and subgraywacke; they consist of the same mineral assemblage and cements as those found in the Tumbling Run Member. Margins of many quartz grains and quartzite fragments are deeply sutured by pressure solution.

Four relatively persistent and several thin, nonpersistent, anthracite beds have been identified in the Schuylkill Member in the western parts of the Southern and Western Middle Anthracite fields. The consistent stratigraphic position of the Lykens Valley No. 1 bed with respect to upper contact of the Schuylkill in the Southern and Western Middle fields supports the conclusion that the Schuylkill and Sharp Mountain Members are conformable in those areas. The four coal beds are the Lykens Valley Nos. 3, 2, 1½ and 1 (Fig. 3). Although several of these beds are more than 4 m (14 ft) thick at some localities, they commonly average only a few feet thick.

The upper contact of the Schuylkill Member with the Sharp Mountain Member is at the base of a conglomerate typical of the Sharp Mountain, which rests conformably upon the finer grained rocks of the Schuylkill. This coarseness and the resistance to erosion of the basal part of the Sharp Mountain Member serves to differentiate it from the underlying Schuylkill.

Sharp Mountain Member. The Sharp Mountain Member, which is the youngest unit assigned to the Pottsville Formation in the Anthracite region, was named by Wood and others (1956, p. 2671) for Sharp Mountain at Schyulkill Gap. White (1900, p. 801), Moore and others (1944, p. 680); Meckel (1967, p. 230), and Wood and others (1969, p. 74), recognized the persistence and character of the basal conglomerate of this unit throughout the Appalachian Plateaus Province. The member crops out at or near the crests of Pottsville ridges that surround the four fields of the Anthracite region. The Sharp Mountain ranges from about 15 m (50 ft) to about 488 m (1600 ft) in thickness. The greatest thickness is preserved along the southern margin of the region and lesser thickness along the northern margin. The thickness data suggests that the axis of the depositional basin of the Pottsville Formation probably lay south of Sharp Mountain, but this distance is unknown because of post-Pennsylvanian erosion.

The basal conglomerate of the Sharp Mountain rests conformably upon conglomeratic sandstone, sandstone, siltstone, and shale in the upper part of the Schuylkill. The basal conglomerate commonly forms a series of moderately to steeply dipping ledges or a near vertical wall that rises abruptly above finer grained Schuylkill beds. In some localities, the basal conglomerate has weathered into gravels that mantle the surrounding area. The upper contact of the Sharp Mountain is the base of the underclay

beneath the Buck Mountain (No. 5) coal bed or, where the underclay is absent, the contact is the base of this coal bed. The Buck Mountain coal bed is considered to be continuous throughout the region and is correlated with the Red Ash coal bed in the Northern field.

Fresh and weathered rocks in the Sharp Mountain Member are chiefly medium gray. Tabular and lenticular beds are about equally abundant, whereas wedge- and irregular-shaped beds are uncommon. Most strata are either cross-laminated or parallel-bedded. The orientation of simple and planar cross-bedding suggests deposition by northeast flowing currents. Most beds range from 1.2 to 3 m (4 to 10 ft) in thickness, although some beds are from 10 cm to 1.2 m (4 in to 4 ft) thick. Conglomerate and conglomeratic sandstone beds are generally thicker than beds of siltstone and shale. Normal graded bedding is common, whereas reverse graded bedding is generally sparse. Plant debris (compressions and impressions) are abundant in all rock types but are well preserved only in the siltstone and shale throughout the member. The gravel weathered from the Sharp Mountain Member is distinguished by its coarse size, well-rounded shape, and unfractured condition. Generally, the coarse sandstone and conglomerate of the Sharp Mountain are a well cemented protoquartzite or subgraywacke like those rocks of the Schuylkill Member.

Three persistent coal beds, the Scotty Steel Nos. 2 and 3 and the Little Buck Mountain (No. 4), occur in the Sharp Mountain Member (Fig. 3). The Scotty Steel No. 3 coal is more than 5.5 m (18 ft) thick, averaging more than 3 m (10 ft). It is economically the most important of the three beds. The Scotty Steel No. 2 averages less than .6 m (2 ft) thick, whereas the less widespread Little Buck Mountain coal bed averages about 2 m (7 ft), of which 1.2 m (4.1 ft) is coal.

Llewellyn Formation. The centers of the four anthracite fields and the semianthracite fields are underlain by the Llewellyn Formation. The Llewellyn Formation was named by Wood and others (1962) for a town in the central part of the Southern Anthracite field. Previously these rocks were referred to as an informal stratigraphic unit known as the "coal measures" (Smith, 1895, p. 1920).

Natural exposures of the Llewellyn are sparse, but there are many manmade exposures developed during surface and underground mining. Many billions of tons of mine waste have been dumped at the surface; consequently, a great deal is known about rocks in the surface pits but little is known about the rocks between the mines.

The base of the Llewellyn is the base of the shale or underclay below the Buck Mountain (No. 5) coal bed or, where the shale is absent, at the base of the coal bed. The upper limit of the Llewellyn is the present erosional surface at most places, except where mantled by Quaternary alluvium. The Llewellyn Formation has a maximum thickness of about 1066 m (3,500 ft) in the central part of the Southern field.

Freshly broken and weathered rocks of the formation are generally light- to dark-gray, black, or brownish. The lithology varies greatly, including conglomerate, sandstone, siltstone, shale, clay, coal, and small amounts of marine limestone. The Llewellyn Formation is characterized by many lateral variations in rock type; locally these may account for abrupt changes in internal between-datum horizons. Over greater distances, however, thicknesses are rather even between these datum horizons. For example, local thickness variations are numerous and abrupt between the Buck Mountain (No. 5) coal bed and the coal beds of the Mammoth coal zone, between coal beds within the Mammoth coal zone, and between the top coal bed of the Mammoth zone and the Diamond (No. 14) coal bed. But the average thickness between the Buck Mountain (No. 5) and Diamond is about 274 m (900 ft), with a range in variation of 236 to 290 m (775 to 950 ft). These local variations between adjacent horizons probably resulted from differential compaction of the finer grained sediments.

Conglomerate and conglomeratic sandstone occur randomly in the Llewellyn. A conglomerate bed that overlies the roof shale of the Primrose (No. 11) coal bed is traceable over a large part of the northern margin of the Southern field. A series of conglomerate beds crop out between the Nos. 22 and 25 coal beds in the central part of the Southern Anthracite field. Similar conglomeratic beds are present in the Llewellyn Formation in the other three anthracite fields but are less common.

Most conglomerate in the Llewellyn is poorly to moderately sorted, but locally some is well sorted and closely resembles the basal conglomerate of the Sharp Mountain Member of the Pottsville Formation. Conglomerate beds below the Peach Mountain (No. 18) contain pebbles as much as 5 cm (2 in) in diameter, with an average of 1.3 cm (0.5 in) in diameter. The conglomerates above that bed locally contain cobbles averaging 7.6 cm (3 in) in diameter and averaging 1.9 cm (¾ in) in diameter. The larger clasts are mainly vein quartz and quartzite with smaller amounts of chert, schist, gneiss, slate, sandstone, siltstone, and shale that are similar to clasts in conglomerates of the Pottsville Formation. The percentage of clasts from metamorphic terranes increases upward stratigraphically, probably indicating an increasing exposure of metamorphic rocks in the source area.

Fine- to coarse-grained sandstone is present throughout the Llewellyn. Bedding ranges in thickness from 1.3 cm to 4.6 m (0.5 in to 15 ft), and averages about 3.8 cm (1.5 in) in thickness. Tabular beds predominate, but lenticular beds are common, and wedge-shaped and irregular beds are locally common. Although most strata are parallel laminated, small- to large-scale simple and planar cross-strata are common in many places.

Siltstone and shale beds range from 2.5 cm to .6 m (1 in to 2 ft) in thickness. Many sequences of these beds are 6 to 15 m (20 to 50 ft) thick. At many localities, the siltstone and shale beds are carbonaceous, contain large amounts of plant debris, and are intercollated with beds of anthracite. The underclays or shales of some anthracite beds are characterized by abundant *Stigmaria* impressions and a few beds contain upright tree trunks. Well-preserved impressions of leaves and stems are common in the roof shales of many anthracite beds.

The rocks of the Llewellyn are predominantly subgray-wacke. Some coarse grained sandstone and conglomerate approaches protoquartzite. The rocks in the lower part of the formation contain higher percentages of common quartz and vein quartz and smaller percentages of rock fragments, unidentified clay minerals, sericite, and other mica minerals than those of the upper parts of the formation. Other constituents include fragments of chert, schist, slate, siltstone, chlorite, ilmenite, leucoxene, magnetite, rutile, tourmaline, zircon, sphene, limonite, hematite, andesene, halloysite, and carbonaceous material.

The rocks of the Llewellyn are cemented principally by silica minerals, sericite, silt- and clay-sized quartz fragments, limonite, hematite, and carbonaceous material. The grains range from angular to well-rounded; the average is round. Many grains of quartz and quartzite are sutured, but when they are embedded in a fine-grained matrix of non-quartz minerals, suturing generally is absent.

In addition to the clastic rocks, limestone also occurs in the Northern field. Ashburner (1886, p. 447–449) reported on four thin beds of limestone, several of which crop out in and near the City of Wilkes-Barre. Other limestone outcrops have been discovered recently by Eggleston and Edmunds (unpublished data). The Mill Creek limestone of Ashburner (1886), containing marine fossils, is the most persistent (Ashburner, 1886; and Chow, 1951). Its stratigraphic position in the Llewellyn Formation, between the Snake Island and No. 1 coal beds, is shown in Figure 3. The limestone is generally siliceous, ferruginous, and generally less than .9 m (3 ft) thick.

Clastic rocks in the Llewellyn are commonly tabular, lenticular, and wedge-shaped. The beds are usually .3 to .6 m (1 to 2 ft) thick, but range from 1.3 cm to 6 m (½ in to 20 ft) thick. Thin- to thick-channel sandstone deposits are sparse, but locally conspicuous. Many beds are graded; reverse grading is rare. Although parallel laminations predominate over cross-lamination, small- to large-scale simple and planar cross-strata are abundant. The cross laminations, cross-beds, ripple marks, oriented plant fragments, and an increase in pebble diameter to the southeast indicate deposition by northwestward flowing streams. Preservation of ripple marks and oriented plant fragments is best in very fine and medium-grained sandstone and siltstone, but well-preserved plant fossils are most common in shale adjacent to anthracite beds. Plant debris is abundant in all rock types. Sandstone-filled channel cutouts are sparse but locally conspicuous.

Forty anthracite beds in the Llewellyn in the Southern field are sufficiently thick, widespread, and economically important to be identified and named; many have been mined. The beds have been numbered upward from the base, starting with 5 and ending with 29. The more widely persistent and thicker beds are: the Buck Mountain (No. 5), the Skidmore (No. 7), Bottom Split (No. 8), Middle Split (No. 8½), Top Split (No. 9), Holmes (No. 10), Primrose (No. 11), Diamond (No. 14), Tracy (No. 16), and Peach Mountain (No. 18). These coal beds are confined to the lower 457 m (1,500 ft) of the Llewellyn; most are in the lower 198 m (650 ft). The coal beds average less than 3 m (10 ft) in thickness but may be as much as 15 m (50 ft) thick; at a few localities, thickening has increased to 29 m (95 ft) or more due to structural deformation.

The coal bed names and numbers listed apply to coal beds of the Llewellyn in the Southern and Western Middle Anthracite fields. The same or stratigraphically equivalent beds in the Eastern Middle and Northern Anthracite fields have somewhat different names and numbers. Generalized columnar sections showing the major coal beds in each field and their general stratigraphic relationship are presented in Figure 3.

The Buck Mountain coal bed (No. 5) is an economically important, relatively thick (2 to 3 m [7 to 10 ft]), and a very persistent coal bed. Because it is so widespread over the entire Anthracite region, it constitutes an important stratigraphic marker bed that probably correlates with the Red Ash coal bed in the Northern field. Another significant economic and stratigraphic unit is the Mammoth coal zone. It lies about 61–91 m (200–300 ft) above the Buck Mountain coal bed, and occurs in as many as three splits (Top [No. 9], Middle [No. 8½], Bottom [No. 8]), which total as much as 20 m (65 ft) of coal. Where it occurs as only one bed, it is commonly 15 m (50 ft) thick. Because of its persistence and unusual thickness, the Mammoth coal zone is easily recognized in drilling logs and is used as a marker bed for correlations. In the Northern field, it is correlated with the Pittston (or Baltimore) coal bed (Fig. 3).

Other coal beds are less extensive, thinner, and somewhat more lenticular. Beds above the Faust (No. 21) crop out in small parts of the Southern field; they are rarely prospected or mined because they are so variable in quality and thickness.

Roof and floor rocks of the Llewellyn coal beds are chiefly shale and siltstone, but in places are sandstone and conglomerate. The floor rock of the Pottsville coal beds is also mainly shale and siltstone, but the roof rock is most commonly sandstone or conglomerate. In both formations, however, the type of roof and floor rock varies laterally and only rarely does one rock type persist for any distance along strike or downdip. Shale and clay partings commonly occur within the coal beds and constitute 20 to 40 percent of most beds.

Biostratigraphy

Lesquereux (1879–1884) was the first to use plant megafossils extensively for biostratigraphic purposes in the United States. He identified the specimens in large collections made by both himself and R. D. Lacoe, and summarized both the horizontal (geographic) and vertical (chronologic) problems involved in studying the sequence. He established tentative correlations between the Northern and Southern Anthracite fields, and between the Anthracite region and the bituminous region of western Pennsylvania. C. D. White (1900) subsequently refined these early interpretations and made interregional stratigraphic correlations, including comparisons with western European floras. A major interest of White's was the Pottsville Formation, and he published an extensive volume on the floras of the Pottsville in the Southern Anthracite field in 1900. Darrah (1937) extended intercontinental correlations on the Upper Pennsylvanian floras. His scheme of floral succession was followed by more detailed work by Read and Mamay (1960, 1964). Darrah (1969) published a comprehensive volume on Upper Pennsylvanian floras in which floras of the Llewellyn Formation in the Southern Anthracite field were described and correlated with floras from the bituminous coal region of Pennsylvania.

The floral zonation for the Pennsylvanian and Mississippian of the Appalachian region (Read and Mamay, 1964) is presented in Figure 4. Despite Read and Mamay's placement of the post-Pottsville (Llewellyn) rocks completely in the Late Pennsylvanian, the authors believe that the lower portion of the Llewellyn Formation is latest Middle Pennsylvanian in age (Wood and others, 1969; Lyons and others, 1985). White (1900) correlated the Buck Mountain (No. 5) coal bed, which lies at or near the base of the Llewellyn, with the Lower Kittanning coal bed in the middle part of the Allegheny Formation of central and western Pennsylvania. Read confirmed this correlation by both oral (1954) and written communication (1955), and stated that these coals contain a flora characteristic of the upper part of his *Neuropteris rarinervis* floral zone (9). In addition, Olekshyshyn (1982) confirmed from paleobotanical studies that the shale just below the Buck Mountain coal bed is of late Middle Pennsylvanian age (Westphalian D), equivalent to the middle and upper parts of the Allegheny Formation. According to Read and Mamay (1964), the Llewellyn Formation correlates with the upper part of the Allegheny and lower part of the Conemaugh Formation. However, recent investigations suggest a younger age. Darrah (1969, p. 26) noted a marked change in the floras that occur above the middle of the Conemaugh of western Pennsylvania. Although rare, the chief indicators of this change are *Lescuropteris moorii* and *Danaeites emersoni,* which have been found associated with the Tracy (No. 16) coal bed. They are somewhat more common higher in the section, near the Peach Mountain (No. 18), and Salem (No. 22) coal beds, as are some of the associated species listed above. Wood and others (1969) found *Sphenophyllum oblongifolium* and *Pecopteris feminaeformis* near the Faust (No. 21) coal bed. Eggleston and others (unpublished data) collected extensively just above the No. 25 coal bed and found *Lescuropteris moorii* and *Sphenophyllum oblongifolium.* Darrah (1969) has suggested the possibility of correlation of the upper part of the Llewellyn Formation with the Monongahela Group (Late Pennsylvanian age) or the Waynesburg Formation (Late Pennsylvanian and Early Permian) in western Pennsylvania (Berryhill and others, 1971).

The presence of marine limestone in the Northern Anthracite field offers another biostratigraphic marker. Chow (1951) identified various species of crinoids, brachiopods, pelecypods, gastropods, cephalopods, and trilobites in the Mill Creek limestone of Ashburner (1886). Chow (1951) postulated a brackish water environment during deposition on the basis of such evidence as dwarfing of the mollusks and normal sizes, but depleted species of brachiopods. Chow (1951) agreed with I. C. White (1903) in correlating the Mill Creek with the Ames Limestone of

System and Series	Floral zone	Name	Appalachian region except for Southern anthracite field	Southern anthracite field	Midcontinent region
PENNSYLVANIAN / UPPER	12	*Danaeites* spp.	Upper part Monongahela Formation.	Not known.	Missouri and Virgil Series.
	11	*Lescuropteris* spp.	Lower part Monongahela Formation and upper part Conemaugh Formation.	Not known.	In midcontinent region, zones 11 and 12 are not separable and are together designated the zone of *Odontopteris* spp.
	10	Neuropteris flexuosa and *Pecopteris* spp.	Lower part Conemaugh Formation and upper part Allegheny Formation.	Post-Pottsville rocks undifferentiated.	Upper part of Des Moines Series.
PENNSYLVANIAN / MIDDLE	9	*Neuropteris rarinervis*	Lower part Allegheny Formation.	Upper part Sharp Mountain Member, Pottsville Formation.	Lower part of Des Moines Series.
	8	*Neuropteris tenuifolia*	Major part Kanawha Formation.	Not known.	Major part of Atoka Series.
	7	*Megalopteris* spp.	Base of Kanawha Formation.	Not known.	Base of Atoka Series.
PENNSYLVANIAN / LOWER	6	*Neuropteris tennesseeana* and *Mariopteris pygmaea.*	Upper part New River Formation and upper part Lee Formation.	Schuylkill Member, Pottsville Formation.	Bloyd Shale, Morrow Series.
	5	*Mariopteris pottsvillea* and *Aneimites* spp.	Lower part New River Formation.	Lykens Valley No. 4 coal bed and adjacent strata of Tumbling Run Member, Pottsville Formation.	Locally, basal strata of Pennsylvanian System in midcontinent region.
	4	*Neuropteris pocahontas* and *Mariopteris eremopteroides*	Pocahontas Formation.	Lykens Valley No. 5 and No. 6 coal beds and adjacent strata of Tumbling Run Member, Pottsville Formation.	No floras known.
MISSISSIPPIAN	3	*Fryopsis* spp. and *Sphenopteridium* spp.	Mauch Chunk Formation.	Mauch Chunk Formation.	Chester Series. Similar flora occurs in Stanley Shale.
			No floras known.	No floras known.	Meramac Series. No floras known.
	2	*Triphyllopteris* spp.	Upper part of Pocono and Price Formations.	Upper part of Pocono Formation.	Osage Series. No floras known.
	1	*Adiantites* spp.	Lower part of Pocono and Price Formations.	Lower part of Pocono Formation.	Kinderhook Series. Only spores and fossil wood known.

Figure 4. Mississippian and Pennsylvanian floral zones of the Appalachian region (modified from Read and Mamay, 1964, tables 1-4).

the Conemaugh Group of western Pennsylvania on the basis of the similarity in faunal species and the eastern extent of the distribution of the Ames. A lack of abundant corals, crinoids, foraminifera, and bryozoa in the Mill Creek limestone of Ashburner (1886) indicates that the area may have been a constricted part of the Ames sea.

DEPOSITIONAL HISTORY

The type of sediments and the mechanism of deposition in the Pennsylvania Anthracite region during the Carboniferous were strongly controlled by tectonism adjacent to the region. This tectonic activity was apparently caused by the interaction of the North American and African plates as they periodically collided and separated. During times of uplift associated with collision, large volumes of clastic sediments were eroded and carried westward into the deepening Appalachian geosyncline as the mountains were upthrust near the continental margin. The mechanism of orogenic deformation is still a source of great debate. Geophysical and geological studies revealed one or more large-scale or master décollements, with characteristics similar to those described for the southern Appalachians by Harris and Milici (1977), that appear to be related to differences in competency between the Paleozoic cover rocks and the crystalline basement complex. The master décollements appear to have developed southeast of the region and to have extended northwestward by horizontally directed forces generated during four major episodes of continental collision. The first episode, the Taconic orogeny, began near the middle of Ordovician time; the second, the Acadian orogeny, began near the end of Middle Devonian time; the third (unnamed) orogeny occurred in Late Mississippian through Early Pennsylvanian time and culminated with the deposition of the thick conglomeratic sequences of the Pottsville Formation; and the fourth, the Alleghany orogeny, extended from Permian to early Triassic time. Stratigraphic evidence suggests that between these major orogenic episodes, smaller-scale pulses locally rejuvenated the source areas and erosional action from time to time. The total amount of crustal shortening across the Anthracite region resulting from these events was probably between 80 and 161 km (50 and 100 mi) in the southwestern part of the Southern Anthracite field (Cloos, 1940).

Deformation during the Devonian to Early Mississippian Acadian orogeny occurred mainly southeast of the Anthracite region. Coarse-grained clastics, eroded from the rocks in the orogenic belt, were carried northwestward into and across the region. They were deposited unconformably on a pre-Mississippian erosional surface of low topographic relief; these sediments ultimately formed the Pocono Formation. Subsequently, terrestrial sediments were carried from the southeast into a subsiding, asymmetric basin and deposited in upper flood plain or in other fluvial environments. These sediments, including fine to coarse sand, silt, and clay, became the largely reddish strata of the Mauch Chunk Formation. The axis of the depositional basin lay to the southeast of that formation's present-day southernmost outcrops; thus, the thickest Mauch Chunk Formation accumulated contiguous to the south margin of the Southern Anthracite field in an area where it has since been removed by erosion.

The stratigraphy and composition of the red beds support the hypothesis that the Mauch Chunk accumulated as well-drained fluvial upper delta plain deposits that were derived from a rapidly eroding highland source area to the southeast. The broad plain covered a differentially subsiding basin that permitted the accumulation of a thick wedge of fluvial red sediments. The wedge was thickest to the southeast, near the axis of the basin, and thinnest to the north, where epeirogenic upwarping in central and western New York and northern Pennsylvania occurred along the cratonic margin. This uplifting may have restricted Mauch Chunk deposition northward. The abundance of mudcracks, animal tracks, raindrop impressions, and plant debris in all rocks of the Mauch Chunk demonstrate that the surface of the depositional plain was at many times above sea level and was suitable for animal and plant life. Small- to medium-scale planar cross beds also indicate deposition by streams on a fluvial plain. Although the origin of the red color in the Mauch Chunk rocks is still in question, it is generally believed to be syndepositionally developed in a well-drained oxidizing environment (Wood and others, 1969, p. 68; Meckel, 1970, p. 53).

During the time of middle Mauch Chunk deposition, an andesite or diorite mass unroofed in the source area shed clastic sediments to the northwest, as indicated by the quantity of andesite clasts in the middle member. Because calcite is a cementing and interstitial material in the rocks in the middle and upper members of the Mauch Chunk, their source area may have contained some limestone, dolomite, or marble. Because many conglomerates in the upper member of the Mauch Chunk contain granule- to cobble-sized clasts of red shale, siltstone, and sandstone in their basal parts, the conglomerate beds must have accumulated near previously deposited finer grained red rocks that were being eroded and/or cannibalized. The Mauch Chunk delta prograded northwestward until Early Pennsylvanian time, when uplift to the north caused the cessation of further progradation.

Meanwhile, lower Pottsville Formation sediments were accumulating in the Southern field as a facies equivalent of the terminal Mauch Chunk deposits. Detritus consisting of gray polymictic gravels, coarse sand, and small amounts of silt and clay were carried onto the flood plain from the southeast source. Swamps developed during periods of less intense sedimentation. The Pottsville Formation represents the alluvial aspect of the northward-prograding Mauch Chunk delta complex. Rocks in the base of the Pottsville are intercalated with Mauch Chunk rocks. The Pottsville thins markedly to the north, due in part to increased distance from the source area, but more importantly to encroachment onto the more stable northern side of the depositional basin. Only the gravels assigned to the Sharp Mountain Member were deposited in the Northern field. Figure 5 presents a series of schematic drawings by Edmunds and others (1979) that depict a depositional model for rocks of the Pennsylvanian Period.

The drab colors of the rocks and preservation of carbonaceous material and anthracite suggest deposition in a reducing environment. Sedimentary structures, thickness patterns, and a southeastward increase in grain size indicate that the rocks of the Pottsville were derived from a source southeast of the area. Meckel (1967) determined that the fall line and source area lay approximately 113 km (70 mi) southeast of the southeastern margin of the Anthracite region, in the vicinity of Philadelphia. The Tumbling Run and Sharp Mountain Members of the Pottsville Formation, and the upper member of the Mauch Chunk Formation are the only stratigraphic units in which gneiss and granite and relatively unstable garnet, epidote, staurolite, kyanite, and sillimanite are found, suggesting that igneous and high-temperature metamorphic rocks were exposed in the source area (Wood and others, 1969). The remainder of the source material for these members was sedimentary rock.

Each of the three Pottsville members is defined by a thick sequence of vertically decreasing grain size, which is interpreted to represent fluvial deposition from a recurring uplift of the source area to the southeast. The Tumbling Run and Sharp Mountain contain coarser sediment, which could represent episodes of more intensive uplift in the source area during early deposition of these two members.

Sediment accumulated mainly in a series of north- to northwest-trending, thin to thick lobes separated by thinner se-

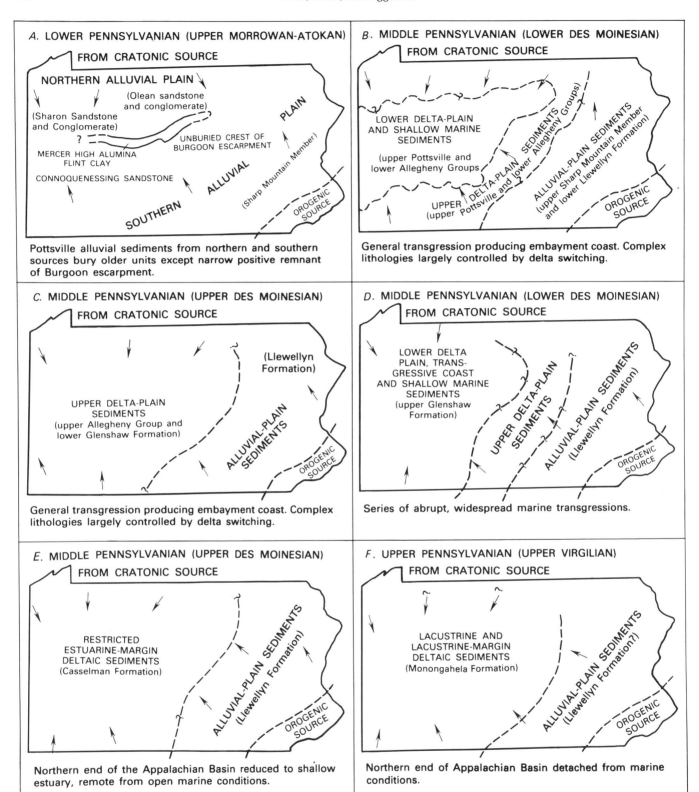

Figure 5. Pennsylvanian paleogeography and depositional environments (from Edmunds and others, 1979).

quences of finer-grained sediments. Conglomerate in the thick lobes contains cobbles as much as 20 cm (8 in) in diameter. In contrast, the diameter of the cobbles in thin lobes reaches a maximum diameter of about 13 cm (5 in). The greater size of the cobbles in thicker lobes suggests that they were the sites of the large alluvial fans of major streams and that the thinner lobes were the sites of inter-alluvial fans deposited by smaller streams. The deposition of the larger size cobbles also suggests that the source area was undergoing renewed uplift or that the sites of deposition were rapidly subsiding.

The end of Pottsville deposition was marked by the formation of a very extensive swamp, in which the plant matter of the Buck Mountain (No. 5) and its northern equivalents, the Dunmore and Red Ash, accumulated. The stratigraphic equivalence of these beds is suggested by their similar stratigraphic positions above the Sharp Mountain Member and by their content of the same fossil macroflora. Deposition of the Buck Mountain coal bed was terminated in most places by an influx of interbedded fine gravel and coarse- to fine-grained sand. The sequence of events that deposited the Buck Mountain coal bed and associated younger rocks of the Llewellyn Formation was repeated more than 40 times in the basin during Late Pennsylvanian time as other local to very extensive, thin- to thick-coal beds developed.

More than 40 swamps, covering hundreds to thousands of square miles, existed for more than one hundred, perhaps for as many as hundreds of thousands of years, in the region. These expansive swamps developed on a broad, flat alluvial plain. At places they were filled by clastic material from mountains in the southeast source area. The clastics were deposited as alluvial fans and in some areas as blankets of fine to coarse detritus on the alluvial plain. Large, extensive blankets of coarse sand or gravel do not seem to have been deposited in the lower or middle parts of the Llewellyn Formation, but many were deposited in the upper part of the formation. These more extensive coarse deposits suggest that renewed uplift of the source area took place before the end of Pennsylvanian deposition, an early effect of the Alleghany orogeny that later extended northwestward, deforming all Pennsylvanian and older rock in the region.

The thickness of some anthracite beds indicate that plant growth continued for long periods of time in a nearly stable swamp environment. Based on plant megafossils, it is evident that during the Late Pennsylvanian, tropical to subtropical conditions prevailed over a broad region from Pennsylvania to Alabama (Lyons and others, 1985) in which conditions were favorable for lush and prolific vegetation. Various estimates have been made for peat accumulation time and subsequent compression rates to produce anthracite. According to Ashley (1907, p. 42), a 12-m-(40-ft-)thick coal bed would require peat accumulation for 12,000 years. More recently, Altschuler and others (1983) found that in the Everglades the rate of peat accumulation is about 30 cm (1 ft) per 1000 years. Using these data and applying Ryer and Langer's (1980) compression rates, a 12-m-(40-ft-)thick anthracite bed would represent more than 400,000 years of accumula-

tion! Other studies indicate that the growth rate of tropical peats, probably more similar to the conditions during Carboniferous deposition, is considerably higher. For example, Anderson (1964) determined that in Northwest Borneo forest swamps, peat growth could reach 1 m per 300 to 400 years, approximately 10 times greater than Altschuler and others (1983) Everglades number. In any case, thick coal appears to represent very long periods of generally uninterrupted accumulation of plant detritus. The Mammoth coal beds are probably the best examples of persistent, thick coal. The Mammoth can be traced over great distances in the Southern and Middle fields, as can its equivalent, the Pittston coal zone in the Northern Anthracite field.

The flood plain on which the Late Pennsylvanian age swamps formed was bounded to the southeast by a rising highland area and on the west and northwest by a distant fluctuating continental coastline. A brief marine incursion from the western sea produced thin beds of limestone in the Northern field. They contain the marine or brackish-water faunal assemblage found in the Mill Creek limestone (Chow, 1951). Conditions to the northeast are unclear because erosion has removed the Pennsylvanian rocks there. The floodplain was underlain by a subsiding asymmetric depositional basin trending northeast–southwest, whose steep southeastern limb probably extended only a few miles southeast of the modern Anthracite region. The longer northwestern limb was much broader and extended into central Pennsylvania and perhaps all the way to the distant epicontinental coastline. Some evidence exists for the presence of the northeast-trending Waverly arch, which is northwest of the Northern Anthracite field and extends westward into the semianthracite fields. The position of the arch might have marked the northern termination of the Pottsville Formation.

STRUCTURE

Structural deformation of Carboniferous strata in the Anthracite region occurred during the Alleghany orogeny of Early to Middle Permian, and possibly Triassic, time. Probably some of the secondary orogenic pulses during Pottsville and Llewellyn deposition were precursors to the main orogenic activity. Many folds and faults formed in the region; the principal structural features are shown on Figure 6.

The Anthracite region is in a northeast-trending structural depression within the Valley and Ridge Province of east-central and northeastern Pennsylvania. The boundary of the depression is difficult to define, but to the north it is at the structural front of the Appalachian Mountains; to the east, the west edge of the Pocono Plateau; to the south it is the outcrop of the Tuscarora Sandstone; and to the west it is in the contorted outcrop belt of Middle Devonian rocks. Each coal field of the Anthracite region is a complexly folded and faulted synclinorium, with structural trends between N55°E and N85°E. The outlying semianthracite fields to the west are only mildly deformed in comparison to the four anthracite fields. The Northern field contains two sub-basins

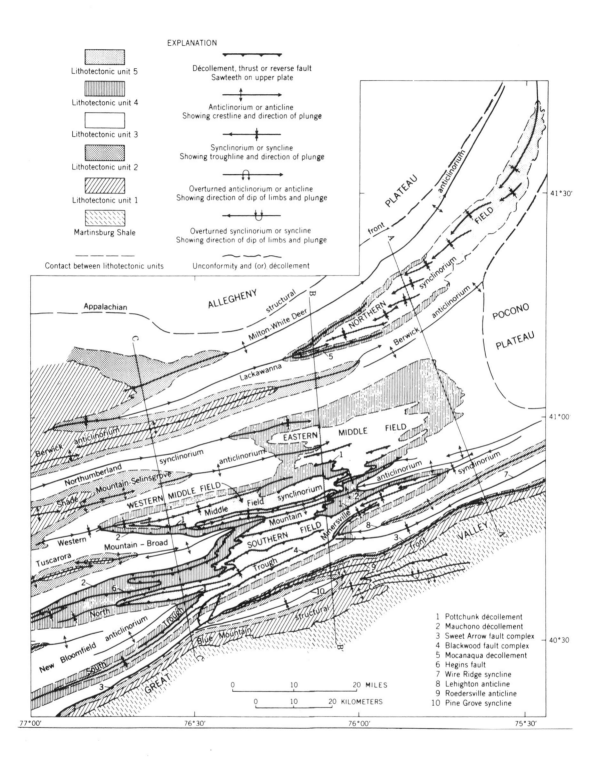

Figure 6. Tectonic map of the Anthracite region (from Wood and Bergin, 1970, p. 150). Lithostratigraphic units: 1–Early Silurian to early Middle Devonian age, 2–Middle and early Late Devonian age, 3–Late Devonian to Late Mississippian, 4–Late Mississippian age, 5–Late Mississippian to Late Pennsylvanian age.

that are almost equal in length, the deeper Wyoming basin to the southwest and the Lackawanna basin to the northeast. Each contains many thrust-faulted anticlines and synclines. The Eastern Middle field consists of several closely clustered thrust-faulted synclines and anticlines, whereas the Western Middle field is made up of two large thrust-faulted adjacent synclines, a greatly deformed intervening major anticline, and many lesser anticlines and synclines. The Southern field is the most highly deformed, with several highly faulted, closely spaced synclinal basins. Deformation is most complex toward the southeast, where it is characterized by hundreds of thrust, reverse, tear, and bedding-plane faults and tightly compressed, commonly overturned folds.

Arndt and Wood (1960) determined that the structural features of the region formed progressively in a sequence of five structural stages. These stages, classified on the basis of increasing complexity, are 1) folding of horizontal strata into broad anticlines and synclines, 2) low-angle thrusting and imbricate faulting, followed by formation of subsidiary folds on the larger folds to develop anticlinoria and synclinoria, 3) folding of low-angle and high-angle thrust and offsetting of preexisting structural features by high-angle thrusts, 4) development of overturned folds and offsetting of overturned folds by tear faults and high-angle thrusts, and 5) development of recumbent folds and nappes. According to Arndt and Wood (1960), all of these stages occurred during the Alleghany orogeny, as the orogenic forces were continuously transmitted from southeast to northwest in the Anthracite region with gradually increasing intensity. Rocks to the southeast, then, experienced a longer period of deformation than those to the northwest. Recently, Nickelsen (1979), working mostly in the Western Middle field, identified seven stages of structural deformation during the Allegheny orogeny.

Wood and Bergin (1970) noted that not only does the structural complexity vary geographically, but it also varies stratigraphically. They defined five lithotectonic units in the region, each of which occupies a particular stratigraphic zone. These units each control the vectoral resolution of stresses, resulting in characteristic assemblages of structural features in each unit. In Wood and Bergin's Unit 5, the relatively competent rocks of the upper member of the Mauch Chunk Formation are commonly deformed into long, concentric, symmetric, open, en echelon folds broken by low-angle thrust and bedding faults and fewer reverse faults. In contrast, rocks of the Llewellyn Formation range from competent to incompetent, are folded more tightly into numerous shorter, narrower, lower amplitude, commonly disharmonic, en echelon anticlines and synclines broken by reverse faults and low-angle thrust and bedding faults.

Coal in the region has been thickened by flowage associated with folding and faulting. Commonly, the coal thickens in the axis of synclines and is increased as much as three- to four-fold, but this thickening is not predictable. Thrust faults often create local thickening of the coal by dragging of the less competent coal and of the enclosing strata. Structural thickening can be seen in stripmine highwalls and has also been reported in underground mining and in drill hole data.

Coal Quality

Pennsylvania anthracite is a low-sulfur, high-Btu, moderately high-ash coal. Major sources of analytical data come from the U.S. Bureau of Mines (1944), a summary of anthracite data by Deasy and Griess (1963), and a report on the chemical data from 53 anthracite samples by Swanson and others (1976). The latter report included analysis for proximate, ultimate, Btu, forms-of-sulfur, 15 oxides, and 36 elements (Table 1).

Sulfur, on an as-received basis, ranges from 0.3 to 5.1% and averages 0.8%. Analysis of sulfur forms gives an average of 0.02% sulfate, 0.35% pyritic sulfur, and 0.48% organic sulfur. Sulfur content generally increases toward the west and is highest in the Northern Anthracite field (Fig. 7a). The low sulfur content of the anthracite may be due, in part, to metamorphism and/or the fresh-water depositional environment of the organic matter and enclosing strata. Research indicates that coal beds with a marine roof rock generally contain more sulfur than those of fresh-water or brackish-water origin (Horne and others, 1979). Based on analyses by Swanson and others (1976), ash content ranges between 5.2 and 45.1%, and averages about 12.6%. The ash content varies greatly in geographic distribution, but appears to be higher in the Northern field (Fig. 7b). The Btu value is high, ranging between 6,700 and 14,400 and averaging 12,780.

By definition, fixed carbon increases with coal rank; it averages about 80% in the Pennsylvania anthracite. In the western parts of the Southern and Western Middle fields, the coal is of slightly lower rank where it grades into semianthracite. According to Levine and Davis (1983), the west to east increase in rank across the region is attributed to increasing depth of burial. Wood and others (1969) noted that the fixed carbon content of the coal increases toward the core of tightly folded synclines and toward complexly deformed thrust faults. They conclude that structural deformation is extremely important in determining the rank of anthracite and semianthracite.

SUMMARY

In conclusion, coal-bearing strata in the Pennsylvania Anthracite region were deposited on a broad alluvial plain that overlay a subsiding, asymmetric basin. The Pottsville and Llewellyn Formations were laid down as fluvial and paludal deposits containing an abundance of plant material, which is reflected in the gray hues of the coal-associated rocks. The juxtaposition of coarse clastics and swamp deposits shows clearly that tectonism adjacent to the Anthracite region controlled the type of sediments, the sequence of deposition, and the rate of basin subsidence within the region during the interval from Early Mississippian to Late Pennsylvanian time. Numerous persistent, thick coal beds within the Llewellyn Formation indicate long periods of tectonic quiescence in which vegetation flourished in widespread swamps. The lack of marine influence in most of the sequence may in part explain the generally low sulfur content of the coals. After deposition and coalification, probably in Permian

TABLE 1. ANALYSES FOR 38 PENNSYLVANIA ANTHRACITE REGION SAMPLES*

	Arithmetic mean (abundance)	Observed range minimum	maximum	Geometric mean (expected value)	Geometric deviation
Proximate and ultimate analyses					
Moisture	1.4	0.5	3.9	1.3	1.5
Volatile matter	6.5	3.8	11.2	6.3	1.3
Fixed carbon	79.5	39.8	87.0	78.8	1.2
Ash	12.6	5.2	45.1	11.1	1.6
Hydrogen	2.4	1.7	3.5	2.3	1.2
Carbon	80.1	43.2	88.2	79.5	1.1
Nitrogen	.8	.5	1.4	.8	1.3
Oxygen	3.2	1.3	9.0	3.1	1.3
Sulfur	.8	.3	5.1	.7	1.6
Btu	12,780	6,730	14,360	12,690	1.1
Forms of sulfur					
Sulfate	0.02	0.00	0.09	0.01	2.0
Pyritic	.35	.03	4.47	.16	2.8
Organic	.48	.17	.83	.45	1.5

Note: All values are in percent, except Btu, and are reported on the as-received basis.

*Source: Swanson and others (1976, p. 25).

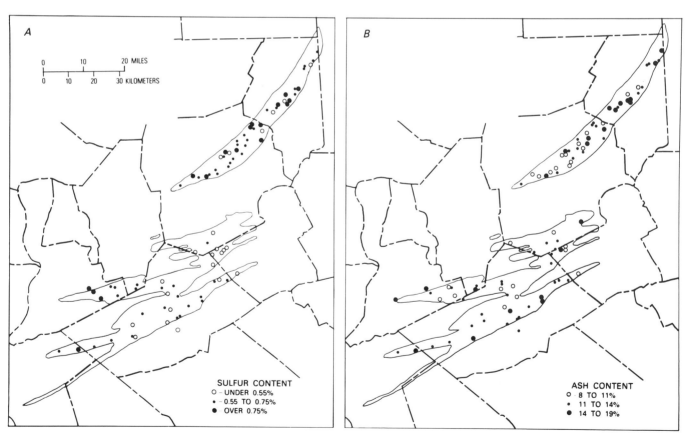

Figure 7. Percentages of sulfur and ash in anthracite samples from the Pennsylvania Anthracite region (Deasy and Griess, 1963, p. 26–27).

time, tectonism again influenced the region above a décollement zone as rocks moved progressively northwestward during the Alleghany orogeny. Structural deformation during this orogeny evolved in a series of stages, folding and faulting the coal-bearing strata and affecting the coal rank.

REFERENCES CITED

Altschuler, Z. S., Schnepfe, M. M., Silber, C. C., and Simon, F. O., 1983, Sulfur Diagenesis in Everglades Peat and Origin of Pyrite in Coal: Science, v. 221, p. 221–227.

Anderson, J.A.R., 1964, The structure and development of the peat swamps of Sarawak and Brunei: Journal of Tropical Geography 18, Singapore, p. 7–16.

Arndt, H. H., and Wood, G. H., Jr., 1960, Late Paleozoic orogeny in eastern Pennsylvania consists of five progressive stages. U.S. Geological Survey Professional Paper No. 400-B, p. B182–B184.

Arndt, H. H., Averitt, P., Dowd, J., Frendzel, D. J., and Gallo, P. A., 1968, Pennsylvania Anthracite, in Mineral Resources of the Appalachian Region: U.S. Geological Survey Professional Paper 580, p. 121–133.

Ashburner, C. A., 1886, Report on the Wyoming Valley limestone beds, in Lesley, Peter, ed., Annual Report of the Geological Survey of Pennsylvania for 1885, Pennsylvania Geological Survey, 2nd Series, p. 437–458.

Ashley, G. H., 1907, The maximum rate of the deposition of coal: Economic Geology, v. 2, p. 34–47.

Barrell, J., 1907, Origin and significance of the Mauch Chunk Shale: Geological Society of America Bulletin, v. 18, p. 449–476.

Berryhill, H. L., Jr., Schweinfurth, S. F., and Kent, B. H., 1971, Coal-bearing Upper Pennsylvanian and Lower Permian rocks, Washington area, Pennsylvania: U.S. Geological Survey Professional Paper 621, 47 p., 8 pl.

Chow, M. M., 1951, The Pennsylvanian Mill Creek Limestone in Pennsylvania: Pennsylvania Geological Survey, 4th Series, Bulletin G26, 36 p.

Cloos, E., 1940, Crustal shortening and axial divergence in the Appalachians of southeastern Pennsylvania: Geological Society of America Bulletin, v. 51, no. 6, p. 845–872.

Darrah, W. C., 1937, American Carboniferous Floras: Compte Rendu, 2nd International Congress of Carboniferous Stratigraphy and Geology, v. 1, p. 109–129.

——, 1969, A critical review of the Upper Pennsylvanian floras of the eastern United States with notes on the Mazon Creek flora of Illinois: Gettysburg, Pennsylvania, privately printed, 220 p., 80 pl.

Deasy, G. F., and Griess, P. R., 1963, Atlas of Pennsylvania Coal and Coal Mining, Part II: Anthracite: Bulletin of the Mineral-Industries Experiment Station, No. 80, The Pennsylvania State University, 123 p.

Edmunds, W. E., Berg, T. M., Sevon, W. D., Piotrowski, R. C., Heyman, L., and Richard, L. V., 1979, The Mississippian and Pennsylvanian (Carboniferous) Systems in the United States—Pennsylvania and New York: U.S. Geological Survey Professional Paper 1110-B, p. B1–B33.

Fenneman, N. M., 1938, Physiography of eastern United States: New York, McGraw-Hill, 714 p.

Harris, L. D., and Milici, R. C., 1977, Characteristics of thin-skinned style deformation in the Southern Appalachians, and potential hydrocarbon traps: U.S. Geological Survey Professional Paper 1018, 40 p.

Horne, J. C., Ferm, J. C., Caruccio, F. T., and Baganz, B. P., 1979, Depositional models in coal exploration and mine planning in Appalachian Region, in Ferm, J. C., and Horne, J. C., eds., Carboniferous depositional environments in the Appalachian Region, Carolina Coal Group: Columbia, South Carolina, University of South Carolina, p. 544–575.

Lesley, J. P., 1876, The Boyd's Hill gas well at Pittsburgh, Pennsylvania: Pennsylvania Geological Survey, 2nd series, Report L. app. E, p. 217–237.

Lesquereux, L., 1879–1884, Description of the coal flora of the Carboniferous formation in Pennsylvania and throughout the United States: Pennsylvania Geological Survey, 2nd Series, Report P, v. 1 and 2, 694 p., (1880); v. 3, p. 695–977, (1884); Atlas (1879).

Levine, J. R., and Davis, A., 1983, Tectonic history of coal-bearing sediments in eastern Pennsylvania eastern Pennsylvania using coal reflectance anisotropy: Pennsylvania State University Special Report SR-118, 314 p.

Lyons, P. C., Meissner, C. R., Jr., Barwood, H. L., and Adinolfi, F. G., 1985, North American and European megafloral correlations with the upper part of the Pottsville Formation of the Warrior coal field, Alabama, USA: Compte Rendu, 10th International Congress of Carboniferous Stratigraphy and Geology (Madrid, Spain, September 1983).

Meckel, L. D., 1967, Origin of Pottsville Conglomerates (Pennsylvanian) in the Central Appalachians: Geological Society of America Bulletin, v. 78, p. 223–257.

——, 1970, Paleozoic alluvial deposition in the Central Appalachians—A summary, in Fisher, G., Pattijohn, F. J., Reid, J. C., Jr., and Weaver, K. N., eds., Studies of Appalachian Geology—Central and Southern: New York, Wiley Interscience, p. 49–67.

Moore, R. C., chairman, and others, 1944, Correlation of Pennsylvanian formations of North America [Correlation chart 6]: Geological Society of America Bulletin, v. 55, no. 6, p. 657–706.

Nickelsen, R. P., 1979, Sequence of structural stages of the Allegheny Ocogeny, at the Bear Valley Strip Mine, Shamokin, Pennsylvania: American Journal of Science, vol. 279, p. 225–271.

Oleksyshyn, J., 1982, Fossil plants from the Anthracite Coal Fields of eastern Pennsylvania: Pennsylvania Geological Survey, 4th Series, General Geology Report 72, 157 p.

Read, C. B., and Mamay, S. H., 1960, Upper Paleozoic floral zones of the United States: U.S. Geological Survey Professional Paper 400-B, p. B381–B383.

——, 1964, Paleozoic floral zones and floral provinces in the United States: U.S. Geological Survey Professional Paper 454K, p. K1–K35.

Ryer, T. A., and Langer, A. W., 1980, Thickness change involved in the peat-to-coal transformation for a bituminous coal of Cretaceous age in central Utah: Journal of Sedimentary Petrology 50, p. 987–992.

Smith, A.D.W., 1895, Report on the Anthracite region, in Lesley, J. P., and others, eds., A summary description of the geology of Pennsylvania: Pennsylvania Geological Survey, 2nd. series, Final report, v. 3, pt. 1, p. 1916–2152.

Swanson, V. E., Medlin, J. H., Hatch, J. R., Coleman, S. L., Wood, G. H., Jr., Woodruff, S. D., and Hildebrand, R. T., 1976, Collection, chemical analysis, and evaluation of coal samples in 1975: U.S. Geological Survey, Open-File Report 76-468, 503 p.

U.S. Bureau of Mines, 1944, Analyses of Pennsylvania anthracitic coals: U.S. Bureau of Mines Technical Paper 659, 271 p.

White, C. D., 1900, The stratigraphic succession of the fossil floras of the Pottsville Formation in the Southern Anthracite field, Pennsylvania: U.S. Geological Survey, Annual Report, 20, pt. 2 (1898–99), p. 749–953.

White, I. C., 1903, The Appalachian Coal Field: the Conemaugh Series: West Virginia Geological Survey, Report, vol. 2, p. 225–332.

Wood, G. H., Jr., and Bergin, M. J., 1970, Structural controls of the Anthracite Region, Pennsylvania, in Fisher, G. W., Pettijohn, F. J., Reed, J. C., Jr., and Weaver, K. W., eds., Appalachian Geology—Central and Southern: New York, Wiley Interscience, p. 147–160.

Wood, G. H., Jr., Trexler, J. P., and Arndt, H. H., 1962, Pennsylvanian rocks of the southern part of the Anthracite region of eastern Pennsylvania: U.S. Geological Survey Professional Paper 450-C, p. C39–C42.

Wood, G. H., Jr., Trexler, J. P., Arndt, H. H., Yelenosky, A., and Soren, J., 1956, Subdivision of the Pottsville formation in Southern Anthracite field, Pennsylvania: American Association of Petroleum Geologists Bulletin, v. 40, no. 11, p. 2669–2688.

Wood, G. H., Jr., Trexler, J. P., and Kehn, T. M., 1969, Geology of the west-central part of the Southern Anthracite field and adjoining areas, Pennsylvania: U.S. Geological Survey Professional Paper 602, 150 p.

MANUSCRIPT ACCEPTED BY THE SOCIETY APRIL 16, 1986

Geological Society of America
Special Paper 210
1986

Origin of thick, low-sulphur coal in the Lower Pennsylvanian Pocahontas Formation, Virginia and West Virginia

Kenneth J. Englund
John F. Windolph, Jr.
Roger E. Thomas
U.S. Geological Survey
National Center
Reston, Virginia 22092

ABSTRACT

Clastic sediments in the Pocahontas Formation of the east-central Appalachian basin in Virginia and West Virginia were deposited in a series of stacked delta lobes along the southeastern shoreline of a Carboniferous Appalachian seaway. These sediments prograded northwestward and were depositionally continuous with precursor Mississippian coal-bearing strata presently located primarily to the southeast in the faulted and folded belt of the Appalachians. During periodic stillstands in Early Pennsylvanian time, coastal currents and waves reworked and segregated sand along the delta front, forming a system of curvilinear barrier-bars. Behind these protective barriers, vegetation flourished in swamps on the abandoned delta lobes. An analysis of the relationship of coal occurrences to the geometries of sandstone units indicates that the origin of thick, low-sulfur coal in the Pocahontas Formation can be attributed to the initial and continuing accumulation of peat on the periodically inactive delta lobes. Conversely thin, impure, and discontinuous peat (coal) accumulated in the shale-dominated interlobe areas. An increase in the sulfur content of the coal to the northwest may have resulted from the proximity of marine conditions to the distal ends of the delta lobes. The genetic relation of coal distribution and sulfur content to the delta system provides a basis for designing exploration programs in coal-bearing strata of the Appalachian basin, particularly for predicting both the quantity and the quality of the coal.

INTRODUCTION

Strata overlying coal beds have been subjected to in-depth investigations, particularly to determine the relationship between roof-rock characteristics and various coal quality and quantity parameters. For example, the origin of high-sulfur coal has been widely attributed to the marine- or brackish-water deposition of the overlying strata (Williams and Keith, 1963; Ferm and others, 1976; Horne and others, 1978). This concept may present a feasible explanation for the origin of the high-sulfur content of some coal beds but it is not applicable to high-sulfur coal beds where the roof rock is identified as a fresh-water deposit (Cecil and others, 1981). Likewise, the thinning or "cutout" of a coal bed can be related to fluvial scouring associated with the deposition of roof rock; however, variations in coal bed thickness can

also be caused by syndepositional processes such as vegetation accumulation and preservation. In contrast to these efforts to relate coal quality and quantity to roof-rock characteristics, this paper focuses attention on the relationship of coal thickness and sulfur content to the distribution and thickness of underlying strata, specifically to deltaic sandstone lobes.

This study of the Pocahontas Formation is supplemented by data from previous investigations in the subject area, including: (1) geologic mapping (Englund, 1968, 1981; Englund and others, 1977a; Meissner, 1978, 1981; Meissner and Miller, 1981; Miller and Meissner, 1978; Stricker, 1981; and Windolph, 1983); (2) regional stratigraphic studies (Englund, 1969, 1971, 1974; Englund and Henry, 1981; Englund and others, 1977b, 1979; Miller,

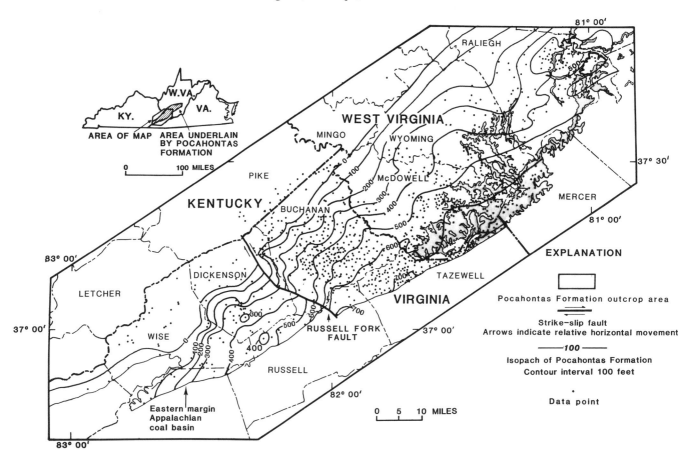

Figure 1. Isopach map of the Pocahontas Formation in southwestern Virginia and southern West Virginia, modified from Englund (1974).

1974); (3) coal resource assessments (Englund and Teaford, 1980; Meissner, 1979, Meissner and Heermann, 1982; Windolph, 1986; and Windolph and others, 1977); and (4) core drilling programs (Englund and others, 1983; Henry and others, 1981; Schweinfurth and others, 1976). Additional data on the sulfur content of the Pocahontas No. 3 coal bed were obtained from several of the above investigations and from reports by Cooper and others (1942, 1944), Medlin and Coleman (1976), Simon and Englund (1983), Trent and others (1982), and Zubovic and others (1979, 1980). Analyses used in this report are of samples collected by standard sampling methods (that is, channel samples that excluded partings more than .95 cm [3/8 in] in thickness).

Peat deposition in the east-central Appalachian basin during Early Pennsylvanian time was associated with a regressive trend in the Appalachian basin that began in early Late Mississippian time (Englund and others, 1981). The southeastern coast of the receding seaway was successively occupied by northwestward prograding deltas and widespread peat swamps.

LOCATION

The Pocahontas Formation underlies an area of approxi-

mately 9,000 sq km (3,500 sq mi) in southeastern West Virginia and southwestern Virginia at the eastern edge of the Appalachian coal basin. Correlative beds have been recognized to the northeast as far as the Anthracite fields of Pennsylvania (Read and Mamay, 1964, p. K6) and to the southwest as far as the Cumberland Gap area of Kentucky and Tennessee (Englund, 1979, p. C14). Exposures are limited to the eastern edge of the coal basin where the formation crops out in a broad dissected area of relatively flat-lying beds in West Virginia, and in a narrow belt of upturned or faulted beds across Virginia to the southwestern corner of the state. A few small outliers are preserved in the trough of the Hurricane Ridge syncline 4 to 8 km (2.5 to 5 mi) southeast of the Appalachian coal basin. From a maximum thickness of about 229 m (750 ft) in the central part of the outcrop belt, the formation thins northwestward for about 48 km (30 mi) to where it is truncated in the subsurface beneath younger Pennsylvanian rocks at an average depth of about 457 m (1,500 ft) below the valley floors (Fig. 1). Sandstone, which is locally conglomeratic or in part, calcareous, constitutes about 70 percent of the formation, finer clastics—siltstone, shale, and underclay—total 28 percent of the formation, and coal the remaining 2 percent. Clastics were derived from the Appalachian orogenic belt to the southeast and accumulated in extensive deltaic systems bordering the seaway. The abundance of sediments may have contributed to load-induced subsidence that resulted in the thickest accumulations in the southeasternmost part or trough of the basin. Infilling by deltaic clastic wedges during marine regression to the northwest recorded an idealized facies relationship in which marine shale, barrier-bar sandstone, bay-fill shale, distributary sandstone, and swamp deposits are found in lateral sequences. Northwestward wedging out of the Pocahontas Formation resulted from the tonguing out of the lower beds and erosion of upper beds prior to the deposition of younger Pennsylvanian strata.

This paper presents the depositional history of thick, low-sulfur coal in the Pocahontas Formation, Virginia and West Virginia, with emphasis on the relation of coal quantity and quality to the distribution and character of underlying sediments.

DEPOSITIONAL SETTING

In the east-central Appalachian basin and in nearby outcrop belts of the faulted and folded Appalachians, Upper Mississippian and Lower Pennsylvanian strata constitute a southeastward-thickening wedge of interbedded limestone, sandstone, siltstone, shale, coal, and claystone as much as 1,524 m (5,000 ft) thick (Fig. 2a). These strata are assigned to seven formations, in ascending order: the Greenbrier Limestone, Bluefield Formation, Hinton Formation, and Princeton Sandstone of Late Mississippian age; the Bluestone Formation of Late Mississippian and Early Pennsylvanian age; and the Pocahontas and New River Formations of Early Pennsylvanian age. Of this sequence, only the basal Greenbrier Limestone represents a thick and widespread marine incursion (Fig. 2b). It consists mostly of medium-gray, thick-bedded, very finely to coarsely crystalline limestone with a few oolitic, cherty, and argillaceous beds. Marine invertebrates are found throughout the formation. Marine deposition prevailed during the accumulation of most of the overlying Bluefield Formation. This formation consists largely of medium- to medium-dark-gray, greenish-gray, and grayish-red, partly calcareous shale interbedded with limestone and argillaceous limestone. In easternmost exposures the formation includes siltstone and sandstone beds as much as 24 m (80 ft) thick, and a few thin coal beds. These coal beds are associated with rooted underclay and carbonaceous shale representing the first seaward encroachment of terrestrial mud, sand, and fresh-water swamp deposits in Late Mississippian time. Limestone and calcareous shale beds, which predominate in the lower part of the formation, contain abundant marine fossils including brachiopods, bryozoans, crinoids, and blastoids. Plant fossils, including megaspores, are found locally in the formation. Minor periodic regressions during Bluefield deposition mark the beginning of a regressive trend that accelerated with the deposition of later Mississippian and Early Pennsylvanian sediments.

The Bluefield is overlain by the Hinton Formation, which is characterized by an abundance of grayish-red, partly calcareous shale, and siltstone with minor amounts of medium-gray and greenish-gray shale, sandstone, fossiliferous limestone, and coal or carbonaceous shale underlain by rooted underclay. The basal unit of the Hinton, the Stony Gap Sandstone Member, is a well-sorted orthoquartzite that was deposited as a sequence of coalescing offshore bars (Englund and others, 1979, p. 9). The thickest and most widespread of several marine units in the formation is the Little Stone Gap Member (Avis Limestone of Reger, 1926). It is an abundantly fossiliferous limestone and calcareous shale ranging in thickness up to 30 m (100 ft). The most widely distributed of several sandstone members in the upper part of the formation is a locally conglomeratic orthoquartzite identified as the Tallery Sandstone Member. During deposition of these units of the Hinton Formation, shallow-marine, barrier-bar, tidal-flat, and fresh-water swamp environments prevailed.

The Hinton is unconformably overlain by the lithically distinctive Princeton Sandstone, which ranges from a polymictic conglomerate to a coarse conglomeratic subgraywacke as much as 18 m (60 ft) thick. Princeton Sandstone matrix consists of light-gray, fine- to coarse-grained, thick-bedded to massive, calcite-cemented sandstone. Clasts in the formation are diverse in composition, size, and abundance, and consist of well-rounded to angular fragments of quartz, shale, siltstone, limestone, chert, and ironstone. The variety of lithic fragments, ranging from locally derived limestone and shale to quartz and chert from more distant sources, indicates that the Princeton Sandstone was deposited in a high-energy environment. These coarse, fluvial clastics accumulated on a highly eroded surface and were reworked by storm waves and longshore currents associated with a marine incursion at the base of the overlying Bluestone Formation.

Except for an overall decrease in marine influence, the lithology and depositional environment of strata in the Bluestone Formation are similar to those of the Hinton. The widespread Pride Shale Member at the base of the Bluestone is a dark-gray silty shale that contains sparse marine and brackish-water faunal assemblages. It represents predominantly silt and clay infilling of a large shallow marine embayment or lagoon. The Pride is overlain locally by the Glady Fork Sandstone Member representing tidal-creek and other intertidal sediments. The gray member, overlying the Glady Fork and merging with the Pride in areas beyond the distribution of the Glady Fork, represents a major seaward progradation of terrestrial coal-bearing deposits. In addition to several thin coal beds, the gray member contains beds of carbonaceous shale with fresh- or brackish-water ostracodes and pelecypods. The overlying red member is a sequence of mostly grayish-red, partly calcareous shale and siltstone deposited in a tidal-flat environment associated with fresh-water marshes. It contains several thin beds of coal, underclay, and nodular argillaceous limestone that may represent part of an ancient soil profile. The Bramwell Member is the youngest of the Mississippian strata in the Bluestone. It was a marine transgression across the lower coastal plain represented by the underlying red member. Carbonaceous shale containing fresh- and brackish-water faunas, found at the base of the Bramwell, grades upward to silty shale and calcareous siltstone that contain thin limestone beds and

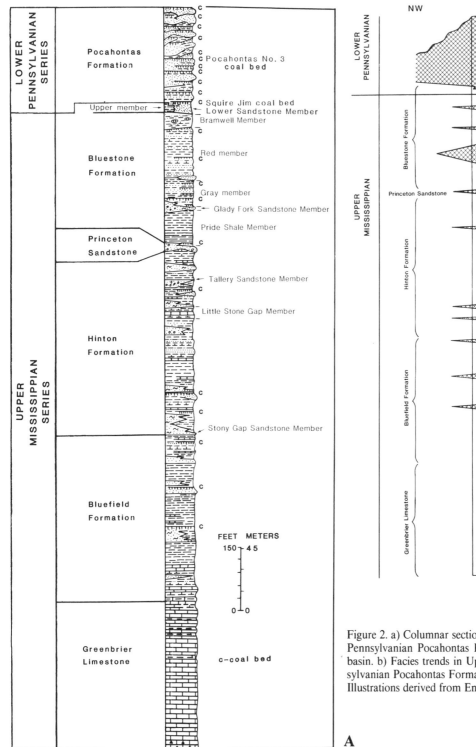

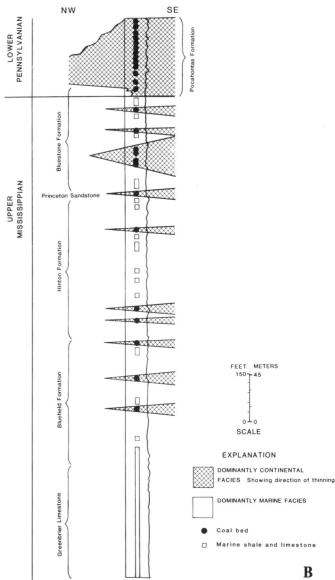

Figure 2. a) Columnar section of Upper Mississippian Series and Lower Pennsylvanian Pocahontas Formation in the east-central Appalachian basin. b) Facies trends in Upper Mississippian Series and Lower Pennsylvanian Pocahontas Formation in the east-central Appalachian basin. Illustrations derived from Englund and others (1986).

highly diverse marine faunas. The Bramwell Member, together with the greenish-gray and grayish-red shale of the upper member of the Bluestone Formation, constitute a prodeltaic sequence that preceded and later overlapped the deposition of the basal deltaic wedge or lower sandstone member of the Pocahontas Formation.

The depositional trends established in Late Mississippian time show that the Appalachian seaway regressed slowly toward the northwest in a series of regressive-transgressive events, thereby producing a predominance of terrestrial coal-bearing sediments in the east-central Appalachian basin in Early Pennsylvanian time (Fig. 3). The earliest Pocahontas deposits consist of sand that accumulated as a series of merging delta lobes prograding toward the northwest over the nearshore marine muds (Fig. 4). The coarsest sediments, including sand and quartz-pebble gravel, accumulated in the major distributary channels (Fig. 5). The orientation of the lobes in conjunction with decreasing grain size toward the edges of the lobes show that clastics prograded to the northwest from a southeastern source, similar to the trend established in underlying Mississippian strata.

During deposition of the upper part of the lower member of the Pocahontas Formation, decreasing sand dispersal was accompanied by a southeastward encroachment by nearshore muds of the upper member of the Bluestone Formation over areas of relatively thin sand, mostly in the interlobe areas. In the final phase of the deposition of the lower sandstone member of the Pocahontas, very fine-grained sand graded into silt and clay at the top of the distributary lobes. Several feet of rooted underclay developed on the lobe surfaces prior to the accumulation of peat deposits that are recorded by as much as 1.2 m (4 ft) of coal in the Squire Jim coal bed (Fig. 6). Widespread peat accumulation coincided with a stillstand—a period when the influx of clastics was minimal—and the stabilized shoreline led to the development of a barrier system consisting of lithically and texturally mature quartz sand (Fig. 7). Growth of this barrier system continued during the initial deposition of the middle sandstone member of the Pocahontas Formation. This member consists of several coalescing lobes between the Squire Jim and Pocahontas No. 3 coal beds. Delta lobe switching in this interval is marked by the local development of the relatively thin Pocahontas No. 1, No. 2, and No. 2A coal beds. The major lobes of the middle member are superimposed over those of the lower sandstone member (Fig. 8). Sand at the distal edges of the lobes was reworked and winnowed by waves and longshore currents and, as a result, the barrier system is thickest just seaward of the major distributary lobes.

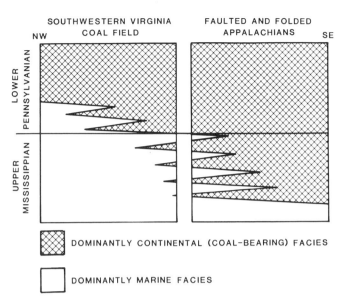

Figure 3. Depositional trends in Upper Mississippian and Lower Pennsylvanian rocks in the east-central Appalachian basin, from Englund and others (1986).

Continued marine regression during deposition of the upper part of the middle sandstone member was accompanied by a northwestward progradation of sand in distributary channels over and beyond the barrier system. As the distributary systems of the middle sandstone member waned, the deposition of sand was followed by the accumulation of fine-grained terrigenous sediments, including silt and clay, over the lobes.

Subsequent abandonment of the major distributary systems permitted the development of an extensive swamp in which very thick peat, represented by the Pocahontas No. 3 coal bed, was deposited. The No. 3 is the thickest and most widely distributed of the Pocahontas coal beds, attaining thicknesses of 107 cm (42

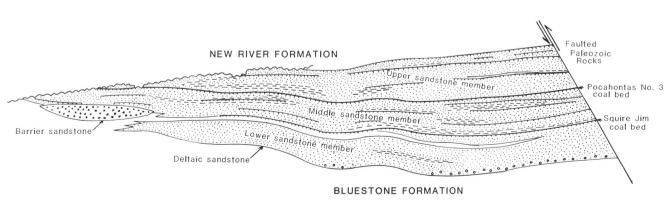

Figure 4. Diagrammatic cross section of the Pocahontas Formation in Buchanan and Tazewell Counties, Virginia.

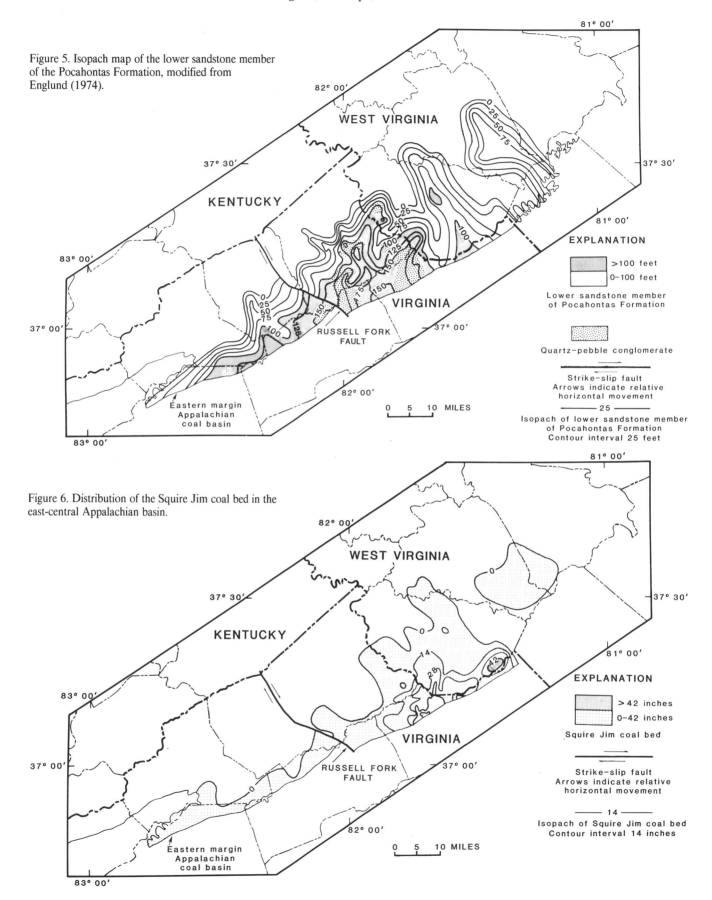

Figure 5. Isopach map of the lower sandstone member of the Pocahontas Formation, modified from Englund (1974).

Figure 6. Distribution of the Squire Jim coal bed in the east-central Appalachian basin.

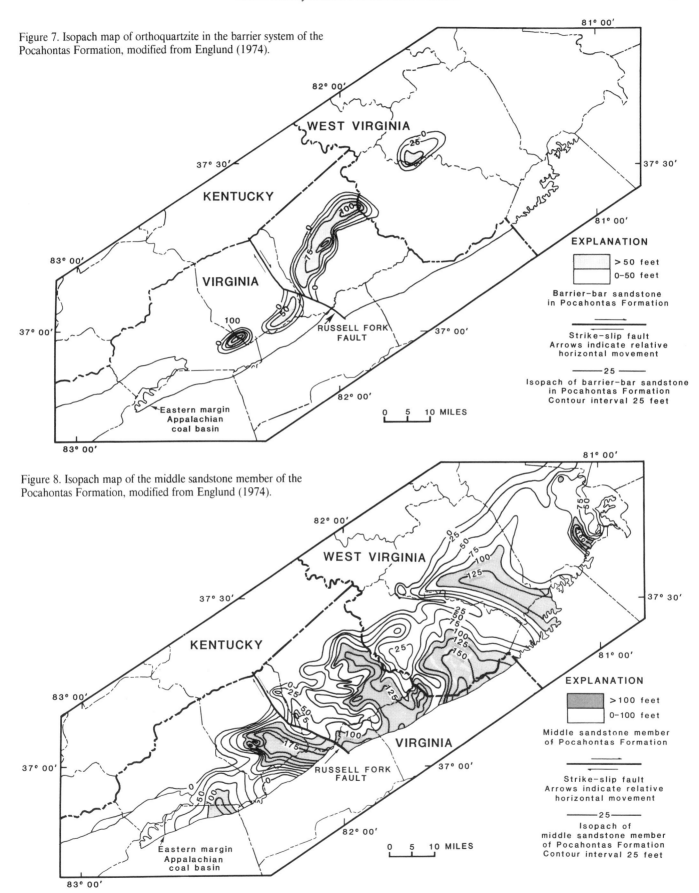

Figure 7. Isopach map of orthoquartzite in the barrier system of the Pocahontas Formation, modified from Englund (1974).

Figure 8. Isopach map of the middle sandstone member of the Pocahontas Formation, modified from Englund (1974).

Figure 9. Distribution of the Pocahontas No. 3 coal bed in southwestern Virginia and southern West Virginia.

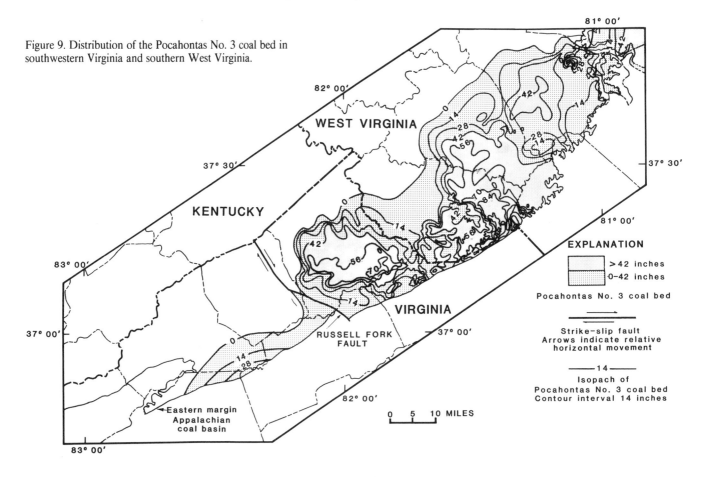

in) or more over large areas (Fig. 9). Variations in the thickness of the Pocahontas No. 3 coal bed indicate that the thickest peat accumulated over abandoned distributary lobes. However, for the first time in the sequence, the coal swamp extended well beyond the lobes and across the former interdistributary and back-barrier areas. The unusual extent of the Pocahontas No. 3 can be attributed to the abandonment of the main distributary systems and the consequential limited influx of terrigenous clastics. Deposition was very likely accompanied by widespread shoreline stability, perhaps a major stillstand, but supporting evidence, such as a barrier system along the seaward edge of the Pocahontas No. 3 coal bed, has been removed by the truncation of strata at the overlying unconformity.

Sulfur in the Pocahontas No. 3 coal bed ranges from a minimum of about 0.4 percent over the sandstone lobes to a maximum of about 1.0 percent at the northwestern or seaward margin of the deposit (Fig. 10). Throughout the lobe and marginal areas, the sulfur content is predominantly organic sulfur.

The upper sandstone member of the Pocahontas represents a resumption of deltaic sedimentation similar to that of the underlying member. Several coal beds, including the relatively thick Pocahontas No. 4 and No. 6, resulted from the accumulation of peat on abandoned delta lobes. The shift of the major axis of the

delta systems to the northeast has also affected the distribution of coal, including the Pocahontas No. 6 bed, which is more extensive to the northeast.

DEPOSITIONAL MODEL

The analysis of net-sandstone distribution patterns in the Pocahontas Formation (Figs. 5 and 8) indicates that sandstone (consisting of a subgraywacke with a relatively low quartz content of 50–60 percent) was deposited in a lobate, river-dominated delta system. A comparison of the geometry of the sandstone lobes with coal isopach maps (Figs. 6 and 9) confirms earlier observations that the thickest peat was deposited over the principal lobes (Englund, 1974, p. 43). Similar relations were recognized by Kaiser and others (1978, p. 83), who pointed out that thick sand and lignite areas coincided in the deltaic facies of the Jackson Group of the Texas Gulf Coast area. In both cases, laterally extensive thick coal and lignite were inferred to have accumulated as peat in blanket swamp deposits over inactive or abandoned sandstone lobes. This relationship can be demonstrated in the deltaic deposits of the Pocahontas Formation by reference to the distribution of the widespread Squire Jim and Pocahontas No. 3 coal beds. The Squire Jim coal bed (Fig. 6) is

Figure 10. Distribution of sulfur in the Pocahontas No. 3 coal bed.

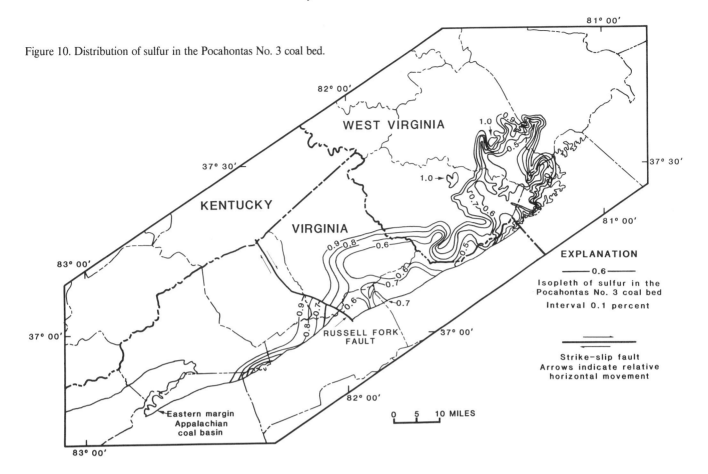

almost totally confined to the area occupied by the underlying lower sandstone member, and the coal has a similar lobate distribution pattern. Because of the stacking of the principal lobes (Englund, 1974, p. 43) and associated distributary channels, the Squire Jim coal bed was locally scoured prior to the deposition of the overlying lobe. In the interlobe areas and over minor or thin lobes, the coal position is represented by a few inches of carbonaceous shale and underclay. The thickest coal (>107 cm [42 in]) is limited to areas where the underlying sandstone is more than 15 m (50 ft) thick.

A similar relation exists between the middle sandstone member of the Pocahontas and the overlying Pocahontas No. 3 coal bed (Figs. 8 and 9). The coal is almost entirely confined to the areas underlain by sandstone and it is thickest over the central or thickest part of the underlying lobe. Scour associated with the distributary channels of the overlying sandstone has modified the coal-bed thickness by cutting into or locally eroding the coal in the lobe areas. In places along the extreme southeastern edge of the lobes, a slight influx of sediments due to minor reactivation of drainage from the southeast is responsible for splits or clastic wedges in the coal.

In addition to abundant thickness data, extensive exploration and mining of the Pocahontas No. 3 coal bed have provided much information on the distribution of sulfur in the coal. The total sulfur content, based on approximately 270 analyses, is 1 percent or less. It is lowest in the thickest coal, increases towards the periphery of the lobes, and is highest to the northwest in the direction of the contemporaneous marine environment. The ash content and thin partings in the coal also increase towards the lobe margin.

The occurrence of high-quality, low-sulfur coal in the Pocahontas Formation has received much attention because of its environmental and economic importance, but also because it can provide data concerning the origin of low-sulfur coal. In contrast to the physical depositional models that have related the low-sulfur content of the coal to the absence of marine roof rock, Cecil and others (1983) have attributed the formation of low-ash and low-sulfur coal in Pennsylvanian strata of the Appalachian basin to a major climatic change that began in latest Mississippian or earliest Pennsylvanian time. They postulated that rainfall exceeded evapotranspiration and, because of the ever-wet climate, the water originating as rainfall was low in dissolved solids. Furthermore, the organic acids characteristic of the swamp system resulted in intense leaching of the remaining mineral matter. Physical aspects of the depositional history presented here support the existence of a humid, high rainfall, ever-wet climate.

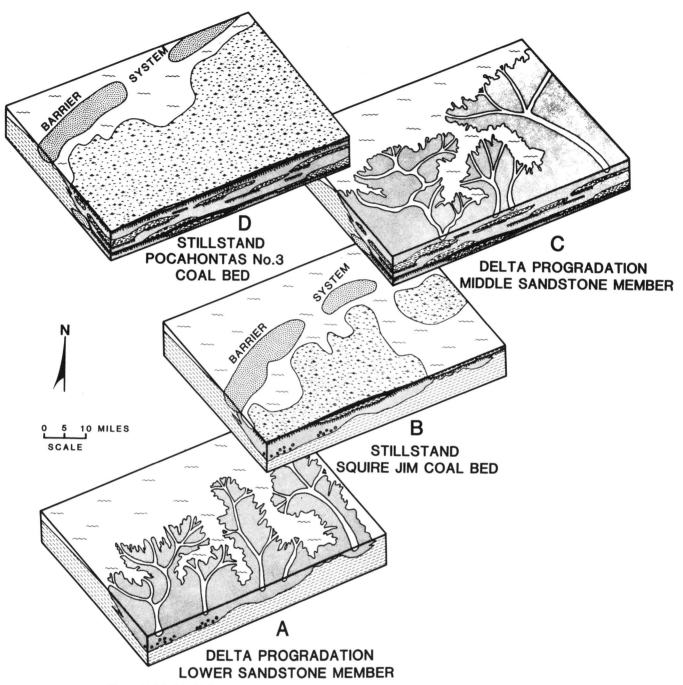

Figure 11. Model of inferred depositional systems of the Pocahontas Formation showing regressions (A, C) and stillstands (B, D).

However, the data derived from this study indicate that a flood of terrestrial clastics into the previously marine-dominated basin in response to high rainfall and associated conditions probably began in earliest Late Mississippian time. This influx of terrestrial clastics into the basin was further influenced by the capacity of the basin to accommodate these sediments through subsidence. Continuous, slow subsidence during Late Mississippian and Early Pennsylvanian times is well documented by the shallow-water character of the nearly 1,524 m (5,000 ft) of strata in these series. Imbalance between subsidence (capacity of the basin to accommodate sediments) and the influx of sediments controlled the extent of terrestrial progradation into the basin. Terrestrial progradation or marine incursion records periods when the sediment influx was respectively greater than or less than the local accommodating capacity of the basin. Periods of balance or near balance between these two influences were marked by the development of stillstands and widespread peat formation, accompanied by minimal subsidence and clastic sedimentation.

The last southeastward encroachment of marine muds took place during the late stages of deposition of the lower sandstone member as recorded in the upper member or tongue of the Bluestone Formation. In succeeding sediments of the Pocahontas Formation, terrestrial deposition was dominant and, because of this, the alternating periods of transgression and regression in underlying strata were replaced by alternating periods of regression and stillstand (Fig. 11). During those stillstands, when there was neither marine transgression nor significant terrestrial progradation, extensive swamps flourished across the abandoned distributary lobes.

The imbalance between rates of subsidence and sediment influx during deposition of the Pocahontas Formation was further modified by an additional factor—differential compaction. Two relationships demonstrate the effects of compaction. The first is shown by the encroachment of nearshore marine mud into the interlobe areas and over thin sand along the fringe of the principal lobes, thus demonstrating the positive aspect of the high-sand central lobe. Second, because of the greater compactability of sediments in the shale-dominated fringe area, carbonaceous muds or thin peat beds were deposited in water that was too deep for optimum plant growth and the accumulation of thick peat.

The relationship of thickness and sulfur content of the Pocahontas coal is similar to that noted in some modern coastal peat deposits. Anderson (1983) identified extensive low-ash peat deposits with a domed convex surface along the north coast of Borneo. These coastal deposits have been used as modern analogs for low-ash, low-sulfur coal of Early and Middle Pennsylvanian age in the eastern United States (Neuzil and Cecil, 1984). Cameron and Schruben (1983) report that the Great Heath in the coastal area of Maine contains domed deposits of ombrogenous peat that is low in ash and sulfur. A surrounding strip or moat area contains a high-ash muck consisting of organic-rich clay and silt. This modern analog would account for the deposition of thick, low-ash, low-sulfur peat where peat accumulation was dependent on high rainfall, which in turn contributed little if any mineral matter to the peat. This observation is concordant with the high rainfall, ever-wet climate postulated by Cecil and others (1983). The increase in the sulfur content noted towards contemporaneous brackish or marine environments is also evident in many modern analogs.

CONCLUSIONS

Data derived from studies of the distribution of the Pocahontas coal beds and associated strata have been used to develop a model (Fig. 11) that shows: 1) extensive peat accumulations developed on abandoned delta lobes during stillstands in a regressive delta-dominated sequence; 2) the thickest peat having the lowest sulfur content accumulated over the thickest part of sandstone lobes; 3) carbonaceous shale or thin coal beds accumulated in the interlobe areas; 4) the total sulfur and ash contents and partings in the coal increased toward the fringe areas; 5) scouring associated with the vertical stacking of sandstone lobes was responsible for the erosion of coal beds locally in areas of thick sandstone, and 6) splits in the coal beds recorded minor reactivation of drainage from the southeast. As an alternative to the use of the roof rock to explain sulfur distribution in coal, the model proposed here demonstrates that the geometry, thickness, and orientation of underlying delta lobes can be used to predict the occurrence of thick, low-sulfur coal in the Pocahontas Formation.

REFERENCES CITED

Anderson, J.A.R., 1983, The tropical peat swamps of western Malesia, *in* Gore, A.J.P., ed., Ecosystems of the World 4B Mires, swamp, bog, fen and moore: Amsterdam, Elsevier Scientific Publishing Company, p. 181–199.

Cameron, C. C., and Schruben, Paul, 1983, Variation in mineral matter content of a peat deposit in Maine resting in glacio-marine sediments, *in* Raymond, Robert, Jr., and Andrejko, M. J., eds., Mineral matter in peat—Its occurrence, form, and distribution: Los Alamos, New Mexico, Los Alamos National Laboratory, p. 63–76.

Cecil, C. B., Stanton, R. W., Dulong, F. T., Ruppert, L. F., and Renton, J. J., 1981, A geochemical model for the origin of low-ash and low-sulfur coal: *in* Roberts, T. C., ed., Geological Society of America Cincinnati '81, Fieldtrip Guidebooks, v. 1, Stratigraphy, sedimentology: Washington, D.C., American Geological Institute, p. 175–177.

Cecil, C. B., Stanton, R. W., Neuzil, S. G., Dulong, F. T., and Ruppert, L. F., 1983, Paleoclimate controls on coal beds and associated rocks in the central Appalachian basin: Geological Society of America Abstracts with Programs, v. 15, no. 6, p. 541.

Cooper, H. M., Snyder, N. H., Abernethy, R. F., Tarpley, E. C., and Swingle, R. J., 1942, Analyses of mine, tipple, and delivered samples, *in* Analyses of West Virginia coals: U.S. Bureau of Mines Technical Paper 626, p. 39–323.

——, 1944, Analyses of mine, tipple, and delivered samples, *in* Analyses of Virginia coals: U.S. Bureau of Mines Technical Paper 656, p. 31–144.

Englund, K. J., 1968, Geologic map of the Bramwell quadrangle, West Virginia-Virginia: U.S. Geological Survey Geologic Quadrangle Map GQ-745, scale 1:24,000.

——, 1969, Relation of the Pocahontas Formation to the Mississippian-Pennsylvanian systemic boundary in southwestern Virginia and southern West Virginia: Geological Society of America Abstracts with Programs, v. 1, pt. 4, p. 21.

——, 1971, Displacement of the Pocahontas Formation by the Russell Fork fault, southwest Virginia: U.S. Geological Survey Professional Paper 750-B, p. B13–B16.

——, 1974, Sandstone distribution patterns in the Pocahontas Formation of southwest Virginia and southern West Virginia, *in* Briggs, Garrett, ed., Carboniferous of the southeastern United States: Geological Society America Special Paper 148, p. 31–45.

——, 1979, The Mississippian and Pennsylvanian (Carboniferous) systems in the United States—Virginia: U.S. Geological Survey Professional Paper 1110-C, 21 p.

——, 1981, Geology of the Jewell Ridge quadrangle, Buchanan and Tazewell Counties, Virginia: U.S. Geological Survey Geologic Quadrangle Map GQ-1550, scale 1:24,000.

Englund, K. J., and Henry, T. W., eds., 1981, Mississippian-Pennsylvanian boundary in the central part of the Appalachian Basin (Part I: southwestern Virginia-southern West Virginia), *in* Roberts, T. G., ed., Geological Society of America Cincinnati '81. Fieldtrip Guidebooks, v. 1, Stratigraphy, sedimentology, Washington, D.C., American Geological Institute, p. 153–194.

Englund, K. J., and Teaford, N. K., 1980, Maps showing coal resources of the Jewell Ridge quadrangle, Buchanan and Tazewell Counties, Virginia: U.S. Geological Survey Miscellaneous Field Studies Map MF-1211, scale 1:74,500.

Englund, K. J., Arndt, H. H., Henry, T. W., Meissner, C. R., Jr., Windolph, J. F., Jr., and Warlow, R. C., 1977a, Geologic map of the New River Gorge area, Fayette, Raleigh, and Summers Counties, West Virginia: U.S. Geological Survey Open-File Report OF-77-76, Map A.

Englund, K. J., Windolph, J. F., Jr., Warlow, R. C., Henry, T. W., Meissner, C. R., Jr., and Arndt, H. H., 1977b, Stratigraphic section of the New River Gorge area, Fayette, Raleigh, and Summers Counties, West Virginia: U.S. Geological Survey Open-File Report OF—77-76, Map C, scale 1:1,200.

Englund, K. J., Arndt, H. H., and Henry, T. W., eds., 1979, Proposed Pennsylvanian System stratotype, Virginia and West Virginia—Field trip no. 1, Ninth International Congress of Carboniferous Stratigraphy and Geology, Washington: American Geological Institute Selected Guidebook no. 1, 136 p.

Englund, K. J., Henry, T. W., and Cecil, C. B., 1981, Upper Mississippian and Lower Pennsylvanian depositional environments, southwestern Virginia and southern West Virginia, *in* Roberts, T. G., ed., Geological Society of America Cincinnati '81. Fieldtrip Guidebooks, Vol. 1, Stratigraphy, sedimentology, Washington, D.C., American Geological Institute, p. 171–175.

Englund, K. J., Windolph, J. F., Jr., Weber, J. C., Thomas, R. E., and Dryden, J. W., 1983, Test drilling for coal in 1982-83, in the Jefferson National Forest, Virginia, Part I: Lithologic descriptions and geophysical logs of coreholes in the southwestern Virginia coal field, Dickenson, Lee, Scott, and Wise Counties, Virginia: U.S. Geological Survey Open-File Report OF—83-628, 374 p.

Englund, K. J., Gillespie, W. H., Johnson, P. L., and Pfefferkorn, H. W., 1986, Depositional model for Upper Mississippian and Lower Pennsylvanian coal-bearing rocks of southwestern Virginia: *in* McDowell, R. C., and Glover, Lynn, III, eds., Studies in Appalachian Geology: Virginia Polytechnic Institute and State University, Department of Geological Sciences Memoir 3 (in press).

Ferm, J. C., Horne, J. C., and Melton, R. A., 1976, Depositional models applied to coal exploration and development: paper presented at the American Institute of Mining Engineers Annual Meeting, Las Vegas Nevada, February 1976, 12 p.

Henry, T. W., Englund, K. J., Johnson, P. L., Mory, P. C., and Windolph, J. F., Jr., 1981, Description and correlation of core from five deep drill holes in Carboniferous rocks along the New River Gorge, West Virginia: U.S. Geological Survey Open-File Report OF—81-1339, 88 p.

Horne, J. C., Howell, D. J., Baganz, B. P., and Ferm, J. C., 1978, Splay deposits as an economic factors in coal mining: *in* Hodgson, H. E., ed., Proceedings of the second symposium on the geology of Rocky Mountain coal—1977: Colorado Geological Survey Resource Series 4, p. 89–100.

Kaiser, W. R., Johnston, J. E., and Bach, W. H., 1978, Sand-body geometry and the occurrence of lignite in the Eocene of Texas, *in* Hodgson, H. E., ed., Proceedings of the second symposium on the geology of Rocky Mountain coal—1977, Colorado Geological Survey Resources Series 4, p. 67–87.

Medlin, J. H., and Coleman, S. L., 1976, Geochemistry of Lower Pennsylvanian coal beds, *in* Englund, K. J., Cecil, C. B., Stricker, G. D., and Warlow, R. C., Guidebook to Carboniferous stratigraphy of southwestern Virginia and southern West Virginia: Northeastern and Southeastern Combined Section Meeting, Geological Society of America, Arlington, Va., March 1976, Field Trip Guidebook 3, p. 14–17.

Meissner, C. R., Jr., 1978, Geologic Map of the Duty quadrangle, Dickenson, Russell, and Buchanan Counties, Virginia: U.S. Geological Survey Geologic Quadrangle Map GQ-1458, scale 1:24,000.

——— , 1979, Maps showing coal resources of the Honaker quadrangle, Russell,

Tazewell, and Buchanan Counties, Virginia: U.S. Geological Survey Miscellaneous Field Studies Map MF-1123, scale, 1:62,500.

——— , 1981, Geologic Map of the Shady Spring quadrangle, Raleigh and Summers Counties, West Virginia: U.S. Geological Survey Geologic Quadrangle Map GQ-1546, scale 1:24,000.

Meissner, C. R., Jr., and Heermann, S. E., 1982, Maps showing coal resources of the Big A Mountain quadrangle, Russell and Buchanan Counties, Virginia: U.S. Geological Survey Miscellaneous Field Studies Map MF-1439, scale, 1:62,500.

Meissner, C. R., Jr., and Miller, R. L., 1981, Geologic Map of the Honaker quadrangle, Russell, Tazewell, and Buchanan Counties, Virginia: U.S. Geological Survey Geologic Quadrangle Map GQ-1542, Scale 1:24,000.

Miller, M. S., 1974, Stratigraphy and coal beds of upper Mississippian and lower Pennsylvanian rocks in southwestern Virginia: Virginia Division of Mineral Resources Bulletin 84, 211 p.

Miller, R. L., and Meissner, C. R., Jr., 1978, Geologic map of the Big A Mountain quadrangle, Russell and Buchanan Counties, Virginia: U.S. Geological Survey Geologic Quadrangle Map GQ-1350, scale 1:24,000.

Neuzil, S. G., and Cecil, C. B., 1984, A modern analog of low-ash, low-sulfur, Pennsylvanian-age coal (abs.): Geological Society of America Abstracts with Programs, v. 16, no. 6, p. 84.

Read, C. B., and Mamay, S. H., 1964, Upper Paleozoic floral zones and floral provinces of the United States: U.S. Geological Survey Professional Paper 454-K, p. K1–K35.

Reger, D. B., 1926, Mercer, Monroe, and Summers Counties: West Virginia Geological Survey [County Report], 963 p.

Schweinfurth, S. P., Arndt, H. H., and Englund, K. J., 1976, Description of core from three U.S. Geological Survey core holes in Carboniferous rocks of West Virginia: U.S. Geological Survey Open-File Report OF-76-159, 61 p., 5 figs.

Simon, F. O., and Englund, K. J., 1983, Test drilling for coal in 1982-83 in the Jefferson National Forest, Part 2: Analyses of coal cores from the southwestern Virginia coal fields: U.S. Geological Survey Open-File Report OF-83-620, 23 p.

Stricker, G. D., 1981, Geologic Map of the Crumpler quadrangle, West Virginia: U.S. Geological Survey Geologic Quadrangle Map GQ-1547, scale 1:24,000.

Trent, V. A., Medlin, J. H., Coleman, S. L., and Stanton, R. W., 1982, Chemical analyses and physical properties of 12 coal samples from the Pocahontas field, Tazewell County, Virginia and McDowell County, West Virginia: U.S. Geological Survey Bulletin 1528, 37 p.

Williams, E. G., and Keith, M. L., 1963, Relationship between sulfur in coals and the occurrence of marine roof beds: Economic Geology, v. 58, no. 5, p. 720–729.

Windolph, J. F., Jr., 1983, Geologic Map of the Amonate quadrangle, Buchanan and Tazewell Counties, Virginia and McDowell County, West Virginia: U.S. Geological Survey Open-File Report OF—83-446, scale 1:24,000.

——— , 1986, Maps showing coal resources of the Amonate quadrangle, Buchanan and Tazewell Counties, Virginia, and McDowell County, West Virginia: U.S. Geological Survey Miscellaneous Field Studies Map MF-1730, scale 1:48,000.

Windolph, J. F., Jr., Henry, T. W., and Englund, K. J., 1977, Coal resources of the proposed National Park area of the New River Gorge, Fayette, Raleigh, and Summers Counties, West Virginia: U.S. Geological Survey Open-File Report OF-77-76, Map F, scale 1:100,000.

Zubovic, Peter, Oman, C. L., Coleman, S. L., Bragg, L. J., Kerr, P. T., Kozey, K. M., Simon, F. O., Rowe, J. J., Medlin, J. H., and Walker, F. E., 1979, Chemical analyses of 617 coal samples from the eastern United States: U.S. Geological Survey Open-File Report OF-79-665, 460 p.

Zubovic, Peter, Oman, C. L., Bragg, L. J., Coleman, S. L., Rega, N. H., Lemaster, M. E., Rose, H. J., Golightly, D. W., and Puskas, John, 1980, Chemical analyses of 659 coal samples from the eastern United States: U.S. Geological Survey Open-File Report OF—80-2003, 513 p.

MANUSCRIPT ACCEPTED BY THE SOCIETY APRIL 16, 1986

Discussion of paper by Englund, Windolph, and Thomas. Responses by Englund.

Paul C. Lyons
Question: Do you have any place in the Pocahontas Formation where marine strata overlie the coal beds? If so, would you comment on the associated coal quality, particularly sulfur content?
Response: Confirmed marine deposits do not occur above coal beds in the Pocahontas Formation. The Pocahontas No. 8 coal bed in the overlying New River Formation does have a marine roof but, because of the thinness of the coal, it has not been mined or sampled for analysis.

Jim Fassett
Question: Were the marine and non-marine environments of deposition separated by a continuous barrier-beach system at the time of deposition?
Response: The preserved evidence shows that the barrier sandstones were discontinuous. However, this barrier does delineate the extent of the nonmarine environment, most likely due to high rainfall and low tides, so that there was a net outflow of fresh or brackish water.

Nelson Shaffer (Indiana Geological Survey)
Question: Could the sandstones have acted as a freshwater aquifer that could have transmitted fresh water to promote plant growth and to dilute seawater?
Response: I would not have expected the sandstone to act as an aquifer for two reasons: (1) A layer of impervious clay (underclay) occurs between the sandstone and the overlying coal; (2) the sandstones today are not good aquifers; they are dirty, poorly sorted.

R. L. Lengenheim, Jr. (Dept. Geology, University of Illinois, Urbana)
Question: How far above sea level do you believe the Pocahontas coal swamp stood?
Response: The base of the coal swamp was only slightly above sea level. The top of the bed was substantially higher, depending on rate of compaction applied to the peat; possibly as much as 50 ft.

J. E. Fassett (USGS, Reston)
Comment: The Sears and others (1941) depositional model was the first comprehensive model which explained in a detailed way how transgressive and regressive shoreface sandstones formed. This model was based on a detailed study of Upper Cretaceous sandstone in the southern San Juan Basin. The model indicated a continuously subsiding seaway receiving a varying amount of sediment over time. A high rate of sediment influx would have caused the shoreline to build outward into the seaway, resulting in shoreline regression. A low rate of sediment influx would allow the sea to advance over the land, resulting in shoreline transgression. When the sediment influx exactly balanced subsidence, shoreface sands would build up. Sears and others (p. 103) suggested that thick coal deposits should form landward of upbuilding beach-sand deposits. It seemed to me that your coal model reflected the Sears and others coal model of 1941.

Geological Society of America
Special Paper 210
1986

Structural and depositional history of the Pennsylvanian System in Illinois

C. Brian Trask
Illinois State Geological Survey
Natural Resources Building
615 E. Peabody Dr.
Champaign, Illinois 61820

James E. Palmer
Sigma Consultants, Inc.
P. O. box 1035
Mattoon, Illinois 61938

ABSTRACT

Structures active during the Pennsylvanian Period and paleoenvironments in which Pennsylvanian strata were formed strongly influenced the character and location of coal resources in the Illinois Basin. Sediment filling the basin probably originated in the Canadian Shield and perhaps the highlands of the northern Appalachians. Major river systems transported this sediment to the Illinois Basin, where it was deposited in fluvial and deltaic paleoenvironments on a broad coastal plain and adjacent shallow shelf. Loci of deposition were controlled by the La Salle Anticlinal Belt on the east and the Du Quoin Monocline and the Louden and Salem Anticlines on the west. These structures separated the deeper parts of the basin from the shallow shelf areas to the west and east.

Periodic marine invasions interrupted fluvial and deltaic sedimentation. River systems were able to re-establish themselves following these inundations, which resulted in the creation of a series of elongate, sinuous sandstone/siltstone bodies. Some of these bodies were deposited contemporaneously with coal-forming swamps that occupied vast areas of this coastal plain. These rivers were the Pennsylvanian continuation of the Michigan River System, which carried terrestrial sediment from the Canadian Shield and perhaps the Appalachians to the Illinois Basin during the Mississippian Period. Further exploration will undoubtedly reveal additional peat-contemporaneous channel-fill deposits.

INTRODUCTION

The Illinois Basin contains as much as 975 m (3200 ft) of Pennsylvanian-age alluvial, deltaic, and marine sedimentary rocks deposited in a broad coastal plain of very low relief, which extended at least from Kansas to Pennsylvania. Pennsylvanian strata in the Illinois Basin contain as many as 80 coal beds. Mining has occurred in more than 30 beds.

This report contains a description and analysis of Pennsylvanian-age strata that lie between the Cincinnati Arch to the east and the Ozark Dome to the west. These strata are bounded by the Wisconsin, Kankakee, and Mississippi River Arches to the north and west, and by the Pascola Arch and Nashville Dome to the south. Their original extent and correlations beyond these structural features have been considered by Wanless (1975a) and other workers.

As a result of numerous studies by geologists during the past 150 years, conditions of deposition of Pennsylvanian sediments in the Illinois Basin are probably as well known as in any comparable area of the world. Data summarized and reviewed here are based in part upon the studies and conclusions of these earlier workers.

STRUCTURAL HISTORY

Following an episode of dominantly marine deposition during the Mississippian Period, regional uplift raised the Midcontinent area above sea level and tilted it to the southwest. Rivers flowing down this paleoslope truncated earlier strata to form a basal Pennsylvanian unconformity. Bristol and Howard (1971) have compared this to the modern coastal plain of Georgia and South Carolina. Pennsylvanian strata were deposited on this truncated surface to form an angular unconformity with older rocks. Underlying rocks in the southern and southeastern part of the basin are Upper Mississippian (Chesterian); those in the northern and northwestern parts are Devonian to Ordovician. Pennsylvanian rocks also overlap progressively older Pennsylvanian strata northward, reflecting progressive filling of the basin throughout Pennsylvanian time.

Strata of the Pennsylvanian System were deposited in a subsiding trough open to the south and bordered by broad arches or uplifts to the north, east, and west (Fig. 1). Because those structural features were at or below depositional base level at times, some lithic units were deposited without substantial interruption in an area extending from Pennsylvania to Kansas (Wanless, 1975a). The Illinois Basin was structurally closed on the south during Mesozoic time by uplift of the Pascola Arch (Marcher and Stearns, 1962; Hopkins and Simon, 1975).

The Cincinnati Arch, which borders the Illinois Basin on the east, does not seem to have had much effect on delivery of sediment to the basin from the Canadian Shield or northern Appalachian orogenic belt, though during Mississippian time it separated the drainage basin of the Michigan River System from that of the Ontario River System to the east (Donaldson and Shumaker, 1979). The Rough Creek-Shawneetown Fault System (along the Rough Creek Lineament) in the southern part of the basin exerted little influence on sedimentation during the Pennsylvanian Period, though movement along this fault system may have been the cause of local deepening of Pennsylvanian paleovalleys and syndepositional slumping of flood-plain and deltaic deposits (Nelson and Lumm, 1984). Movement along the Wabash Valley Fault System in southeastern Illinois is entirely post-Pennsylvanian (Bristol and Treworgy, 1979). Similarly, movement along faults in the Fluorspar Area Fault Complex was dominantly post-Pennsylvanian (Trace, 1974), though some movement may have occurred during Pennsylvanian time (Trace, 1974) as evidenced by local thickening of basal Pennsylvanian units (Amos, 1966; Pinckney, 1980). Potter (1957) described slumping in the Caseyville Formation from southern Illinois that may have been caused by movement along the McCormick Fault Zone.

The Cap au Grès Faulted Flexure in western Illinois underwent uplift during Late Mississippian time (Rubey, 1952). Subsequent erosion cut valleys into the structure, but these were rapidly filled and the topography nearly leveled during the early part of the Pennsylvanian Period. The structure was then dormant until post-Pennsylvanian time. Similarly, the Ste. Genevieve Fault

Zone underwent movement during Late Mississippian or Early Pennsylvanian time. Pennsylvanian strata in this area form an angular unconformity with underlying Chesterian rocks (Poor, 1925; Ekblaw, 1925; Desborough, 1961). Basal Pennsylvanian rocks contain a dominantly chert-pebble conglomerate; the angularity of the particles in this conglomerate suggests derivation from a nearby source (Poor, 1925), perhaps the upthrown side of the fault zone. Desborough (1961) has demonstrated that this fault zone contained sufficient relief to deflect streams from the dominant southwesterly transport direction for the basin to a southeasterly direction along the northeast side of the fault zone. The dominant structural features affecting Pennsylvanian deposition were the Du Quoin Monocline and nearby Salem and Louden Anticlines, the La Salle Anticlinal Belt, and the Ozark Dome.

Du Quoin Monocline, Salem and Louden Anticlines

The Du Quoin Monocline and Salem and Louden Anticlines (Fig. 1) extend along the western margin of the Fairfield Basin for nearly 160 km (100 mi). The monocline forms a hinge line separating horizontal to gently dipping strata on the west from more steeply dipping rocks at the margin of the Fairfield Basin. The monocline has local structural relief of about 152 m (500 ft) at the horizon of the Herrin (No. 6) Coal Member and more than 300 m (1000 ft) in rocks of Chesterian (Late Mississippian) age. Maximum growth of the Du Quoin Monocline appears to have occurred during Early and Middle Pennsylvanian time. Topographic expression of this structure may have been sufficient during Early Pennsylvanian time to deflect stream flow from southwesterly to a more southerly direction (Bristol and Howard, 1971). The monocline and Salem and Louden Anticlines may have helped to determine the extent of coal swamps for deposition of both the Springfield (No. 5) and Herrin (No. 6) Coal Members. The Springfield Coal (Fig. 2) thickens abruptly east of these structures, and is generally thin or missing to the west. Conversely, the Herrin Coal (Fig. 3) is thicker to the west and thin or missing on the east. Wanless and others (1969) and Treworgy and Jacobson (1985) suggested that the location of the Herrin coal swamp was determined by two wedges of deltaic sediment on the east and west.

La Salle Anticlinal Belt

The La Salle Anticlinal Belt (Fig. 1), which extends more than 320 km (200 mi) from La Salle County in northern Illinois to Lawrence County in southeastern Illinois, was substantially uplifted in the north prior to deposition of Pennsylvanian rocks. Much of the northern and central area of the La Salle Anticlinal Belt must have been a peninsula or archipelago during Early Pennsylvanian time, because no Morrowan strata were deposited, and Atokan and early Desmoinesian strata are much thinner than to the east or west. Uplift during Mississippian time occurred primarily in the north (H. R. Schwalb, 1984, personal communi-

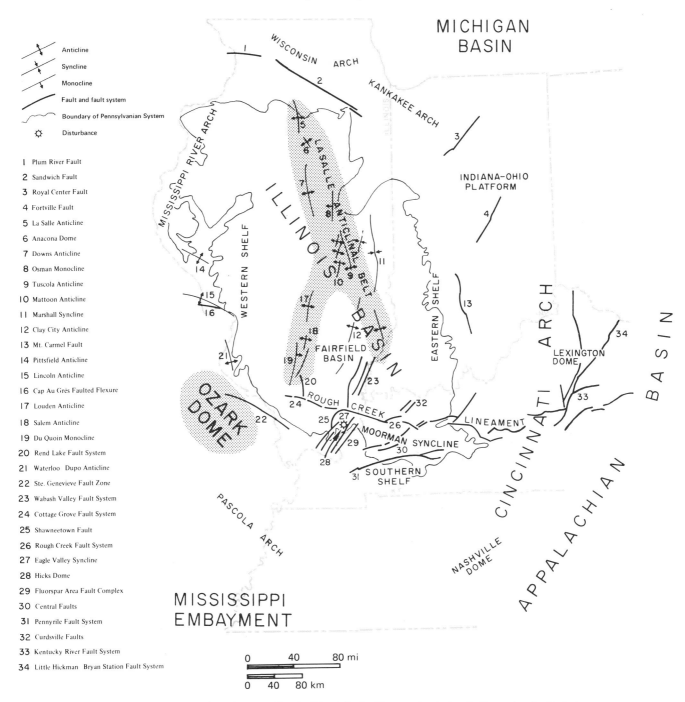

Figure 1. Structures in and surrounding the Illinois Basin. Those active during the Pennsylvanian Period are indicated with a stippled pattern. (After Krausse and Treworgy, 1979).

cation). Clegg (1965) reported that relative uplift took place on the anticlinal belt throughout Pennsylvanian time, and intensive uplift of all Pennsylvanian strata occurred in very Late Pennsylvanian or post-Pennsylvanian time. Current structural relief of the La Salle Anticlinal Belt in east central Illinois is 300 m (1000 ft) at the Colchester Coal Member and 760 m (2500 ft) at the top of the Upper Ordovician Kimmswick Subgroup (Clegg, 1965).

Ozark Dome

The Ozark Dome borders the Illinois Basin on the southwest. Pennsylvanian strata are preserved almost exclusively in caves and sinkholes on the Ozark Dome (Hinds and Greene, 1915; Howe and others, 1967; Wanless, 1975b). The fact that only Desmoinesian strata are preserved (Howe and others, 1967;

Trask and Palmer

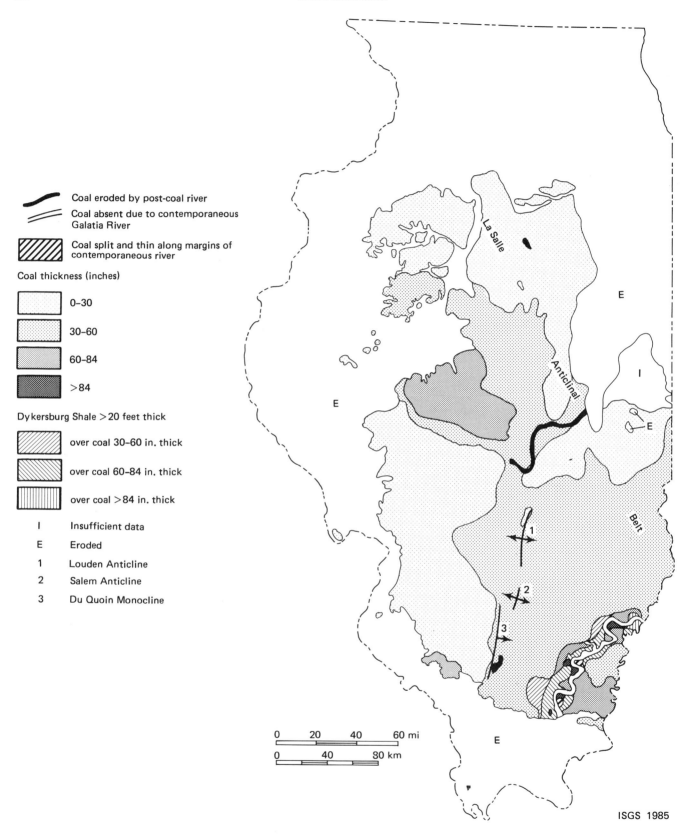

Figure 2. Resources in the Springfield (No. 5) Coal Member of Illinois (after Smith and Stall, 1975; sandstone channels according to Treworgy and Bargh, 1984b).

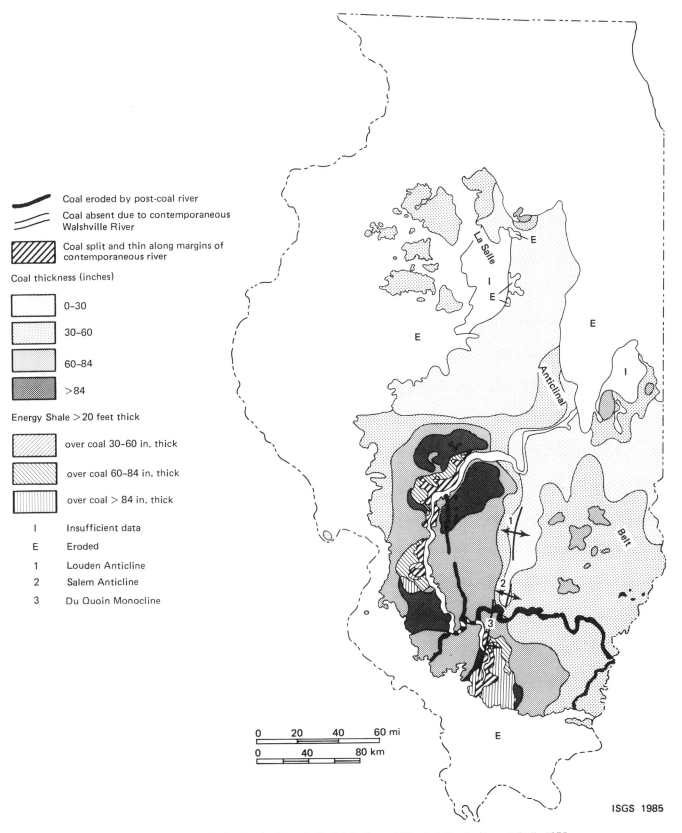

Figure 3. Resources in the Herrin (No. 6) Coal Member of Illinois (after Smith and Stall, 1975; sandstone channels according to Treworgy and Bargh, 1984a).

Figure 4. Thickness of the Pennsylvanian System in the Illinois Basin (after McKee and Crosby, 1975, pl. 11; modified according to Smith and Smith, 1967, and Williams and others, 1982). Paleocurrent rose diagram based on data from Potter (1963, Table 5). Contour interval 500 ft.

sequence. The maximum preserved thickness of Pennsylvanian strata in Illinois is slightly more than 750 m (2500 ft).

Stratigraphic nomenclature is not yet consistent among the three states that occupy the area of the Illinois Basin (Fig. 5). Work to unify terminology is in its early stages (Jacobson and others, 1985). History of deposition is well illustrated, however, by the sequence of strata in Illinois, which occupies 75% of the area of the basin.

The Pennsylvanian System in Illinois comprises seven formations, from the basal Caseyville Formation to the uppermost Mattoon Formation (Hopkins and Simon, 1975). Assigned to the Morrowan, Atokan, Desmoinesian, Missourian, and Virgilian Series of North American Midcontinent terminology, these rocks correlate with the Westphalian and Stephanian Series of Europe. Rocks of the Namurian B and C Stages, which lie below Westphalian A and may be correlative in part with lower Morrowan rocks, may be present in western Kentucky (R. A. Peppers, 1984, personal communication), in southern Illinois (Rexroad and Merrill, 1979), and in sinkholes in western Illinois (Leary, 1981).

Clastic rocks form 90 to 95 percent of the Pennsylvanian System (Atherton and Palmer, 1979). Shales and siltstones are the dominant rock types, although sandstone comprises over half of the rocks in the Caseyville and Abbott Formations (Fig. 6). Limestone is rare in the lower part of the section but increases in abundance upward; locally it constitutes as much as 5 to 10 percent of the rock types in the upper two-thirds of the System. Coal seams comprise no more than 1 to 2 percent of the stratigraphic column except in the Carbondale Formation, which contains most of the coal resources of Illinois.

Depositional Model

During the Pennsylvanian, a broad, shallow, trough-like depression existed in the area of the Illinois Basin (Potter, 1962, 1963). Paleoslope was to the south and southwest toward the developing Ouachita geosyncline and Warrior Basin. Sediments that filled the embayment were dominantly clastic, carried by rivers flowing from the southern Canadian Shield and possibly from highlands of the northern Appalachians (Siever and Potter, 1956; Potter, 1963). The principal source area is believed to have been an orogenic belt, undergoing mild to moderate uplift and erosion. Vertical decrease in recycled components (quartz pebbles, zircon, tourmaline, and rutile) and increase in matrix, feldspar, and garnet suggest unroofing of a crystalline mass (Potter and Glass, 1958).

Sediments were transported by a series of large river systems entering the basin from the east, northeast, and north. Studies of the azimuth of cross-bedding in sandstone (Potter and Siever, 1956; Potter, 1963) have shown that transport direction in the basin was dominantly southwest (Fig. 4), except perhaps where diverted by the Ste. Genevieve Fault Zone and possibly the Du Quoin Monocline. These sediments were deposited on a low-lying coastal plain and adjacent shallow shelf, in a series of fluvial and deltaic systems. Strata are essentially non-marine in the Ca-

Wanless, 1975a) indicates that the Ozarks were elevated during Early Pennsylvanian time. Howe and others (1967) suggested a greater persistence of Desmoinesian strata in this region prior to post-Pennsylvanian erosion. Sinkholes to the south and higher on the uplift are filled with pyrite and hematite (Bretz, 1950). Wanless (1975b) suggested that this resulted from climatic zoning due to differences in height of the Ozark uplift at the time. Bretz (1965, p. 13), however, noted that weak Pennsylvanian rocks flanking the dome are higher than the dome itself; he concluded that Pennsylvanian strata probably once covered all but the St. Francois Mountains.

STRATIGRAPHY AND ENVIRONMENTS OF DEPOSITION

The Pennsylvanian System in the Illinois Basin is thickest in western Kentucky (Smith and Smith, 1967; Williams and others, 1982), where 975 m (3200 ft) of strata are present (Fig. 4). This thick sequence is located just south of a graben that contains Permian rocks at the surface (Kehn, Beard, and Williamson, 1982; Williams and others, 1982) indicating an originally thicker

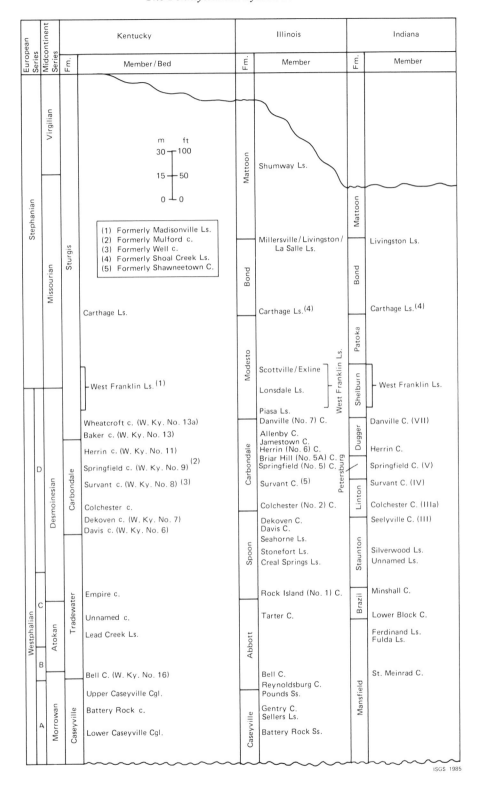

Figure 5. Stratigraphic columns of the Pennsylvanian System in the Illinois Basin, showing principal coals (after Shaver and others, 1970; Hopkins and Simon, 1975; Peppers and Popp, 1979; and Williams and others, 1982). New names not cited in these references are from Jacobson and others (1985). Modifications from these references according to Russel A. Peppers (1984, personal communication).

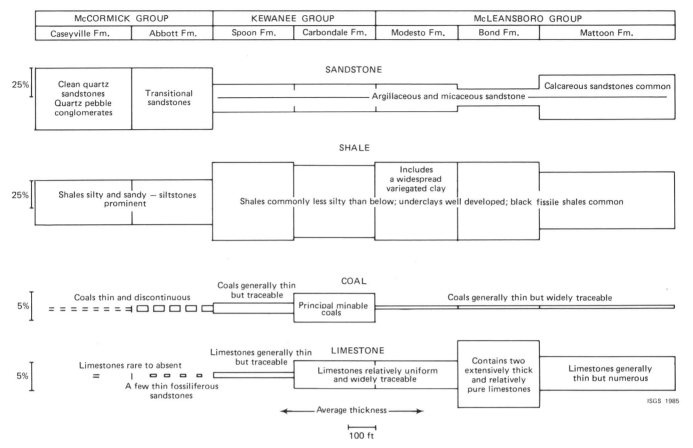

Figure 6. Lithologic composition of formations in the Pennsylvanian System (from Kosanke and others, 1960).

seyville and Abbott Formations, but become more marine upward and are dominantly marine in the Bond Formation (Fig. 5).

Deposition of sediments filling the Illinois Basin was controlled by structures we have already identified as being active during the Pennsylvanian Period. The La Salle Anticlinal Belt on the east and the Du Quoin Monocline and Salem and Louden Anticlines on the west separated the Fairfield Basin from the shelf areas to the east and west (Fig. 1). This is reflected in the basin fill by thinning of the section and absence of units on the shelf and over these positive structures. Ambrose (1983a, b) documented the effect these structures had on narrowing the depositional trough and amplifying tides during Spoon time.

Early Clastic Infilling—Caseyville, Abbott, and Spoon Formations

During the early part of the Pennsylvanian Period, basin fill consisted primarily of sandstone, siltstone, and shale. The lower three formations (Caseyville, Abbott, and Spoon, Fig. 7a) reach a combined thickness of more than 300 m (1000 ft) in parts of southeastern Illinois, between the La Salle Anticlinal Belt and the Du Quoin Monocline. The effect of the Du Quoin and La Salle

structures can be seen in thinning of these units in the eastern and western parts of the basin.

The Caseyville Formation (Fig. 7b) is the lowermost Pennsylvanian formation in Illinois. The Caseyville reaches 150 m (500 ft) in thickness in southern Illinois, but its common maximum is 100 m (350 ft). The formation rests on an unconformable surface. Paleovalleys cut into underlying Mississippian rocks trend dominantly southwest (Bristol and Howard, 1971). These channels have a relief ranging from a few meters to as much as 137 m (450 ft), causing abrupt changes in thickness of the formation.

The Caseyville Formation consists primarily of sandstone and shale (Fig. 6). Caseyville sandstones contain only minor amounts of rock fragments, feldspar, mica, and detrital matrix. Quartz arenites dominate Caseyville sandstones. Quartz occurs commonly as well-rounded granules and pebbles, locally forming a conglomeratic phase. These particles were probably derived from reworked sedimentary rocks in the source area (Potter and Glass, 1958). Individual sandstone units are elongate, mainly channel-phase; they are up to 76 m (250 ft) thick (Wanless, 1975a). One marine limestone (Sellers Limestone Member) has been described from the Caseyville of southeastern

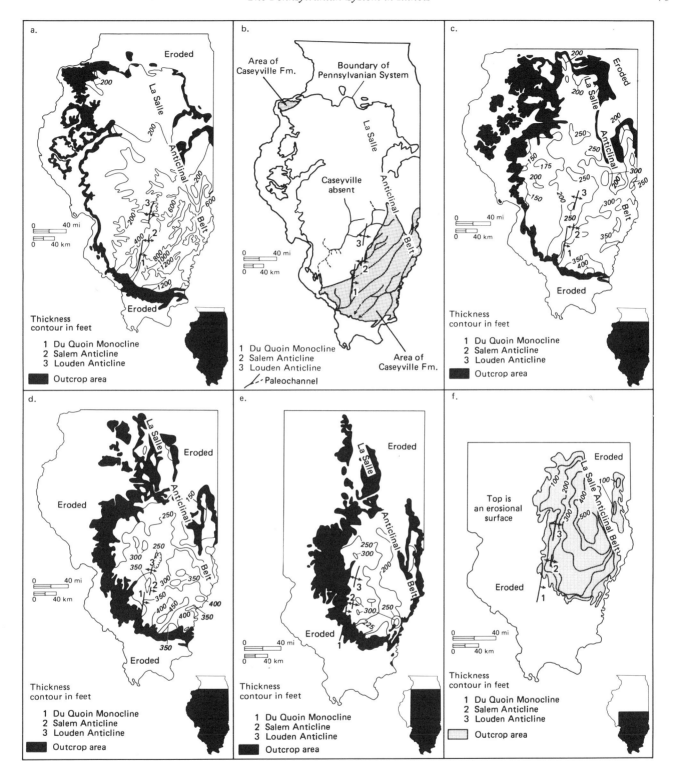

Figure 7. a) Combined thickness of Caseyville, Abbott, and Spoon Formations in Illinois (after Hopkins and Simon, 1975). b) Occurrence of Caseyville Formation in Illinois (after Hopkins and Simon, 1975). Location of sub-Pennsylvanian paleochannels from Bristol and Howard (1971). c) Thickness of Carbondale Formation in Illinois (after Hopkins and Simon, 1975). d) Thickness of Modesto Formation in Illinois (after Hopkins and Simon, 1975). e) Thickness of Bond Formation in Illinois (after Hopkins and Simon, 1975). f) Thickness of Mattoon Formation in Illinois (after Hopkins and Simon, 1975).

Illinois, but it is limited in extent to the type area (Hopkins and Simon, 1975). Coals in the Caseyville Formation are lenticular and discontinuous.

The overlying Abbott Formation, which overlaps the Caseyville northward, is the basal Pennsylvanian formation throughout most of Illinois where the Caseyville is absent. It pinches out beneath overlying Pennsylvanian strata in northern and northeastern Illinois and against some prominent anticlinal structures. The Abbott Formation reaches a maximum thickness of 90–100 m (300–350 ft) in the deepest part of the basin in southern Illinois, though it is commonly less than 30 m (100 ft) thick in the western part of the state.

Like the underlying Caseyville, the Abbott Formation is composed mainly of sandstone, siltstone, and shale (Fig. 6). Compared to the Caseyville, Abbott sandstones contain more rock fragments, clay, feldspar, and mica. They are mineralogically less mature and texturally more poorly sorted. Sandstone units of the Abbott are also primarily elongate but not as thick as those in the Caseyville. Limestone is rare. Abbott coal seams are lenticular, but more extensive than Caseyville coals.

The Spoon Formation, which overlaps the Abbott in northern and northeastern Illinois and on some major anticlinal structures, is present throughout most of the area in which Pennsylvanian strata occur. It is as much as 100 m (350 ft) thick in the deepest part of the basin in southern Illinois, but only a few m (less than 30 m; 100 ft) in areas of northern and western Illinois.

There is less sandstone and more coal and limestone in the Spoon Formation than in underlying formations (Fig. 6), reflecting a gradual change from dominantly clastic infilling during deposition of sediments forming the Caseyville and Abbott Formations to widespread marine invasions and coal swamps characteristic of the later part of the Desmoinesian Epoch. Spoon sandstones contain more clay matrix, rock fragments, feldspar, and mica, than those of the Abbott Formation. The presence of garnet in Spoon sandstones (Potter and Glass, 1958) suggests metamorphic rocks in the source area; garnet increases in abundance in overlying formations. Sandstone occurs in both elongate and sheet bodies. Marine limestones, though thin and few in number, are laterally extensive, particularly in the upper part of the formation, indicating regionally persistent marine invasions. Coals are thicker and more widespread in the Spoon Formation, although they are lenticular in the lower two-thirds of the formation. The widespread coal horizons (Davis, Dekoven, Seelyville) found in the upper Spoon reflect smoothing of pre-Pennsylvanian topography.

Widespread Coal Swamps—Carbondale and Modesto Formations

The Carbondale and Modesto Formations represent a time when extensive coal-forming swamps developed over broad areas of the North American continent. These swamps ranged in magnitude from individual deltaic swamps (such as those that may have formed the Jamestown and Briar Hill Coal Members) to broad coastal-plain swamps (such as those forming the Herrin and Springfield Coals).

The Carbondale Formation (Fig. 7c) occurs throughout the basin where Pennsylvanian strata are present, overlapping the underlying Spoon Formation northward. It is less than 45 m (150 ft) thick in the western and northern parts of the state, but reaches more than 120 m (400 ft) in the south. The Carbondale Formation thins sharply over the Du Quoin, Louden, Salem, and La Salle structures.

Potter and Glass (1958) referred to Carbondale sandstones as subgraywackes (mainly equivalent to sublitharenite of Folk, 1980). Garnet is an abundant accessory mineral in the upper part of the formation. Sandstone occurs as elongate units up to 30 m (100 ft) thick and as associated widespread thinner sheet-like bodies 6 m (20 ft) or less in thickness. Wide-spread limestones (Fig. 6) record periodic, regionally extensive marine invasions. Most of the coals of economic interest occur in the Carbondale Formation of Illinois and correlative rocks in Indiana and Kentucky. Rocks of the Carbondale Formation reflect a time of widespread development of coal swamps on a broad coastal plain of low relief. The Colchester Coal Member at the base of the Carbondale is believed to be one of the most widespread coals in the United States (Hopkins and Simon, 1975). Wanless and Wright (1978) have suggested that this coal and others in the Carbondale Formation developed on a platform formed by several coalesced deltas.

Because of post-Pennsylvanian erosion, the overlying Modesto Formation (Fig. 7d) is not as extensive as the Carbondale. It thickens from less than 40 m (125 ft) along the La Salle Anticlinal Belt in east-central Illinois to more than 60 m (200 ft) in northern Illinois and to a maximum of more than 135 m (450 ft) in the south. Although the Modesto Formation thins over the La Salle Anticlinal Belt, the effect of the Du Quoin Monocline and related structures is less pronounced. The depocenter of the formation is located more to the west, and the Modesto is thick over the Du Quoin Monocline. The thin succession in the central part of the basin overlies the Louden Anticline.

Modesto sandstones occur in both elongate bodies (as much as 24 m [80 ft] thick) and more widespread sheet-like bodies (commonly less than 6 m [20 ft] thick). Marine limestones are thicker and less argillaceous than Carbondale limestones; these represent repeated episodes of regional transgression. Modesto coals are widespread but thin (Fig. 6).

Extensive Marine Invasions—Bond and Mattoon Formations

Late Pennsylvanian time in the Illinois Basin was characterized by extensive, prolonged marine invasions. The uppermost Pennsylvanian formations (Bond and Mattoon) contain thick, widely quarried limestones.

The Bond Formation (Fig. 7e), overlying the Modesto, is primarily restricted to the central part of the basin. It is less than

— Paleochannel (dashed where inferred)

1 Louden Anticline
2 Salem Anticline
3 DuQuoin Monocline

Figure 8. Major channel-fill sandstones in the Illinois Basin formed contemporaneously with coal swamps. After Jacobson (1983, Oraville channel), Treworgy and Bargh (1984a, Walshville channel; 1984b, Galatia channel), Eggert (1982, Galatia channel), Beard and Williamson (1979, Henderson channel), and Treworgy and Treworgy (1983, lake from poster paper illustration).

45 m (150 ft) thick in eastern Illinois, but exceeds 90 m (300 ft) in southeastern Illinois. The La Salle Anticlinal Belt strongly influenced deposition of sediments forming the Bond Formation. Activity of the Du Quoin Monocline and Salem and Louden Anticlines was subdued during Bond time but the formation is locally thinner over small, individual structures, including parts of the Louden and Salem Anticlines. The Du Quoin Monocline is located in an area where the Bond Formation is eroded; therefore, any activity of this structure is not apparent in Figure 7e.

Bond sandstones are much like those in the underlying Modesto Formation. The Bond Formation contains a high percentage of marine limestone and calcareous claystone and shale (Fig. 6). The Carthage and Livingston/Millersville/La Salle Limestone Members, which bound the Bond Formation, are the thickest and purest Pennsylvanian limestones in Illinois and are extensively quarried. Bond coal seams are widespread, but they are thin and have little potential for economic development.

The youngest Pennsylvanian unit in Illinois, the Mattoon Formation, is limited to two small areas in southeastern Illinois (Fig. 7f). Although it locally exceeds 180 m (600 ft) in thickness in eastern Illinois, it is truncated by erosion and its original thickness and extent are unknown. The pattern of Mattoon distribution is obviously controlled by the La Salle Anticline Belt and the Du Quoin Monocline and Louden and Salem Anticlines. How much of this is a reflection of syndepositional structural activity (if any) and how much is a result of postdepositional structural movement and erosion cannot be determined.

The Mattoon Formation comprises a complex succession (Fig. 6) of thin limestones, coals and underclays, thick gray shales, black fissile shales, and several well-developed sandstones (Atherton and Palmer, 1979). Sandstones occur in elongate bodies as much as 30 m (100 ft) thick. The thin, widespread limestones reflect less marine influence during deposition of sediments forming the Mattoon Formation than in the underlying Bond. Coals are thin but widespread, and a few are of economic interest because they occur at shallow depths.

PERSISTENCE OF A MAJOR RIVER SYSTEM IN PENNSYLVANIAN STRATA OF THE ILLINOIS BASIN

Elongate sandstone bodies are prominent features in coal-bearing sequences of the Illinois Basin. Although many of these sandstones fill erosional troughs in coal beds, some (Fig. 8) have been shown to have been deposited contemporaneously with coal-forming peat (e.g., Johnson, 1972; Hopkins, 1968; Treworgy, 1981; Jacobson, 1983). Flow of water in the paleoriver systems that deposited these sandstones was generally to the south and southwest. Channels in which these rivers flowed apparently formed stable sluiceways through the swamps that enabled water (and sediment) to cross the vast swamp areas from source areas on the north and east to the basin of deposition to the south and west of the coastal plain.

Courses of major rivers are not easily changed. Potter (1978) has demonstrated the stability and longevity of several large river systems. When channel rerouting occurs, it is often on a small scale, a result of local differential compaction or structural dislocation.

Swann (1963), in his pioneering work on the origin of the Mississippian Chesterian Series, recognized the "Michigan River System" that existed throughout Chesterian (Late Mississippian) time, supplying delta-forming clastic sediments to the then dominantly marine Illinois Basin (Fig. 9). Uplift and withdrawal of seas at the close of the Mississippian Period permitted substantial erosion of upper units of the Chesterian Series by major streams (Bristol and Howard, 1971). These streams appear to have been part of the Michigan River System as it persisted through the close of the Mississippian Period.

Subsequently, as basin filling resumed during Early Pennsylvanian time, the same major drainage system deposited clastic sediments, forming the Caseyville Formation. Evidence suggests deposition of this formation by major rivers that crossed the basin flowing southwest. In a study of the Caseyville in southern Illinois, Koeninger and Mansfield (1979) concluded that deposition of the formation appears to have been "not unlike the Ganges portion of the Ganges-Brahmaputra delta as described by Morgan (1970)."

Strata of the Abbott and Spoon Formations overlying the Caseyville Formation contain extensive, thin marine limestones (see Fig. 5) that indicate episodic returns of marine environments to the Illinois Basin following nearly continuous terrestrial erosion and deposition since the close of the Mississippian Period. Although numerous examples of channel cut-and-fill deposits are recognized in the Abbott Formation, no major channel has been identified that might be considered a continuation of the Michigan River System. However, within the Spoon Formation, Jacobson (1983) has described a major channel (Oraville channel, Fig. 8) that may have been a segment of the Michigan River System. This stream eroded or prevented deposition of the Murphysboro coal in an area in southwestern Illinois. Coal along the margins of the channel is thicker, and is split by crevasse-splay and overbank deposits, resulting in formation of low-sulfur coal (<2.5% sulfur) in a moderately extensive area adjacent to the channel.

Probably the largest fluvial deposit known in the Pennsylvanian System of the Illinois Basin begins at the level of the Seahorne Limestone Member of the Spoon Formation. Palmer and others (1979) reported that the river that deposited these sediments (collectively termed the Highland fluvial complex) persisted throughout a major portion of the Desmoinesian Epoch (upper Spoon through Carbondale Formations), until it appears to have been disrupted and its deposits covered by an extensive marine invasion that occurred at the time of deposition of the Piasa Limestone Member of the Modesto Formation.

The Walshville paleoriver (Fig. 3), one of the rivers that deposited the Highland fluvial complex, was active at the time of the Herrin coal swamp. Johnson (1972) has demonstrated the contemporaneity of this river with the Herrin coal by identifying floodplain and crevasse-splay deposits, which cause the coal to be thin or split locally along the margins of the channel deposits. Proximal to this body of clastic rocks, the coal thickens, perhaps as a result of subsidence along the trend of the channel. Thickening and splitting of peat as a result of differential compaction in the vicinity of distributaries has also been identified in the Mississippi River delta (Fisk, 1960).

The Walshville river crossed the basin north of the Louden Anticline and flowed west of and parallel to this structure and the Salem Anticline and Du Quoin Monocline throughout most of its remaining course. Resources in the Herrin coal are greatest in

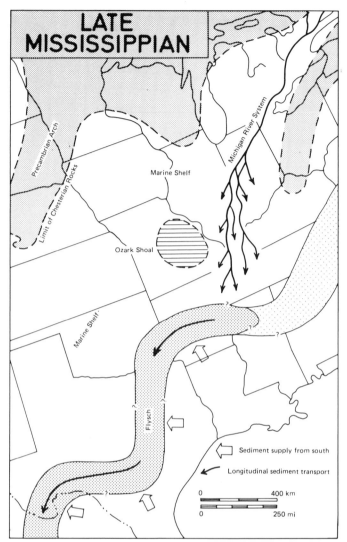

Figure 9. Late Mississippian Michigan River System (after Sedimentation Seminar, 1969). Limit of Chesterian rocks east of Michigan River System after Pryor and Sable (1974).

this smaller sub-basin west of the Du Quoin Monocline and Salem and Louden Anticlines. Wanless and others (1969) and Treworgy and Jacobson (1985) have suggested that, following withdrawal of marine waters, the Walshville channel and an extensive peat swamp developed in a topographically low area between two deltaic wedges, one located in western Indiana and southeastern Illinois and the other in west central Illinois. The locus of deposition of the eastern wedge may have been controlled by the Du Quoin Monocline and Salem and Louden Anticlines, over which this wedge thins. Deltaic sediments perhaps were deposited in a more rapidly subsiding area between these structures and the La Salle Anticlinal Belt. The Du Quoin, Salem, and Louden structures also may have helped to contain this small sub-basin to the west, further localizing fluvial activity.

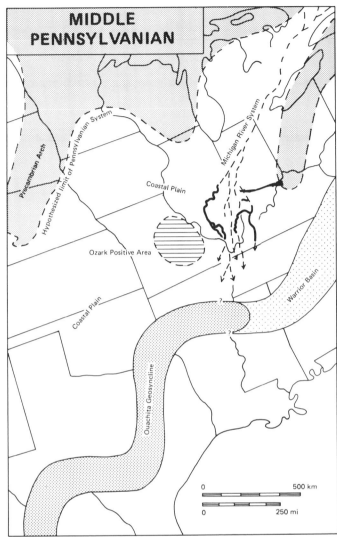

Figure 10. Middle Pennsylvanian Michigan River System. Solid lines represent known channel-fill sandstones (see Fig. 8); dashed lines are inferred routes in areas where channels are unknown.

On the north edge of the Fairfield Basin, near a projected point of convergence of the Salem and Louden Anticlines with the La Salle Anticlinal Belt, a large lake developed at the time of the Herrin swamp (Treworgy and Jacobson, 1985; Treworgy and Treworgy, 1983). A clastic wedge deposited in this lake resulted in the splitting of the Herrin coal along the margins of the lake and thinning of the coal under the wedge. Location of the lake may have been determined by activity of the Louden and Mattoon Anticlines and the La Salle Anticlinal Belt (Treworgy and Jacobson, 1985).

The Galatia paleochannel (Fig. 2) in southeastern Illinois and southwestern Indiana contained a river that was active at the time of the swamp that deposited the Springfield coal (Hopkins, 1968; Hopkins and others, 1979; Eggert, 1982). This paleochan-

nel is filled with sandstone and siltstone. Coal is thicker near this sinuous clastic body. Along its margins, coal is split into numerous benches by siltstone and shale. This fluvial deposit has been mapped over a distance of more than 240 km (150 mi) throughout the extent of the Springfield coal in southwestern Indiana and southeastern Illinois.

The Henderson paleochannel in western Kentucky (Beard and Williamson, 1979) is more than 32 km (20 mi) long where it has been mapped in Henderson and Webster Counties. Sandstone is the dominant rock type filling the paleochannel. Though it is eroded into the Springfield coal bed, one of the channels in a succession of at least two stacked sandstones is believed to have existed contemporaneously with the Baker coal bed of Kentucky (Allen D. Williamson, 1984, personal communication).

We consider these major channels (Fig. 8) to represent a continuance during Pennsylvanian time (Fig. 10) of the drainage pattern established by the Michigan River System in Late Mississippian time. Headwaters were located on the Canadian Shield to the north and possibly highlands of the northern (and perhaps central) Appalachians to the east. Water flowed across a southwestward-sloping piedmont to the broad coastal plain of the Illinois Basin. Channel systems developed in the swamps and permitted passage of this water through the swamps and into the sea to the south and southwest.

The Michigan River System was important in the development of low-sulfur coal resources in the Illinois Basin. During early stages of marine transgression, rivers overflowed their banks and cut crevasses through levees, flooding the coal swamps and covering portions of the peat near the channels with thick deposits of silt and clay. Where these sediments formed dense, impermeable layers thick enough to isolate the peat from later marine invasions, they prevented influx of sulfates. Allgaier and Hopkins (1975) reported that sulfur is markedly lower in Herrin coal overlain by more than 6 m (20 ft) of non-marine shale than in coal covered by thinner, non-marine shale layers. This effect has also been reported in the Murphysboro coal of southwestern Illinois (Jacobson, 1983) and the Springfield coal of southeastern Illinois (Hopkins, 1968; Hopkins and others, 1979) and southwestern Indiana (Eggert, 1982). We believe that other components of the system may be recognized as studies of the Pennsylvanian System in the Illinois Basin are continued.

ACKNOWLEDGMENTS

An earlier version of this manuscript was reviewed by W. John Nelson, Russell J. Jacobson, Russel A. Peppers, and Howard R. Schwalb of the Illinois State Geological Survey. Their comments resulted in extensive revision of the manuscript. The authors also appreciate the critiques of Paul C. Lyons and Charles L. Rice of the U.S. Geological Survey, Thomas C. Buschbach of St. Louis University, and Peter W. Whaley of Murray State University.

REFERENCES CITED

Allgaier, G. J., and Hopkins, M. E., 1975, Reserves of the Herrin (No. 6) Coal in the Fairfield Basin in southeastern Illinois: Illinois State Geological Survey Circular 489, 31 p.

Ambrose, W. A., 1983a, Tide-dominated deltaic deposits of the Spoon Formation (Pennsylvanian) in the southern Illinois Basin, a shallow embayment [M.A. thesis]: University of Texas at Austin, 105 p.

——, 1983b, Tide-dominated deltaic deposits of the Spoon Formation (Pennsylvanian) in a narrow, subsiding trough, southern Illinois: Geological Society of America Abstracts with Programs, v. 15, p. 514.

Amos, D. H., 1966, Geologic map of the Golconda Quadrangle, Kentucky-Illinois, and part of the Brownfield Quadrangle in Kentucky: U.S. Geological Survey Geologic Quadrangle Map GQ-546, scale 1:24,000.

Atherton, E., and Palmer, J. E., 1979, The Mississippian and Pennsylvanian (Carboniferous) Systems in the United States—Illinois: U.S. Geological Survey Professional Paper 1110-L, 42 p.

Beard, J. G., and Williamson, A. D., 1979, A Pennsylvanian channel in Henderson and Webster Counties, Kentucky: Kentucky Geological Survey, Series XI, Information Circular 1, 12 p.

Bretz, J. H., 1950, Origin of the filled sink-structures and circle deposits of Missouri: Geological Society of America Bulletin, v. 61, p. 789–834.

——, 1965, Geomorphic history of the Ozarks of Missouri: Missouri Geological Survey and Water Resources, v. 41, Second Series, 147 p.

Bristol, H. M., and Howard, R. H., 1971, Paleogeologic map of the sub-Pennsylvanian Chesterian (Upper Mississippian) surface in the Illinois Basin: Illinois State Geological Survey Circular 458, 14 p.

Bristol, H. M., and Treworgy, J. D., 1979, The Wabash Valley Fault System in southeastern Illinois: Illinois State Geological Survey Circular 509, 19 p.

Clegg, K. E., 1965, The La Salle Anticlinal Belt and adjacent structures in east-central Illinois: Illinois Academy of Science Transactions, v. 58, p. 82–94.

Desborough, G. A., 1961, Sedimentational and structural dating of Rattlesnake Ferry fault in southwestern Illinois: American Association of Petroleum Geologists Bulletin, v. 45, p. 1401–1411.

Donaldson, A. C., and Shumaker, R. C., 1979, Late Paleozoic molasse of central Appalachians, *in* Donaldson, A. C., Presley, M. W., and Renton, J. J., eds., Carboniferous coal—Short course and guidebook: Volume 3: West Virginia Geological and Economic Survey Bulletin B-37-3 Supplement, p. 1–42b.

Eggert, D. L., 1982, A fluvial channel contemporaneous with deposition of the Springfield Coal Member (V), Petersburg Formation, Northern Warrick County, Indiana: Indiana Geological Survey Special Report 28, 20 p.

Ekblaw, G. E., 1925, Post-Chester, pre-Pennsylvanian faulting in the Alto Pass area: Illinois Academy of Science Transactions, v. 18, p. 378–382.

Fisk, H. N., 1960, Recent Mississippi River sedimentation and peat accumulation, *in* Compte Rendu, 4th International Congress of Carboniferous Stratigraphy and Geology, Heerlen: Maestricht, The Netherlands, Ernest van Aelst Publishing, p. 187–199.

Folk, R. L., 1980, Petrology of sedimentary rocks: Austin, Hemphill Publishing Company, 182 p.

Hinds, H., and Greene, F. C., 1915, The stratigraphy of the Pennsylvanian Series in Missouri: Missouri Bureau of Geology and Mines, v. 13, Second Series, 407 p.

Hopkins, M. E., 1968, Harrisburg (No. 5) Coal reserves of southeastern Illinois: Illinois State Geological Survey Circular 431, 25 p.

Hopkins, M. E., and Simon, J. A., 1975, Pennsylvanian System, *in* Willman, K. B., and others, eds., Handbook of Illinois Stratigraphy: Illinois State Geological Survey Bulletin 95, p. 163–201.

Hopkins, M. E., Nance, R. B., and Treworgy, C. G., 1979, Mining Geology of Illinois coal deposits, *in* Palmer, J. E., and Dutcher, R. R., eds., Depositional and structural history of the Pennsylvanian System of the Illinois Basin. Part 2: Invited papers: Illinois State Geological Survey Guidebook 15a, p. 142–151.

Howe, W. B., Anderson, K. H., and McCracken, R. H., 1967, Paleozoic rocks, *in* U.S. Geological Survey and Missouri Division of Geological Survey and Water Resources, Mineral and water resources of Missouri: Missouri Geological Survey and Water Resources, v. 43, Second Series, p. 16–18.

Jacobson, R. J., 1983, Murphysboro Coal, Jackson and Perry Counties—Resources with low to medium sulfur potential: Illinois State Geological Survey Illinois Mineral Notes 85, 19 p.

Jacobson, R. J., Trask, C. B., Ault, C. H., Carr, D. D., Gray, H. H., Hasenmuller, W. A., Williams, D., and Williamson, A. D., 1985, Unifying nomenclature in the Pennsylvanian System of the Illinois Basin: Illinois State Academy of Science Transactions, v. 78, p. 1–11.

Johnson, D. O., 1972, Stratigraphic analysis of the interval between the Herrin (No. 6) Coal and the Piasa Limestone in southwestern Illinois [Ph.D. thesis]: University of Illinois at Urbana-Champaign, 105 p.

Kehn, T. M., Beard, J. G., and Williamson, A. D., 1982, Mauzy Formation, a new stratigraphic unit of Permian age in western Kentucky: U.S. Geological Survey Bulletin 1529-H, p. H73–H86.

Koeninger, C. A., and Mansfield, C. F., 1979, Earliest Pennsylvanian depositional environments in central southern Illinois, *in* Palmer, J. E., and Dutcher, R. R., eds., Depositional and structural history of the Pennsylvanian System of the Illinois Basin. Part 2: Invited papers: Illinois State Geological Survey Guidebook 15a, p. 76–81.

Kosanke, R. M., Simon, J. A., Wanless, H. R., and Willman, H. B., 1960, Classification of the Pennsylvanian strata of Illinois: Illinois State Geological Survey Report of Investigations 214, 84 p.

Krausse, H.-F., and Treworgy, C. G., 1979, Major structures of the southern part of the Illinois Basin, *in* Palmer, J. E., and Dutcher, R. R., eds., Depositional and structural history of the Pennsylvanian System of the Illinois Basin. Part 2: Invited papers: Illinois State Geological Survey Guidebook 15a, p. 115–120.

Leary, R. L., 1981, Early Pennsylvanian geology and paleobotany of the Rock Island County, Illinois, area - Part 1: Geology: Illinois State Museum Reports of Investigations No. 37, 88 p.

Marcher, M. V., and Stearns, R. G., 1962, Tuscaloosa Formation in Tennessee: Geological Society of America Bulletin, v. 73, p. 1365–1386.

McKee, E. D., and Crosby, E. J., coordinators, 1975, Paleotectonic investigations of the Pennsylvanian System in the United States, part III, Plates: U.S. Geological Survey Professional Paper 853.

Morgan, J. P., 1970, Depositional processes and products in the deltaic environment, *in* Morgan, J. P., ed., Deltaic sedimentation, modern and ancient: Society of Economic Paleontologists and Mineralogists Special Publication 15, p. 31–47.

Nelson, W. J., and Lumm, D. K., 1984, Structural geology of southeastern Illinois and vicinity: Illinois State Geological Survey Contract/Grant Report 1984-2, 127 p.

Palmer, J. E., Jacobson, R. J., and Trask, C. B., 1979, Depositional environments of strata of late Desmoinesian age overlying the Herrin (No. 6) Coal Member in southwestern Illinois, *in* Palmer, J. E., and Dutcher, R. R., eds., Depositional and structural history of the Pennsylvanian System of the Illinois Basin. Part 2: Invited papers: Illinois State Geological Survey Guidebook 15a, p. 92–102.

Peppers, R. A., and Popp, J. T., 1979, Stratigraphy of the lower part of the Pennsylvanian System in southeastern Illinois and adjacent portions of Indiana and Kentucky, *in* Palmer, J. E., and Dutcher, R. R., eds., Depositional and structural history of the Pennsylvanian System of the Illinois Basin. Part 2: Invited papers: Illinois State Geological Survey Guidebook 15a, p. 65–72.

Pinckney, D. M., 1980, Continental rifting under the Illinois Basin and Mississippi River embayment: U.S. Geological Survey Open-file Report 80-622, 56 p.

Poor, R. S., 1925, The character and significance of the basal conglomerate of the Pennsylvanian System in southern Illinois: Illinois Academy of Science Transactions, v. 18, p. 369–375.

Potter, P. E., 1957, Breccia and small-scale lower Pennsylvanian overthrusting in southern Illinois: American Association of Petroleum Geologists Bulletin, v. 41, p. 2695–2709.

——, 1962, Regional distribution patterns of Pennsylvanian sandstones in Illinois Basin: American Association of Petroleum Geologists Bulletin, v. 46, p. 1890–1911.

——, 1963, Late Paleozoic sandstones of the Illinois Basin: Illinois State Geological Survey Report of Investigations 217, 92 p.

——, 1978, Significance and origin of big rivers: Journal of Geology, v. 86, p. 13–33.

Potter, P. E., and Glass, H. D., 1958, Petrology and sedimentation of the Pennsylvanian sediments in southern Illinois—a vertical profile: Illinois State Geological Survey Report of Investigations 204, 60 p.

Pryor, W. A. and Sable, E. G., 1974, Carboniferous of the eastern interior basin, *in* Briggs, G., ed., Carboniferous of the southeastern United States: Geological Society of America, Special Paper 148, p. 281–313.

Rexroad, C. B., and Merrill, G. K., 1979, Conodont biostratigraphy and the Mississippian-Pennsylvanian boundary in southern Illinois: 9th International Congress of Carboniferous Stratigraphy and Geology, Urbana, Illinois, Abstracts of Papers, p. 179–180.

Rubey, W. W., 1952, Geology and mineral resources of the Hardin and Brussels Quadrangles (in Illinois): U.S. Geological Survey Professional Paper 218, 179 p.

Sedimentation Seminar, 1969, Bethel Sandstone (Mississippian) of western Kentucky and south-central Indiana, a submarine-channel fill: Kentucky Geological Survey, Series X, Report of Investigations 11, 24 p.

Shaver, R. H., Burger, A. M., Gates, G. R., Gray, H. H., Hutchison, H. C., Keller, S. J., Patton, J. B., Rexroad, C. B., Smith, N. M., Wayne, W. J., and Wier, C. E., 1970, Compendium of rock-unit stratigraphy in Indiana: Indiana Geological Survey Bulletin 43, 229 p.

Siever, R., and Potter, P. E., 1956, Sources of basal Pennsylvanian sediments in the Eastern Interior Basin: 2. Sedimentary petrology: Journal of Geology, v. 64, p. 317–335.

Smith, W. H., and Stall, J. B., 1975, Coal and water resources for coal conversion in Illinois: Illinois State Water Survey, Illinois State Geological Survey, Cooperative Resources Report 4, 79 p.

Smith, W. H., and Smith, G. E., 1967, Description of Late Pennsylvanian strata from deep diamond drill cores in the southern part of the Illinois Basin: Illinois State Geological Survey, Circular 411, 27 p.

Swann, D. H., 1963, Classification of Genevievian and Chesterian (Late Mississippian) rocks of Illinois: Illinois State Geological Survey Report of Investigations 216, 91 p.

Trace, R. D., 1974, Illinois-Kentucky Fluorspar District, *in* Hutcheson, D. W., ed., A symposium on the geology of fluorspar: Kentucky Geological Survey, Series X, Special Publication 22, p. 58–76.

Treworgy, C. G., 1981, The Seelyville Coal: a major unexploited seam in Illinois: Illinois State Geological Survey, Illinois Mineral Notes 80, 11 p.

Treworgy, C. G., and Jacobson, R. J., 1985, Paleoenvironments and distribution of low-sulfur coal in Illinois, *in* Compte Rendu, 9th International Congress of Carboniferous Stratigraphy and Geology, Urbana, Illinois: Carbondale, Southern Illinois University Press, v. 4, p. 349–359.

Treworgy, J. D., and Bargh, M. B., 1984a, Coal resources of Illinois—Herrin (No. 6) Coal Member: Illinois State Geological Survey map, scale 1:500,000.

——, 1984b, Coal resources of Illinois—Springfield (No. 5) Coal Member: Illinois State Geological Survey map, scale 1:500,000.

Treworgy, J. D., and Treworgy, C. G., 1983, A new feature in the Pennsylvanian of the Illinois Basin—Clastic infilling of a lacustrine basin: Geological Society of America Abstracts with Programs, v. 15, p. 708.

Wanless, H. R., 1975a, Illinois Basin region, *in* McKee, E. D., and Crosby, E. J., coordinators, Paleotectonic investigations of the Pennsylvanian System in the United States: Part 1. Introduction and regional analyses of the Pennsylvanian System: U.S. Geological Survey Professional Paper 853-E, p. 71–95.

——, 1975b, Missouri and Iowa, *in* McKee, E. D., and Crosby, E. J., coordinators, Paleotectonic investigations of the Pennsylvanian System in the United States: Part 1. Introduction and regional analyses of the Pennsylvanian System: U.S. Geological Survey Professional Paper 853-E, p. 96–114.

Wanless, H. R., Baroffio, J. R., and Trescott, P. C., 1969, Conditions of deposition of Pennsylvanian coal beds, *in* Dapples, E. C., and Hopkins, M. E., eds., Environments of coal deposition: Geological Society of America Special Paper 114, p. 105–142.

Wanless, H. R., and Wright, C. R., 1978, Paleoenvironmental maps of Pennsylvanian rocks, Illinois Basin and northern Midcontinent region: Geological Society of America Map and Chart Series MC-23, 32 p.

Williams, D. A., Williamson, A. D., and Beard, J. G., 1982, Stratigraphic framework of coal-bearing rocks in the Western Kentucky Coal Field: Kentucky Geological Survey, Series XI, Information Circular 8, 201 p.

MANUSCRIPT ACCEPTED BY THE SOCIETY APRIL 16, 1986

Discussion of paper by Palmer and Trask. Responses by Palmer.

Joe Sadnecki (Exxon Coal Resources)
Question: To what do you attribute the deviation of sulfur content within individual beds?
Response: Circulation of water above beds may be attributed to some of this deviation.

Paul C. Lyons
Question: Would you tell us what you mean by low-sulfur coal?
Response: In the Illinois basin there are bodies of coal with sulfur as low as 1 percent.

Geological Society of America
Special Paper 210
1986

Styles of coal deposition in Tertiary alluvial deposits, Powder River Basin, Montana and Wyoming

Romeo M. Flores
U.S. Geological Survey
Denver Federal Center
Denver, Colorado 80225

ABSTRACT

A detailed comparison of styles of coal deposition of Tertiary rocks in the Powder River Basin shows that stratigraphic variations, areal distributions, and trends of depositional facies are the results of variations in alluvial settings. Styles of coal deposition are examined in coal-zone intervals, which are treated either as individual or multiple depositional packages. Facies stratigraphic variations display a common interrelationship of channel-levee facies bounded by floodplain and backswamp facies. Anomalously thick, minable coal deposits commonly are split into discrete coal beds separated by complexes of channel-levee facies. The areal distribution of channel deposits and laterally juxtaposed minable coal deposits display a primary north-to-south and secondary west-to-east depositional dip. Measurements of the crossbeds in channel deposits throughout the basin indicated that the direction of sediment transport was generally northeastward. The channel deposits were formed by braided, meandering, and anastomosed fluvial systems. The meandering streams are more commonly associated with backswamps of thick coal accumulation than are other fluvial systems. The south-to-north and west-to-east channel orientations of the fluvial systems are supported by subsurface net percent sandstone distributions within the basin.

The causes of the facies variations, distributions, and trends are deduced from what is generally known about modern alluvial plain environments. The Mahakam River, which drains the intermontane Kutai Basin in Borneo, is proposed as the best modern alluvial analog for the Tertiary deposits of the Powder River Basin. The alluvial plain of the Mahakam River is bordered by wet alluvial fans and consists of vast, continuous peat-forming backswamps that duplicate those of the Tertiary Powder River Basin coal swamps. In addition, the overall depositional elements of the Rio Paraiba do Sul in Brazil and the Upper Columbia and Lower Saskatchewan rivers in Canada are recognizable in the basin's Tertiary rocks, giving rise to a hybrid model of coal deposition in the Powder River Basin. These modern analogs demonstrate that alluvial environments are areas where thick peat deposits, which are precursors of minable coal beds, can accumulate.

INTRODUCTION

Depositional modeling has been recognized as a valuable tool in coal exploration and development for the past two decades. The approaches to depositional modeling of coal-bearing rocks have varied, for example, from generalized isolith mapping of the lithologies of thick stratigraphic units over a large area to specific mapping of the thickness and areal extent of a coal bed or coal zones and associated sediments over a small area. The former modeling approach relies mainly on percentage maps of sandstones, siltstones, and mudstones in order to outline basinal paleodepoaxes and paleodrainages, from which the environments

79

of deposition are deductively interpreted. The latter method of modeling relies on a specific analysis of lithofacies variations, through which the depositional environments are inductively interpreted. Although both modeling approaches are reliable, some tentative results from computer simulation studies of fluvial system aggradation by Allen (1978) and Bridge and Leeder (1979) suggest that some care be exercised in modeling by sandstone percentage. Allen (1978) suggested that both the numerical and areal densities (average sand/mud ratio) of sand bodies in fluvial system stratigraphy are dependent on the rates of basin subsidence and uplift of source areas. In addition, according to Allen (1978), coarsening-upward alluvial suites can be formed during a period of gradually decreasing subsidence, and fining-upward alluvial suites may be a result of an increasing rate of subsidence or mild uplift. Thus, tectonic control on styles of deposition necessitates comparison of results from both modeling approaches.

In order to reduce the probability of misinterpretation resulting from the effects of tectonism, the relationship between depositional environments and the thickness and areal distribution of coal beds in the Powder River Basin in Montana and Wyoming (Fig. 1) was best determined in this study by assiduous facies analysis of coal-bearing intervals viewed as a single sequence or as multiple sequences. The facies analysis was based on 1,095 measured stratigraphic sections in closely spaced and continuous linear exposures of the Tongue River Member of the Paleocene Fort Union Formation and Eocene Wasatch Formation. Outcrop descriptions, which were augmented by data from 550 boreholes, form the basis for construction of three-dimensional regional patterns of facies variations and styles of deposition. Initially, the patterns of vertical and lateral facies variations of coal-bearing intervals were described in detail and precisely defined. The patterns of facies variations were then used as models for prediction and testing of hypotheses.

The purpose of this paper is to analyze the variations in thickness and the areal distribution of minable coal beds in the Tertiary coal-bearing deposits of the Powder River Basin. These variations will be related to stratigraphic and paleogeographic arrangements of associated sediments considered singly or as a complex. The regional patterns of variation of the coal beds and detrital deposits will be assessed and compared with trends of depositional systems previously determined for these Tertiary coal-bearing deposits. The causes of the depositional trends of the coal and associated detrital deposits are, in turn, used to infer the sedimentary processes and depositional styles, which can then be compared with modern peat-forming analogs.

Previous studies indicated that the Tongue River Member of the Fort Union Formation in the Powder River Basin represents an alluvial-plain facies (Brown, 1958; Childers, 1970; Galloway, 1979; Ethridge and others, 1981; Flores, 1981, 1983; Hansen, 1983; Galloway and Hobday, 1983; Flores and Ethridge, 1985). The Wasatch Formation was also interpreted by Seeland (1976), Obernyer (1978), Flores and Warwick (1984), Warwick and others (1984), and Flores and Ethridge (1985) to be composed of alluvial plain deposits that pass rapidly westward into alluvial fan

deposits. Because the coal beds of these rock units are very thick and have been extensively mined, they were thought to provide an excellent opportunity to test the hypothesis of depositional control on the thickness and areal distribution of minable coal beds accumulated in alluvial environments. The results of these studies (Canavello, 1980; Lynn, 1980; Pait, 1982; Toth, 1982; Coss, 1984; Warwick and others, 1984; Weaver and Flores, 1984) did not confirm the hypothesis that the thickness and areal extent of coal beds were related to specific fluvial depositional modes. By failing to confirm that hypothesis, these results led to a re-evaluation of the styles of deposition of coals with emphasis on deposition in an interdeltaic environment, as proposed by Ayers and Kaiser (1984) for the coal beds in the Tongue River Member.

GEOLOGIC AND STRATIGRAPHIC SETTINGS

The Tongue River Member of the Fort Union Formation and the Wasatch Formation are the principal coal-bearing rock units of the Tertiary deposits in the Powder River Basin. These rock units are as much as 1,210 m thick along the basin axis in the vicinity of Buffalo, Wyoming (see Fig. 1; Curry, 1971). These coal-bearing deposits thin towards the northern, southern, and eastern parts of the Powder River Basin. The area of thickening of these rock units occurs adjacent to the western basin margin and coincides with the distribution of conglomeratic units of the Tongue River Member and Wasatch Formation. In addition, this paleodepoaxis is congruent to the pre-Wasatch Buffalo deep fault of Blackstone (1981) that is west of and parallels the basin axis extending from northwest of Sheridan to north of Glenrock, Wyoming (Fig. 1). The Powder River Basin is asymmetrical in cross section, with the basin axis near the western edge. It is bounded by the Bighorn Mountains to the west, the Casper arch, Laramie Mountains, and Hartville uplift to the south, and the Black Hills to the east. The basin is flanked on the north by the Cedar Creek anticline, Miles City arch, and Ashland and Bull Mountain synclines. The Powder River Basin underwent an initial phase of structural configuration during Late Cretaceous time in response to the Laramide orogeny that peaked with marked uplifts of surrounding terrains during Eocene time (Curry, 1971). Thus, during the deposition of the Tongue River Member and Wasatch Formation, the Powder River Basin was affected by periods of subsidence and uplift.

The Fort Union Formation is divided in ascending order, into the Tullock, Lebo Shale, and Tongue River Members. Although the Lebo Shale and Tullock Members are distinguishable in the subsurface (Curry, 1971), they are difficult to differentiate, both from each other and from the Tongue River Member, in surface outcrops in certain parts of the basin (Flores and Ethridge, 1985). These members are coal-bearing in the eastern and northern parts of the basin. However, those coal deposits are neither as numerous nor as thick as coals in the Tongue River Member. The Tullock Member also contains coal in the south-southwestern part of the basin but loses it toward the west-northwest. The Lebo Shale Member grades laterally into a noncoal-bearing, mudstone-

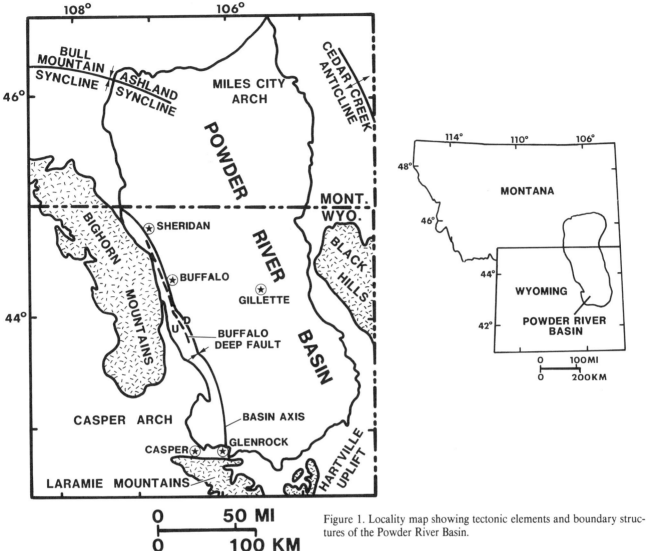

Figure 1. Locality map showing tectonic elements and boundary structures of the Powder River Basin.

dominated interval in the west and northwest parts of the basin. Curry (1971) and Law and others (1979) mapped the Lebo Shale Member in the subsurface as intertonguing with the Tongue River Member. In addition, they correlated the Tongue River Member across the basin axis and showed that it thinned and thickened locally across the axis. The aggradation of the coal-bearing Tongue River Member across the basin axis was also reported by Flores and others (1984) and Hardie and Van Gosen (1986).

The correlation of the Tongue River Member across the basin axis was challenged by Tewalt and others (1983) and Ayers and Kaiser (1984) who proposed that the Lebo Shale Member thickened to as much as 1,250 m in a mudstone-dominated unit along the basin axis where it totally replaced the Tongue River Member. This interpretation ignored the subsurface correlation of the Tongue River Member across the basin axis by Curry (1971) where he measured only as much as 793 m of Lebo Shale Member. The inferred absence of the Tongue River Member

along the basin axis was used by Ayers and Kaiser (1984) to support their hypothesis that a large deep intermontane lake, Lebo Lake, covered the Powder River Basin from north of the Montana/Wyoming state line southward to Casper, Wyoming. This hypothesis assumed that the Lebo lake was deepest along the length of the basin axis and that it was filled by offshore sedimentation (e.g. turbidites) by Tongue River Member deltas that drained a coastal plain from the east, north, and south. Minimum sedimentation was assumed to occur west of the basin axis. The position of the deltas was determined from sandstone (greater than 12 m in thickness) percentage maps, which were interpreted as framework facies other than crevasse splay and overbank sediments. Thus, in this paleoenvironmental scenario, the thick coals were interpreted to be interdeltaic deposits that are elongated parallel to the north-south paleoshoreline of Lebo lake.

The Ayers and Kaiser (1984) interpretation of lacustrine sedimentation along the western extent of the Powder River Basin contradicts the studies of Hose (1955), Mapel (1959),

Childers (1970), Coss (1984), and Weaver and Flores (1984) who recognized coal- and conglomerate-bearing intervals, as much as 420 m and 365 m in thickness, respectively, in the upper part of the Fort Union Formation (Tongue River Member equivalent). If the interdeltaic model by Ayers and Kaiser (1984) is correct, these sediments accumulated in the deep lake bottom. More importantly, the proposed deposition of the Tongue River Member by deltas into a deep lake does not consider the paleoecological analyses of freshwater molluscan fauna in the Powder River Basin (John Hanley, U.S.G.S., personal communication; Hanley and Flores, 1983; Flores and Hanley, 1984). The paleoecology of the Tongue River freshwater molluscan assemblage suggests habitation in discrete small and large interfluve lakes that pass laterally into fluvial axes. This observation is in contrast to the Eocene Green River and Wasatch Formations, which were deposited in and adjacent to the extensive Lake Gosiute (southwest Wyoming and northwest Colorado) where Hanley (1976) traced mollusks of interfluve lakes and adjacent terrestrial habitat laterally to nearshore shallow water (littoral) lacustrine environments and offshore deeper water (sublittoral) lacustrine environments.

The Ayers and Kaiser (1984) model of contemporaneous lacustrine and deltaic sedimentation of the Lebo Shale and Tongue River Members requires a drastic reinterpretation of the Tertiary stratigraphy along the basin axis. This interpretation presumes that along the basin axis, the Lebo Shale Member, which was deposited from middle to late Paleocene time (Ayers and Kaiser, 1984), is directly overlain by the coal-bearing deposits of the Eocene Wasatch Formation. This notion is a radical departure from the stratigraphic framework established in the area of the basin axis by previous works of Hose (1955), Mapel (1959), Horn and Richardson (1958), Culbertson and Mapel (1976), Childers (1970), and Glass (1980). In the central part of the basin the coal-bearing Wasatch Formation, which is difficult to differentiate from the coal-bearing Tongue River Member, grades laterally westward into the conglomeratic Kingsbury and Moncrief Members of the Wasatch Formation. Both the Kingsbury and Moncrief thicken westward. The Kingsbury Member unconformably overlies the Fort Union Formation and contains abundant sedimentary clasts varying from pebble to boulder sizes derived from Mesozoic and Paleozoic rocks. The Kingsbury Member is unconformably overlain by the Moncrief Member, which consists of abundant crystalline rock clasts, varying from pebble to boulder sizes, that were derived from Precambrian rocks. The overall increase upsection of Precambrian crystalline rock clasts in the conglomeratic members of the Wasatch Formation suggests gradual uplift and denudation of core rocks of a relict uplift in the adjoining Bighorn Mountains (Flores and Warwick, 1984).

All the minable coal beds in the Wasatch Formation and Tongue River Member of the Fort Union Formation are contained in stratigraphic units called coal zones. Each coal zone consists of two to seven thin coal beds that commonly merge into a thick coal bed separated vertically from other coal zones by

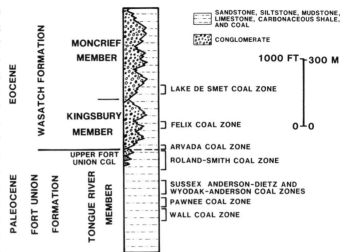

Figure 2. Composite generalized stratigraphic column of the Wasatch Formation and the Tongue River Member of the Fort Union Formation showing positions of studied coal zones.

thick sequences of sandstone, siltstone, mudstone, limestone, and ironstone. Figure 2 shows a generalized composite stratigraphic column for the Wasatch Formation and Tongue River Member of the Fort Union Formation. The coal zones selected for detailed study in the Tongue River Member include the Wall, Pawnee, Wyodak-Anderson, Anderson-Dietz, Sussex, and Roland-Smith coal zones. The coal zones investigated in the Wasatch Formation are the Arvada, Felix, and Lake de Smet (Walters-Healy) coal zones.

DEPOSITIONAL FACIES

In this paper, the lithofacies variations within the Wasatch Formation and Tongue River Member of the Fort Union Formation, which are discussed elsewhere (Obernyer, 1978, Galloway, 1979, Ethridge and others, 1981; Flores, 1981, 1983; Flores and Hanley, 1984; Flores and Warwick, 1984), provide a basis for comparison of facies types between the two rock units. Among the striking results of these studies of the lithofacies variations are those pertaining to vertical sequences, lateral changes, and areal distributions. However, only a limited attempt has been made to compare and contrast these lithofacies variations of the Tongue River Member on a regional basis and no effort has yet been made to relate these lithofacies to those of the Wasatch Formation. Thus, the approach for this analysis is to establish lithofacies relations of the coal zones and to compare and contrast these lithofacies variations on a basinal scale. This approach, in turn, leads to determination of styles of deposition of the Tongue River Member and Wasatch Formation.

Comparison of coal zone lithofacies of the Tongue River Member and the Wasatch Formation indicates that three major lithofacies are common to both stratigraphic units: floodplain, backswamp, and channel-levee facies. Variations exist in the sub-

Figure 3. Coarsening-upward crevasse splay deposits of mudstone, siltstone, and sandstone of the floodplain facies of the Tongue River Member.

Figure 4. Lacustrine or crevasse delta deposits of limestone, mudstone, siltstone, and sandstone of the floodplain facies of the Tongue River Member. Arrows point to slumped deposits (S).

facies of the floodplain and channel-levee facies between these rock units. In addition, an alluvial fan facies commonly occurs in the Wasatch Formation.

ALLUVIAL PLAIN FACIES

Floodplain Facies

Volumetrically, the floodplain facies is the most abundant facies type in both the Tongue River Member and the Wasatch Formation. It consists of interbedded mudstones, siltstones, and sandstones that occur as coarsening-upward sequences or as randomly arranged vertical sequences. The mudstones and siltstones contain root casts, animal burrows, and ripple laminations. The sandstones, which range from lenticular to tabular in shape, have convolutions, ripple laminations, small-scale cross laminations, and burrows (e.g., pelecypod escape structures). These floodplain deposits are interbedded with micritic limestones that often pass laterally into ironstones. The limestones contain freshwater molluscan fossils that are rarely concentrated as coquinal accumulations. Mollusks are also common in the fine-grained detritus of coarsening-upward sequences and in detritus interbedded with fossiliferous limestones. The composition, species abundances, and biofabric of molluscan assemblages preserved in the detritus and fossiliferous limestones provide a basis for recognition of crevasse splay, crevasse or lacustrine delta, and lacustrine subfacies (Figs. 3 and 4) of the floodplain facies. The crevasse splay, which forms by deposition of a sediment lobe through a breach in the levee during floods, developed in the proximal area of the floodplain. Progradation of the crevasse splay towards the distal area of the floodplain leads to debouching into a floodplain lake. This process, in turn, leads to reworking and mixing of shells of lake mollusks with those of the crevasse-splay feeder channel, thus introducing greater diversity of faunal remains into the cre-

vasse or lacustrine delta subfacies (Flores and Hanley, 1984). The fossiliferous limestones represent deposits in the lake proper where carbonates precipitated with no detrital influx.

Backswamp Facies

The backswamp facies, which is the least common facies type, is commonly interbedded with the floodplain facies. The backswamp facies primarily includes coal beds and carbonaceous shale with minor mudstone, siltstone, and sandstone beds and partings. The carbonaceous shales represent a mixture of organic matter and mud. These are common coal interbeds that grade laterally into coal beds. The coal beds are as much as 76 m in thickness (Fig. 5) and are laterally continuous for as much as 96 km (Obernyer, 1978; Glass, 1980; Pierce and others, 1982). However, the thickness of the coals does not reflect partings or beds (e.g. sandstones) that may be thinner than the coals. When the coals are mapped as a single bed, the coal bed extends laterally for as much as 56 km (Pierce and others, 1982; Kent and others, in preparation). The coals vary in rank from lignite to subbituminous and vary from 2.8 to 34.8 percent ash and 0.1 to 2.2 percent total sulfur. The quality of the study coals is summarized in Table 1. Ethridge and others (1981) subdivided the backswamp facies into poorly-drained and well-drained backswamp deposits. They interpreted the thick coals as representative of poorly-drained backswamp deposits. The poorly-drained distal backswamps that developed in the floodplain were not affected by inundation by lake and crevasse splay deposits. The backswamps close to the crevasse splays and lakes were well-drained compared to the poorly drained distal areas. A study by Wolfe (1985) of the paleomacroflora of the floodplain facies in the Tongue River Member indicates that broad-leafed evergreen trees typical of paratropical or subtropical climate (23°C average temperature) were dominant. These trees probably grew on

Figure 5. Very thick (26 m) merged Anderson-Dietz coal bed accumulated in poorly drained backswamp (Spring Creek Mine, Montana).

Figure 6. Multistory channel sandstone of the channel-levee facies of the Tongue River Member (Sussex coal zone). Channel sandstones are thin and narrow and are bounded by abundant fine-grained floodplain deposits.

hummocks that were distributed among hollows containing shrubs and sedges. These vegetal distributions are very similar to those proposed by Flores (1981) for poorly drained backswamps.

Channel-Levee Facies

The floodplain and backswamp facies are commonly bordered by channel-levee facies. The channel deposits have erosional bases overlain by upward-fining sandstones that display large-scale festoon and planar crossbeds in the lower part and small-scale festoon and convolute and ripple laminations in the upper part. Figures 6 and 7 show that the channel sandstones also contain epsilon crossbeds (Allen, 1970) that are marked by mudstone and siltstone laminations or drapes indicating lateral accretion of point bars. The erosional base of channel deposits is often directly overlain by lag conglomerates composed of rounded sandstone, siltstone, mudstone, ironstone, and limestone fragments representing recycled floodplain deposits. The channel sandstones also consist of imbricated, graded, horizontally bedded, and framework-supported conglomerates as much as 9 m thick (Fig. 8). These conglomerates consist of clasts of chert, silicified limestone, quartzose sandstones, and petrified wood fragments that were reworked from extrabasinal Mesozoic and Paleozoic rocks.

The channel sandstones are bounded laterally and above by levee and vertical accretion of clay plug deposits consisting of interbedded mudstones, siltstones, and sandstones. Figure 9 illustrates the common juxtaposition of channel sandstone with levee and vertical accretion deposits. Levee deposits, which are rooted or bioturbated throughout the sequence, show dip of beds away from the channel sandstones indicating overbank sedimentation. Vertical accretion deposits (Allen, 1970), which are rooted in the upper part, are composed of beds that may dip toward and merge

with the upper part of the channel sandstones. In other localities, the vertical accretion deposits on top of the channel sandstones contain flat-lying beds interbedded with fossiliferous limestones or ironstones. These flat-lying vertical accretion deposits formed by deposition of sediments in an abandoned meander loop or oxbow lake during floods; the dipping beds formed proximal to neck cutoffs and flat beds accumulated in more distal areas of the meander loop. Vertical accretion deposits also occur as isolated bodies underlain by erosional bases and overlain by interbedded mudstone, siltstone, sandstone, and carbonaceous shale beds. These vertical accretion sequences, which are bounded by the floodplain-backswamp facies, are interpreted to be channel sandstone-dominated meander loop; thus, such vertical accretion deposits mark the outer limit of the meander belt.

Figure 7. Lateral accretion or point bar deposits of multilateral channel sandstone of the channel-levee facies in the upper part of the interval of the Tongue River Member.

TABLE 1. PROXIMATE ANALYSIS (AS-RECEIVED BASIS), SULFUR CONTENT, AND BTU
OF THE COALS OF THE WASATCH FORMATION AND TONGUE RIVER MEMBER

| | | Percent (average) | | | | Btu |
	Sulfur	Ash	Moisture	Volatile matter	Fixed carbon	
Wasatch coals						
Lake de Smet coal	0.7	8.1	27.0	30.1	34.0	7940
Felix coal*	0.8	7.6	28.1	31.7	32.6	8110
Arvada coal	1.5	9.7	30.5	28.1	31.6	7321
Tongue River coals						
Smith coal	0.7	10.3	31.0	27.2	31.5	6238
Sussex coal	0.5	6.4	21.1	35.6	36.8	9105
Anderson-Dietz coal	0.3	5.7	23.6	30.6	38.8	8978
Wyodak-Anderson coal	0.5	5.6	24.0	33.8	36.5	9040
Wall coal	0.3	4.9	24.5	41.9	40.0	8957
Pawnee coal	0.4	7.6	31.8	27.8	32.7	7381

Compiled from data in Davis and others (1912), Mapel (1959), Matson and Blumer (1973), and Swanson and others (1976).
*Felix coal data compiled by Stephen B. Roberts.

The channel-levee facies represents deposits of braided, meandering, and anastomosed fluvial systems (Obernyer, 1978; Galloway, 1979; Ethridge and others, 1981; Flores, 1981, 1983; Flores and Hanley, 1984; Flores and Ethridge, 1985). The braided or bedload channel deposits are characterized by multilateral channel fills of framework-supported conglomerates and festooned and planar crossbedded pebbly sandstones. The internal structures of the sandstones, which are similar in vertical profile to the braided Donjek River deposits described by Williams and Rust (1969), Rust (1972), and Miall (1978), indicate deposition in longitudinal and transverse bars. The meandering or mixed-load channel deposits consist of lateral point bar accretion and vertical accretion sediments that are either single event or multiple channel fills. The meandering channel deposits display multilateral and multistory lateral relations. The anastomosed or suspended load channel deposits are complexes of multiple, inter-connected, and coeval channel fills that grade laterally into and are areally separated by floodplain-backswamp facies. The channel fills are multilateral in geometry and were deposited in channels of varying sinuosity. The meandering and anastomosed channel deposits are more commonly bounded by floodplain and backswamp facies than the braided channel deposits.

ALLUVIAL FAN FACIES

The alluvial fan facies consists of framework- and matrix-supported conglomerates that are crudely horizontally bedded and imbricated. The conglomerates, which are as much as 47-m thick, are composed of clasts that range in size from pebbles to boulders. The conglomerates are interbedded with minor scour-based, pebbly sandstones in the proximal area. In the distal area, conglomerates are replaced by festooned and planar crossbedded

Figure 8. Framework-supported conglomeratic deposits of braided streams of the Tongue River Member channel-levee facies (Sussex coal zone).

Figure 9. Levee deposits (L) and vertical accretion units (VA), channel-levee facies, marginal to and above the channel sandstone, respectively, of the Tongue River Member.

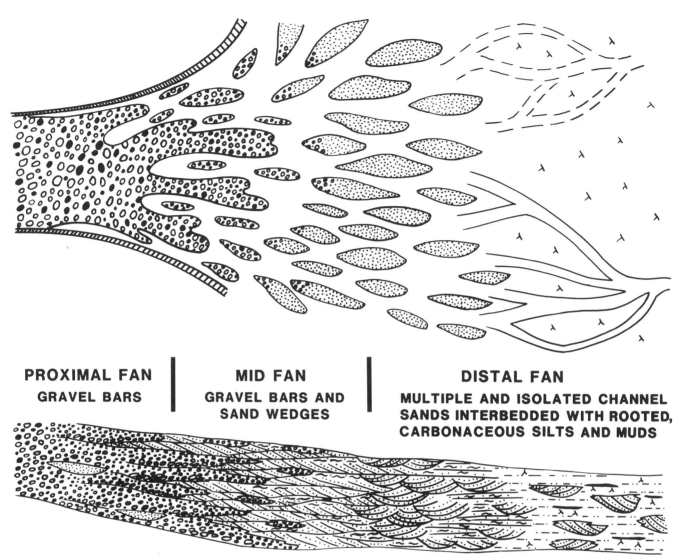

Figure 10. Facies models (vertical and lateral and areal) of the Kingsbury and Moncrief Members of the Wasatch Formation.

channel sandstones flanked by rippled siltstones, cross-laminated sandstones, rooted and variegated mudstones, and coaly carbonaceous shales. The alluvial fan facies characterizes the basin margin deposits of the Kingsbury and Moncrief Members of the Wasatch Formation. Flores and Warwick (1984) described proximal fan, midfan, and distal fan subfacies of the Kingsbury and Moncrief Members (Fig. 10). The proximal fan subfacies is dominated by sheet flood deposition of gravel bars accompanied by some channelized and debris flow deposits. Channelized flow was a dominant process in the midfan and distal fan where channels were integrated and separated by sand bars and floodbasins filled by fine detritus, respectively. The distal fan subfacies merges basinward into the coal-bearing alluvial plain facies. The proximity of the alluvial fan facies and coal-bearing deposits of the alluvial plain facies suggests deposition in a wet, humid environment.

A wet alluvial fan facies may also be found in the upper part of the Fort Union Formation (Tongue River Member equivalent) exposed in the Mowry Basin between Sheridan and Buffalo (Mapel, 1959). These exposures include lenticular conglomerates as much as 91 m thick composed of 0.3 to 6 m thick framework- and matrix-supported gravels. Interbedding of gravels with sandstones, siltstones, and variegated sandstones suggests deposition in a midfan to distal fan.

STRATIGRAPHIC AND AREAL INTERRELATIONSHIPS OF DEPOSITIONAL FACIES

Tongue River Member of the Fort Union Formation

Stratigraphic cross sections (Figs. 11–19) of the coal zones of the Tongue River Member and Wasatch Formation illustrate a

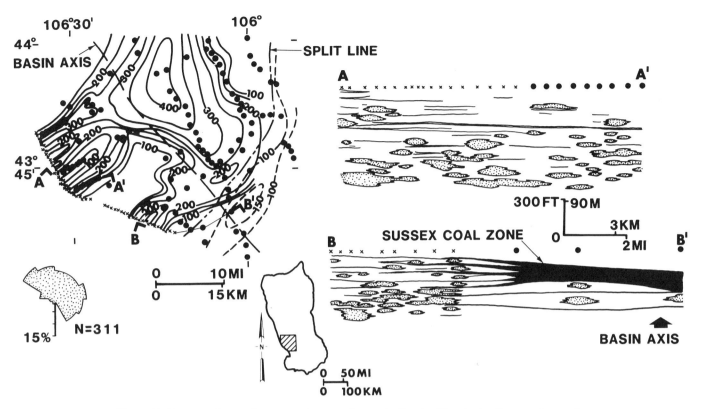

Figure 11. Sussex coal zone. Inset map shows study area in Powder River basin. Cross sections and isopach map show channel sandstones and merged Sussex coal zone. Dots are drillholes and crosses are stratigraphic sections. Solid lines are isopach of channel complex in feet and dashed lines are isopachs of coal in feet. Crossbedding measurements are expressed in a rose diagram. N = number of observations. Data are from Hardie and Gosen, 1986; Coss, 1984; and Bailey and Associates, personal communication.

variety of two-dimensional interrelationships of the depositional facies. The Wall, Pawnee, Anderson-Dietz, Wyodak-Anderson, and Sussex coal zones of the Tongue River Member, which average 15 m in thickness, are commonly split into numerous coal beds by a complex of channel-levee facies. A few of these coal beds are also selectively underlain by a complex of channel-levee facies. A close inspection of these channel-levee facies suggests variations in the lateral relation and genesis of the channel deposits. For example, the Sussex coal zone (Fig. 11), which is as much as 54 m thick bed in the southwest Powder River Basin, is split into several beds (each as much as 6 m thick) towards the west-southwest by channel-levee and floodplain facies complexes. The channel deposits immediately adjacent to and far removed (west) from the merged Sussex coal are composed of multistory and multilateral bodies encased in common to abundant overbank-floodplain deposits. These channel deposits differ in the presence of framework-supported conglomerates typical of braided and coarse-grained meandering streams in the west and fine grained and mixed load meandering streams in the east (adjacent to merged coal). An isopach map (Fig. 11) of the total thickness of the complex of channel deposits shows two parallel bodies that merged to the northeast. Their lengths (as much as 56 km) are

oriented in a southwest-northeast direction. These channel deposit complexes aggraded across the basin axis. The accompanying isopach map of the Sussex coal zone shows northeast-southwest direction of elongation and extension across the basin axis. These observations and the general northeast direction of trough crossbeds of the channel deposits (see Fig. 9) differ from that of Ayers and Kaiser (1984), who suggested that the deposits of the Tongue River Member accumulated in a delta front of the west-southwest flowing Wright delta and in an offshore lacustrine environment. Alternatively, the environment of the Sussex coal zone in this area is here interpreted as contemporaneous meander (east) and braided (west) belts separated by a floodplain and juxtaposed to the east by a poorly drained backswamp. With the appearance of forest vegetation in this backswamp, interfluve sedimentation and fluvial migration were retarded. Continued and prolonged colonization of forest vegetation in the peat-forming swamp restricted fluvial erosion and choked off deposition in the adjoining braided and meander belts, which were floored by readily eroded detrital sediments.

The facies relations of the Sussex coal zone differ from those of the Wall, Pawnee, Anderson-Dietz, Wyodak-Anderson, and Roland-Smith coal zones of the Tongue River Member in the

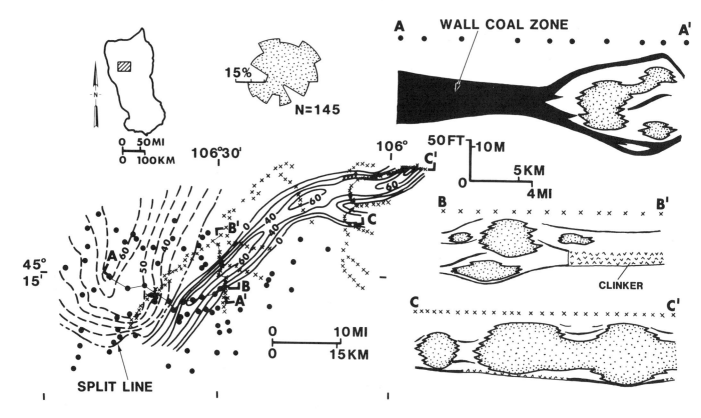

Figure 12. Wall coal zone. Inset map shows study area in the Powder River basin. Cross sections and isopach map show channel sandstones and merged Wall coal zone. Dots are drillholes and crosses are stratigraphic sections. Solid lines are isopachs of channel complex in feet and dashed lines are isopach of coal in feet. Crossbedding measurements are expressed in a rose diagram. N = number of observations. Data from Pait, 1981; Toth, 1982; and Hansen, 1983.

north-central part of the Powder River Basin. The Wall coal zone (Fig. 12) in the northwestern part of the basin is split to the east by a channel-levee complex. These multistory channel deposits indicate deposition in a meandering stream that was commonly bounded by floodplain facies. The channel deposits that intertongue with the Wall coal area as much as 11 km wide. An isopach map of the total thickness of channel deposits that split the Wall coal zone (Fig. 12) displays a channel complex with its length oriented in a generally northeast direction for as much as 60 km. Festoon crossbed measurements from the channel deposits are also oriented generally northeast. The isopach map of the Wall coal zone, which is as much as 18 m in thickness, illustrates north-south direction of elongation subparallel to the length of the juxtaposed channel-levee complex.

The facies relationship and areal pattern of the Wall coal zone are repeated in the Anderson-Dietz coal zone in the same area of the basin. Stratigraphic relations of the depositional facies (Fig. 13) indicate that the Anderson-Dietz coal zone, which is as much as 26 m thick, is split to the east by a complex of channel-level facies bounded by floodplain facies. The channel deposits, which show a multistory lateral relation, were formed by meandering streams. The channel complex, which resulted from coalesced tributaries, is as much as 20 km wide and 40 km in lateral extent where the line of cross section is subparallel to their length. The isopach map of the channel deposits in Figure 12 shows their length orientation in a general northeast direction. Similarly, isopachs of the Anderson-Dietz coal zone also show north to south and west to east directions of elongation. Festoon crossbed measurements show a general northerly direction of sediment transport.

The dominant south-to-north orientation of the depositional dip of minable coal beds and northeast direction of transport of sediments in the northwestern part of the basin appear to refute the northwest-southeast progradation of a Decker delta as proposed by Ayers and Kaiser (1984; Fig. 9). The depositional styles of both the Wall and Anderson-Dietz coal zones are similar to those of the Sussex coal zone in the southwestern part of the basin. Northeast-flowing meandering rivers built meanderbelts stabilized by forested, peat-forming backswamps to the west. Periodic shifts of channel positions along these meanderbelts resulted in small scale expansions and contractions of backswamp margins that influenced splitting of the Wall and Anderson-Dietz coal zones.

In the northeastern part of the Powder River Basin, the facies stratigraphic relationship of the Tongue River Member is exemplified by the Pawnee coal zone (Fig. 14). The Pawnee coal

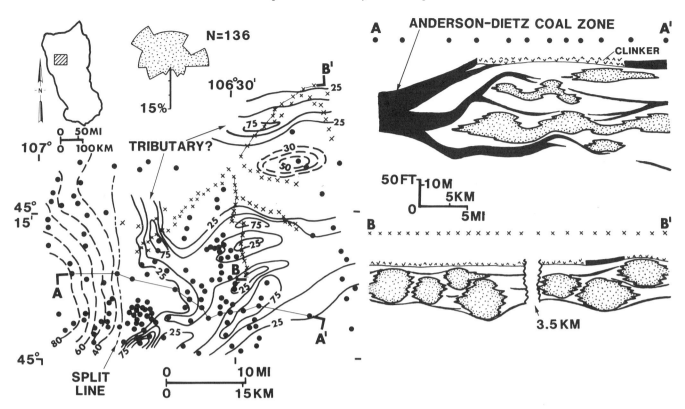

Figure 13. Anderson-Dietz coal zone. Inset map shows location of study area in Powder River basin. Cross sections and isopach map show channel sandstones and merged Anderson-Dietz coal zone. Dots are drillholes and crosses are stratigraphic sections. Solid lines are isopachs of channel complex in feet and dashed lines are isopach of coal in feet. Crossbedding measurements are expressed in a rose diagram. N = number of observations. Data from Toth, 1982, and Hansen, 1983.

zone, which is as much as 13 m thick, is laterally split to the west by younger deposits of a channel-levee complex bounded by floodplain facies. In contrast to channel-levee deposits of the Wall and Anderson-Dietz coal zones, the channel-levee complex, which splits the Pawnee coal zone is thicker, but laterally as extensive (61 m thick and 15 km wide). The multistory and multilateral channel deposits indicate deposition in meandering streams. Figure 14 shows the isopach map of the channel deposits that trend north to south for as much as 75 km. The accompanying isopach map of the Pawnee coal zone, which formed east of the channel deposits, shows the Pawnee's similar north-south elongation. Festoon crossbedding directions show a general northeast paleodrainage orientation. These observations indicate that the Pawnee coal zone was deposited in an alluvial plain somewhat similar to those of the Sussex, Wall, and Anderson-Dietz coal zones. However, in the Pawnee coal zone the peat-forming backswamp developed during the waning stage of channel aggradation in the alluvial plain. The thick and wide channel-levee complex laterally juxtaposed to the Pawnee coal zone suggests deposition in a broad meanderbelt. This indicates the presence of a larger northeast-flowing fluvial system (e.g., trunk stream) during deposition of the Pawnee coal zone that may have drained the axis of the alluvial plain and northeast-flowing transverse streams

(e.g., tributaries) in the western part of the alluvial plain. During the peak of aggradation, the large fluvial system was accompanied by intensive delivery of detritus into the interfluves, which in turn deterred prolonged vegetal growths. However, as fluvial aggradation waned, forest vegetation gradually spread from the distal reaches of the backswamp into proximal areas of the floodplain. Areal extension of forest vegetation stabilized the channels and produced poorly-drained conditions that dominated the Pawnee peat-forming swamp.

The south-north trend of paleodepositional slope for the Tongue River Member in the northeast part of the Powder River Basin is supported by facies trends of the Roland-Smith coal zone (Fig. 15). Unlike the Pawnee coal zone, the Roland-Smith coal zone consists of a channel-levee complex (as much as 3 km wide and 20 km in lateral extent) deposited by anastomosed streams (Flores and Hanley, 1984). The lower part of the coal zone is dominated by lacustrine and crevasse splay subfacies interrupted by backswamp facies consisting of thin coal beds and associated deposits. The upper part (below the coquinoid limestone) of the coal zone consists of the anastomosed channel deposits, which pass laterally into floodplain and backswamp facies; the latter facies consists of thin coal beds and associated deposits. Abundant freshwater mollusks that occur in the lacustrine subfacies

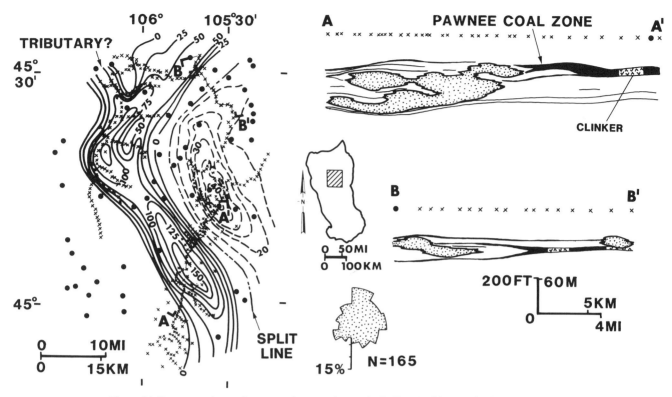

Figure 14. Pawnee coal zone. Inset map shows study area in the Powder River basin. Cross sections and isopach map show channel sandstones and merged Pawnee coal zone. Dots are drillholes and crosses are stratigraphic sections. Solid lines are isopach of channel complex in feet and dashed lines are isopach of coal in feet. Crossbedding measurements are expressed in a rose diagram. N = number of observations. Data from Pait, 1982, and Lynn, 1980.

are interpreted to have inhabited nearshore (littoral) environments in shallow floodbasin lakes. Molluscan assemblages can neither be traced laterally into nor are they interbedded with deep water, offshore (sublittoral) assemblages as was noted in deposits of the more extensive Lake Gosiuite (Eocene) (Hanley, 1976, personal communication). The isopach map of the anastomosed facies (Fig. 15) displays north-trending interconnected diverging and converging channel deposits. The isopach map (Fig. 15) of the Roland coal bed, which formed in backswamps of the intervening floodplains, shows north-south direction of elongation. Festoon crossbedding directions indicate that the floodplain and backswamp environments were bordered by northward flowing anastomosed streams (see Fig. 15). The absence of economic coals in the Roland-Smith coal zone is probably the result of drowning of the backswamps by rapid detrital sedimentation in small floodplains. Although the style of deposition in the Roland-Smith interval was different from that of the Pawnee coal zone, lithostratigraphic relations in both coal zones confirm a northerly paleodepositional slope as noted in the other parts of the basin. These depositional trends contradict the westward progradation of a Moorhead delta in the central Powder River Basin as proposed by Ayers and Kaiser (1984; Fig. 9).

In the Gillette area in the east-central part of the basin, the

northerly direction of paleodepositional slope in other parts of the basin is repeated in the deposits of the Wyodak-Anderson coal zone. The Wyodak-Anderson coal zone, which is as much as 43 m thick, is split to the west by a channel-levee complex bordered by floodplain facies (Fig. 16). The north-south line of split, which is interpreted on the basis of the potentiometric surface-coal map (J. D. Brown, Carter Mining Co., personal communication), is shown in Figure 16. The location of the split line of the Wyodak-Anderson coal zone is similar in areal position to that of the Pawnee coal zone. The south-north depositional dip of the Wyodak-Anderson coal zone is perpendicular to the east-to-west paleodepositional slope of a Gillette delta in the Tongue River Member proposed by Ayers and Kaiser (1984; see Fig. 9) in this part of the Powder River Basin.

Wasatch Formation

The stratigraphic and areal interrelationships of the depositional facies of the Wasatch Formation are generally similar to those of the Tongue River Member of the Fort Union Formation. The Felix, Lake de Smet, and Arvada coal zones (Figs. 15, 17, and 18) of the Wasatch Formation were analyzed and compared with coal zones of the Tongue River Member.

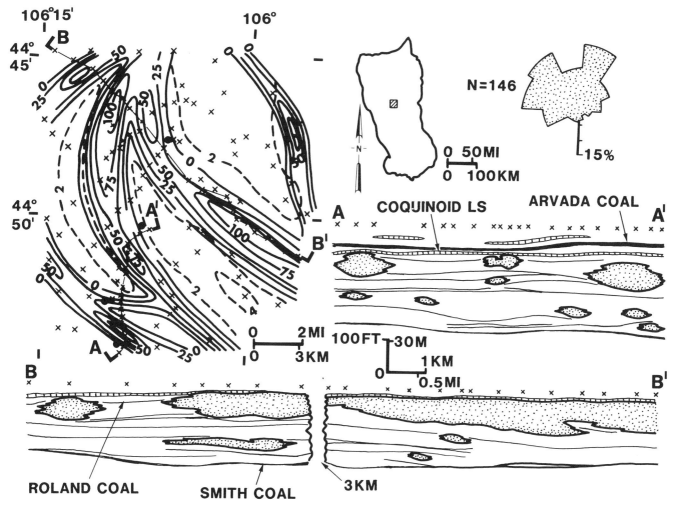

Figure 15. Roland-Smith and Arvada coal zones. Inset map shows study area in the Powder River basin. Cross sections show Roland-Smith and Arvada coal zones; isopach map shows channel sandstone and Roland Coal. Dots are drillholes and crosses are stratigraphic sections. Solid lines are isopachs of channel complex in feet and dashed lines are isopach of coal in feet. Crossbedding measurement is expressed in a rose diagram. N = number of observations. Data are from Canavello, 1980.

Facies stratigraphic variations of the Felix coal zone in the central Powder River Basin slightly depart from those of the Sussex, Wall, Pawnee, Anderson-Dietz, and Wyodak-Anderson coal zones of the Tongue River Member. The Felix coal zone (Fig. 17) is underlain by a channel-levee complex that consists of multistory and multilateral bodies (as much as 15 km wide and 30 km in lateral extent) which were probably deposited in meandering streams (Warwick and others, 1984). Unlike the coal zones of the Tongue River Member the Felix coal zone, which is as much as 9 m thick (Fig. 17), is split to the west by floodplain facies. These observations suggest that the Felix peat-forming backswamp was built on a broad abandoned meanderbelt. This belt consisted of relatively incompactible channel sands that served as a topograhic platform that prevented the Felix back-swamp from detrital inundation. In the outlying area where the channel sands pass into readily compactible floodplain sediments, the overlying Felix coal bed splits. The mode of splitting is by crevasse-overbank influx into the low-lying backswamps.

The thickness of the Felix coal zone, which is thinner than the minable coal beds of the Tongue River Member, was proba- bly controlled by the paleotopography. That is, the rate of subsi- dence due to compaction of the sand platform on which the Felix swamp developed may not have kept pace with the rate of peat accumulation. This condition probably promoted oxidation in the latter stage of swamp development that, in turn, gradually curtailed generation of peat.

The paleohydrology of the Felix coal swamp was probably different from that of the coal zones in the Tongue River Member. In the Felix swamp, peat accumulation was sustained by ground water discharge from the underlying transmissive, permeable channel sand aquifer. Peats in coal zones of the Tongue River Member were primarily sustained by discharge

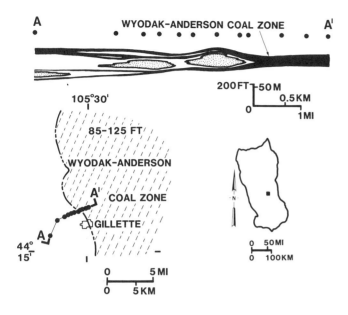

Figure 16. Cross section of the Wyodak-Anderson coal zone and distribution of the merged Wyodak-Anderson coal zone. Inset map shows study area in the Powder River basin. Dots are drill holes.

from a laterally juxtaposed channel sand aquifer. The difference in the paleohydrology may have affected acidity of these peat-forming backswamps. That is, regional upward circulation of groundwater in the Felix swamps probably promoted widespread oxidation that was restricted to the edges of the swamps. Thus, the central parts of the Tongue River Member swamps were more acidic than those of the Felix swamp, a condition that promoted an ombrotrophic swamp.

Perhaps the similarity in variations of facies stratigraphy and areal pattern to those of the coal zones of the Tongue River Member is best exemplified by the Lake de Smet coal zone (Fig. 18). The Lake de Smet coal zone (as much as 76 m thick) is split along its eastern and western boundaries by channel-levee complexes. The isopach maps (Fig. 18) of the Lake de Smet coal zone and laterally juxtaposed channel deposits show a detrital wedge at the western boundary and a north-south elongated body at the eastern boundary of the coal body. The multistory channel sandstones east of the Lake de Smet coal zone were interpreted by Obernyer (1978) to have been deposited in a northeasterly flowing meandering stream. The multilateral channel deposits west of the coal were interpreted by Flores and Warwick (1984) to have been deposited as a distal alluvial fan facies. The presence of the

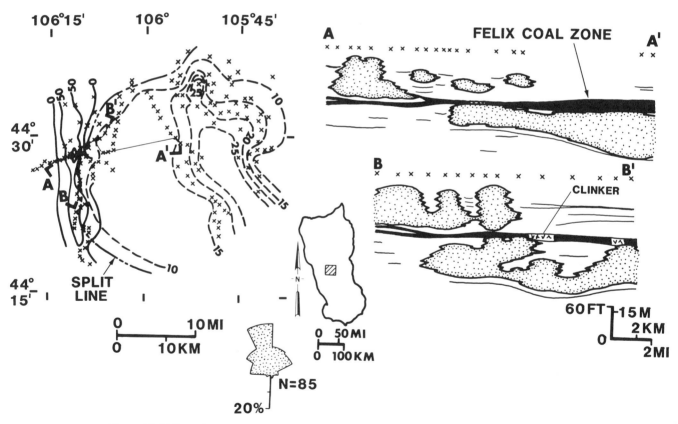

Figure 17. Felix coal zone. Inset map shows study area in Powder River basin. Cross sections and isopach show sandstone that is above and partly splits a bed of the Felix coal zone. Crosses are stratigraphic sections, solid lines are isopachs of channel complex in feet, and dashed lines are isopach of coal in feet. Crossbedding measurements are expressed in a rose diagram. N = number of observations. Data from Warwick and others, 1984; Flores and Warwick, 1984; and Warwick, personal communication.

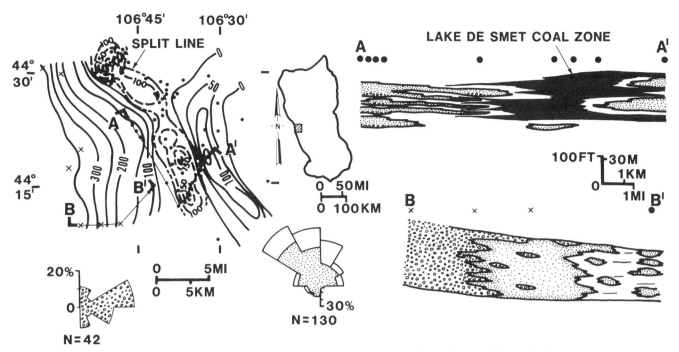

Figure 18. Lake de Smet coal zone. Inset map shows study area in the Powder River basin. Cross sections show Lake de Smet coal zone; isopach shows alluvial fan and channel sandstones and merged Lake de Smet coal bed. Dots are drillholes and crosses are stratigraphic sections. Solid lines are isopachs of channel complex in feet and dashed lines are isopach of coal in feet. Crossbedding measurements are expressed in rose diagrams for the alluvial fan (left) and channel sandstone (right shaded; unshaded includes other channel sandstones). N = number of observations. Data are from Obernyer, 1978.

alluvial fan and the anomalously thick character of the Lake de Smet coal zone are a departure from depositional styles of the coal zones of the Tongue River Member. The Lake de Smet coal zone is about twice as thick as the thickest minable coal bed (as much as 5 km wide and 27 km long) in the Tongue River Member, but it is not as laterally extensive as Tongue River coals. The unique thickness and areal distribution of the Lake de Smet coal zone appear to have been affected by basinal tectonics. Obernyer (1978) suggested that the coal zone accumulated in a downdropped block of the Buffalo deep fault. Flores and Warwick (1984) suggested deposition of the coal on a platform, perhaps on a upfaulted area, east of the subsiding downfaulted (see Buffalo deep fault in Fig. 1) basin axis. This mode of deposition was necessary to prevent drowning of the Lake de Smet swamp vegetation by detrital influx from the nearby alluvial fans. Alternatively, growth of vegetation in raised swamps also may have deterred detrital influx. More importantly, Flores and Warwick (1984) proposed that the poorly drained Lake de Smet backswamp was sustained for a long time by groundwater recharge and discharge from the proximal and distal alluvial fans, respectively. This pattern of paleohydrology is very similar to that of the modern Rio Grande River alluvial fan that discharges groundwater into the alluvial plain of the San Luis Valley in Colorado (Emery and others, 1971). The combined tectonic mode and

paleohydrologic controls on accumulation of the Lake de Smet coal zone present a different style of deposition from that of thick coal beds in the Tongue River Member.

The Arvada coal bed is the lowermost bed in the Wasatch Formation; it formed in an anastomosed fluvial setting much like that of the Roland-Smith coal zone of the Tongue River Member. Figure 15 shows that the Arvada coal bed overlies the coquinoid limestone at the top of the Tongue River Member of the Fort Union Formation. The Arvada coal bed averages 2 m in thickness, in comparison to the Smith and Roland coals, which averages 1.5 m in thickness. The Arvada coal is underlain by lacustrine or crevasse delta-crevasse splay facies and lacustrine facies much like those associated with the Smith coal bed (Flores and Hanley, 1984). The coquinoid limestone, which directly overlies the anastomosed fluvial deposits at the top of the Tongue River Member, represents a lacustrine facies deposited in a large lake. The origin of this lake may have been due to regional subsidence. The lake, in turn, was filled by lacustrine or crevasse deltas and crevasse splays that served as a platform for the Arvada peat-forming swamp. A similar origin of the Smith coal bed was proposed by Flores and Hanley (1984). The Smith and Arvada coal beds are both thin and uneconomic in contrast to thicker coal beds of the Wasatch Formation and Tongue River Member of the Fort Union Formation.

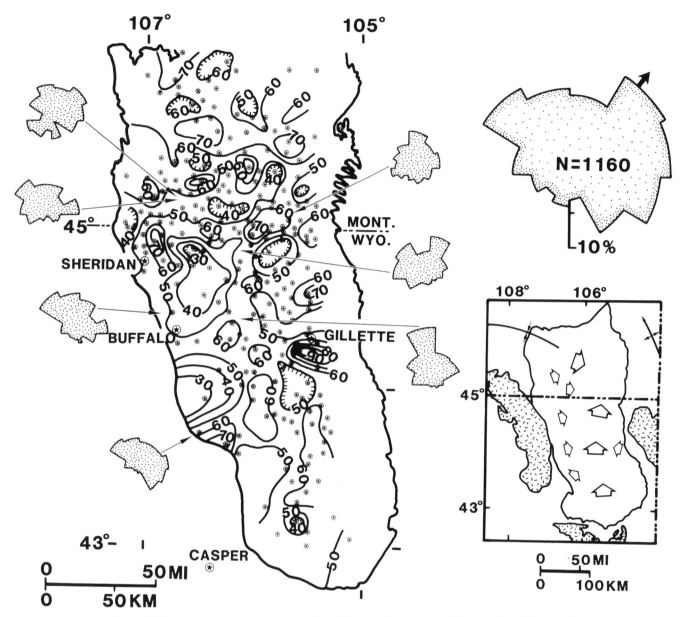

Figure 19. Net sand percent map of the combined Wasatch Formation and Tongue River Member of the Fort Union Formation, modified from Lewis and Hotchkiss (1981). Crossbed rose diagrams are from the channel sandstones of the studied coal zones. Grand total crossbed measurements are expressed in a rose diagram (upper right). Inset map shows schematic diagram of the trunk and tributary streams in the Powder River basin during deposition of the Tongue River Member and Wasatch Formation. See Figure 1 for structural elements of inset map.

COMPARISON WITH BASIN SAND DISTRIBUTION

The investigation by Lewis and Hotchkiss (1981) of basin sandstone aquifers in the Tongue River Member and Wasatch Formation contains information about the styles of deposition. A net sandstone percent map of the combined Tongue River Member and Wasatch Formation modified from Lewis and Hotchkiss (1981) is shown in Figure 19. The map exhibits major north-south and east-west orientations of sandstone bodies

greater than 1.2 in thickness. The distributions of sandstone show an integrated north-south sandstone complex and west-east sandstone complex that is connected to the north-trending complex. The northernmost west-east sand complex contains the greatest areal concentration of high sandstone abundance (greater than 70 percent), although locally the Gillette area contains as much as 90 percent sandstone. The sandstone complexes are interpreted as deposits of trunk (south-north complex) and tributary (west-east complexes) streams. The northerly-oriented trunk stream system served as a secondary system that drained the shallow axis of the basin fed by tertiary systems from the west, south, and east. The northernmost west-east sandstone complex probably represents deposits of a primary trunk stream that merged with the trunk-tributary system to the south. This easterly-oriented trunk stream probably drained the Bull Mountain and Ashland synclines and the south flank of the Miles City arch.

Basin crossbedding distributions shown in Figure 19 indicate sediment influx from the Bighorn Mountains to the west, Casper arch to the southwest, Laramie Mountains to the south, Hartville uplift to the southeast, and Black Hills to the east. These sediments were transported via tributaries to the northerly-flowing secondary trunk stream that flowed along the shallow basin axis. The general northeast direction of sediment transport in this trunk-tributary system (Fig. 19) suggests that the system probably merged at the eastern end of the primary trunk stream. This trunk stream presumably drained between the Black Hills and the Cedar Creek anticline.

The south-to-north and west-to-east paleodepositional slopes of the sand complexes are parallel to the orientations of the channel complexes that split the thick coals in the Tongue River Member and Wasatch Formation. In the south, central, and northeast parts of the basin, the south-to-north paleodepositional dip of the channel sandstones of the Sussex, Felix, Wyodak-Anderson, Roland-Smith, and Pawnee coal zones, respectively, are parallel to the secondary trunk stream. In the west and northwest parts of the basin the west-east depositional dip of the channel sandstones of the Wall and Anderson-Dietz coal zones are parallel to the tributary streams. The northeasterly oriented channel sandstone basinward of the east trending alluvial fan of the Lake de Smet coal zone was probably deposited in a tributary stream. More importantly, the poorly drained backswamps associated with floodplains developed subparallel to the adjoining trunk-tributary streams.

COMPARISON WITH MODERN ANALOGUES

Several studies of modern peat-forming backswamps in alluvial plains provide important information relative to the data on the styles of coal deposition in the Wasatch Formation and Tongue River Member of the Fort Union Formation in the Powder River Basin. Voss (1982), the Transmigration Area Development Project (1983), and Ansyahari and others (1983) show the relationship of peat-forming backswamps to trunk-tributary rivers and floodplain lakes in the modern intermontane Kutai Basin drained by the Mahakam River in Kalimantan, Timur, Borneo. Laippalainen (1980) and the Instituto de Pesquisas Tecnologica (1981) also illustrate the areal geometry and relationship of peat to detrital deposits in a modern intermontane trunk-tributary system, the Rio Paraiba do Sul in the State of São Paulo, Brazil. Modern peat-forming environments in anastomosed fluvial systems in the Upper Columbia River in British Columbia, Canada and Lower Saskatchewan River in Saskatchewan, Canada were investigated by Smith and Smith (1980),

Smith (1983), Clough and Smith (1983), and Dufficy and Smith (1983).

The alluvial plain drained by the trunk-tributary streams of the Mahakam River probably best exemplifies the coal-forming environments of the Tertiary deposits in the Powder River Basin. The alluvial plain is bordered along the basin margin by wet alluvial fans (Voss, 1982). The tectonic setting of the Kutai Basin (Fig. 20), which is bounded by Late Neogene uplifts, is very similar to that of the Powder River Basin. The Kutai Basin is a 97-km wide and 161-km long intermontane basin surrounded on the east, north, and south by Tertiary sedimentary valley-and-ridge fold belts and on the west by a Tertiary volcanic-sedimentary upland (Voss, 1982; Hamilton, 1979). The surrounding uplifts and subsidence of the Kutai Basin probably resulted from continental rifting that opened the Makasar Strait during the Late Neogene time (Samuel and Muchsin, 1975; Hamilton, 1979). These structural movements caused entrenched aggradation of the Mahakam River and its tributaries in the subsiding Kutai Basin. This was accompanied by the river eroding through its older deposits in the valley and ridge fold belt to the east and by deposition of the river sediment load at the Mahakam delta located 105 km farther to the east. The Mahakam River and its tributaries are separated by floodplains covered by poorly drained backswamps and floodplain lakes (Fig. 21). The floodplain lakes, which vary from 3 to 240 sq km coalesced to form a lake that occupied an area of as much as 465 sq km. The floodplain lakes change in size seasonally be enlargement of their shorelines during the rainy season. The principal modes of lake infilling are by lacustrine or crevasse deltas generated by crevassing of the levees of the Mahakam River and its tributaries and by lacustrine deltas fed by short-headed streams that drain mountains and basin margins. The Mahakam River is characterized by a meandering channel morphology and carries a sediment load of mainly mixed sands, silts, and muds. Most of the tributary streams also have meandering channels; however, a few tributaries and short-headed streams developed on anastomosed pattern. Thus, the alluvial plain of the Kutai Basin possesses all the characteristics of the fluvial channel and interfluvial elements that were interpreted in the alluvial settings of the Tongue River Member and the Wasatch Formation.

The most important common element of both modern and ancient alluvial environments is probably the development of poorly drained backswamps. The Mahakam River and its tributaries are stabilized by dense forest vegetation of the backswamps, which consists of broad-leafed evergreens such as *Palaquim, Shorea, Combetocarpus, Mezzetia,* and *Tristana,* all typical of humid tropical climate with average temperatures of 22°C (Ansyahari and others, 1983). In some of the backswamps, the swamp forest is locally replaced by a swamp grassland consisting of various herbaceous plants including grasses and sedges, a few low shrubs, and sometimes small trees. The grassland resulted either from burning of the swamp forest or a natural drying out of vegetation. Ansyahari and others (1983) reported peat deposits more than 3-m thick in the backswamp. The true thickness and geometry of

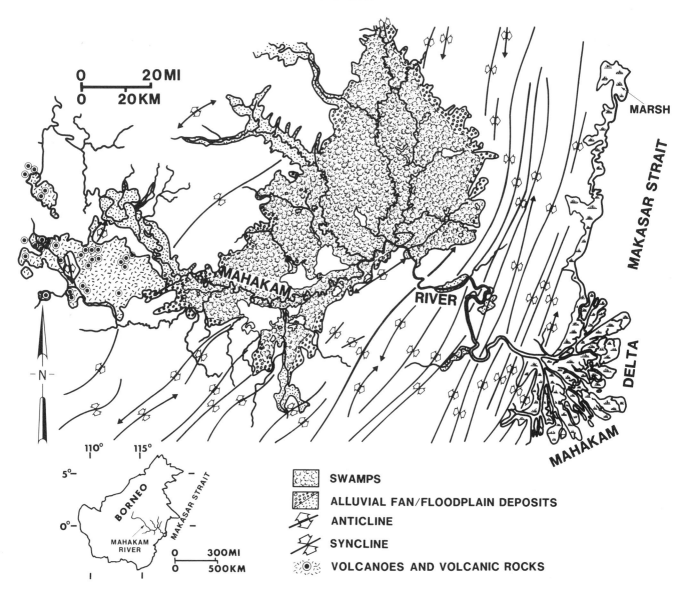

Figure 20. Kutai Basin, drained by the Mahakam River and its tributaries in southeast Borneo. Bounding uplands show tectonic and volcanic elements. Modified from Voss (1982).

the peat deposits are unknown. Selected soil analysis of the upper 400 cm of the peat deposits by Bogor Agriculture University of Indonesia show acidity increasing from average pH 5.6 to 4.4 towards the interior of the peat swamps (Fig. 21). The peat swamps occupy an area 97 km wide and 145 km long (14,065 sq km) throughout the alluvial plain, interrupted only by the trunk and tributary streams and floodplain lakes. The largest and areally most continuous peat swamp in the alluvial plain occupies an area 35 km wide and 72 km long (2,520 sq km). The length of the peat swamps is either parallel or subparallel to the length of the trunk or tributaries of the Mahakam River. Thus, the vast expanse and areal distribution of the peat-forming backswamps in the alluvial plain of the Kutai Basin are analogous to those of

the Tongue River Member of the Fort Union Formation and Wasatch Formation in the Powder River Basin.

The absence of detailed geometry and areal distribution of peat deposits in the Kutai Basin may be provided by the deposits of the peat-forming backswamps of the Rio Paraiba do Sul in the State of São Paulo, Brazil, investigated by the Instituto de Pesquisas Tecnologica (1981). Like the Mahakam River, the Rio Paraiba do Sul is a mixed-load, meandering trunk stream fed by meandering tributary streams. This trunk-tributary stream is entrenched in a 20-km wide and 150-km long graben basin. This intermontane basin is bordered by Precambrian rocks and underlain by Tertiary sedimentary rocks (Instituto de Pesquisas Tecnologica, 1981). However, unlike the Kutai Basin, the peat-forming

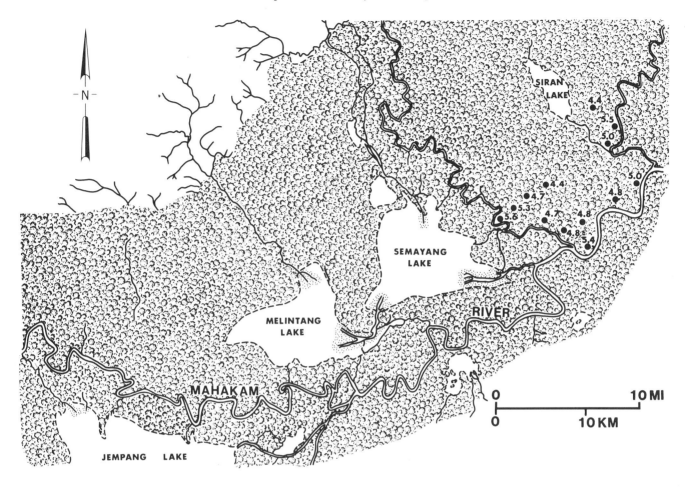

Figure 21. A part of the alluvial plain setting showing poorly drained backswamps, floodplain (crevasse splays, crevasse deltas, and lakes), and channel network of the Makaham River. Peat deposits exhibit pH variation from the margins to the interior of the backswamp. Modified from Transmigration Development Project (1983).

backswamps in the alluvial plain of the Rio Paraiba do Sul are smaller in expanse and are vegetated by herbaceous plants (including sedges, grasses, mosses) and a few trees and shrubs indigenous to a subtropical to tropical climate (Lappalainen, 1980). The peat deposits of the alluvial environment of Rio Paraiba do Sul were classified by Lappalainen (1980) as limnogenic mires in which paludification is around lakes and old river meanders. The peats are strongly minerotrophic because they have been influenced by river floods during their accumulation. The peat deposits are as much as 8.5 m in thickness and are elongate parallel to the length of the Rio Paraiba do Sul (Fig. 22). The bodies of peat, which are as much as 4.3 km wide and 17 km long, are areally distributed in the backswamps on either side of the Rio Paraiba do Sul. The bodies of peat are discontinuous along their length and they are interrupted by tributary streams. The geometry and areal distribution of the peat deposits in the alluvial plain of the Rio Paraiba do Sul are similar to those of the thick coal beds of the Tongue River Member and Wasatch Formation, which are

elongated parallel to depositional slope and laterally juxtaposed to channel-levee complexes.

The best example of a modern peat-forming anastomosed fluvial systems are those of the Upper Columbia River (described by Smith and Smith, 1980, and Smith, 1983) and of the Lower Saskatchewan River (described by Clough and Smith, 1983, and Dufficy and Smith, 1983). These anastomosed rivers have different geological settings, sizes, and origins. The Upper Columbia River system is 1.5 km wide and 120 km long and is situated in an intermontane setting, in contrast to the Lower saskatchewan River system, which is 80 km wide and 120 km long, and is located in a plains setting. The process of anastomosis resulted from lowering of base level or river gradient by aggrading cross-valley alluvial fans for the Upper Columbia River and by basin subsidence and/or regional tilting (e.g. glacial rebound) for the Lower Saskatchewan River. Both anastomosed fluvial systems consist of diverging and converging channels passing laterally into levees, floodplain lakes, crevasse splays, lacustrine or crevasse

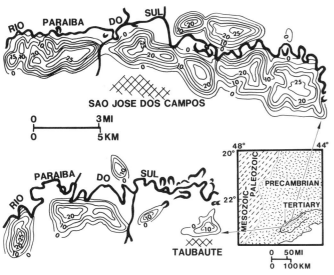

Figure 22. Isopach map of peat deposits in backswamps of the Rio Paraiba do Sul in the State of São Paulo, Brazil. Contour interval in feet.

Figure 23. Anastomosed Upper Columbia River, Alberta, Canada, showing diverging and converging channels separated by levees, floodplains, backswamps, and lakes. Photo courtesy of Derald Smith.

deltas, and backswamps (Fig. 23). The floodplain lakes are aggraded by crevasse splays and lacustrine deltas that served as avulsion routes. Progradation of a crevasse splay and subsequent filling of the floodplain lake by a lacustrine or crevasse delta promoted bifurcation of crevasse channels that served as major conduits during increased discharge. Stabilization of these channels by vegetated levees accompanied by rejoining and abandonment of other channels led to anastomosis. Because of the effects of crevassing in lake-dominated floodplains, associated peat-forming backswamps are frequently drowned by detrital influxes resulting in well developed mud-rich peat deposits.

However, in the Lower Saskatchewan River (Clough and Smith, 1983; Duffy and Smith, 1983) the slow rate of aggradation resulted in greater accumulation of peat bogs (as much as 3.5 m in thickness), which are laterally extensive (as much as 30 sq km area). The extensive peat bogs are isolated from active channels. The variations in areal facies distribution and depositional facies of the Upper Columbia River and Lower Saskatchewan River are similar to those of the Roland-Smith coal zone of the Tongue River and Arvada coal zone of the Wasatch Formation. Of these two fluvial systems, the Lower Saskatchewan River (Fig. 24) is more closely related to the anastomosed fluvial deposits of the Tertiary rocks in terms of scale, peat accumulation, and origin of anastomosis. Flores and Hanley (1984) proposed that regional anastomosis in the Powder River Basin during deposition of the Roland-Smith coal zone was caused by lowering of base level due to damming of the northeast course of the fluvial system by uplift of the Cedar Creek anticline (see Fig. 1).

Studies of modern analog show that thick peat deposits accumulated in vast expanses of backswamps in various alluvial environments from plains settings (as in the Lower Saskatchewan River) to intermontane settings (as in the Mahakam River, Rio Paraiba do Sul, and Upper Columbia River). These modern analogs indicate that accumulation of very thick peat deposits that become coal bodies is common in an intermontane setting and comparable to that of the Tongue River Member and Wasatch Formation in the Powder River Basin.

A PROPOSED HYBRID FLUVIAL MODEL FOR COAL DEPOSITION

The depositional facies of the Tongue River Member of the Fort Union Formation and the Wasatch Formation resemble deposits of the combined alluvial plains of the Mahakam and Saskatchewan rivers and the Rio Paraiba do Sul. Thus, an ideal model of coal deposition in the Tertiary Powder River Basin is a hybrid of those modern fluvial systems. It is proposed that the hybrid fluvial model probably consisted of a coal-forming environment in an alluvial plain that was aggraded by both meandering and anastomosed fluvial systems. In this model the alluvial plain was aggraded vertically, alternately by meandering and anastomosed streams; the anastomosed streams were the principal mode of vertical infilling of floodbasins of the alluvial plain. It is suggested that the anastomosed streams filled the floodbasin to base level at which time anastomosis gave rise to meandering streams that laterally aggraded the floodbasin. The analysis of the development of the fluvial system from anastomosing to meandering streams is the key to understanding accumulation of thick peats (and eventually coals) in backswamps of the alluvial plain.

The architecture of the alluvial plain of the hybrid fluvial model and the evolution of the types of fluvial systems and associated backswamps are displayed in Figure 25. Initially, (Fig. 25A) the system consisted of a flood basin bounded by a meandering stream. The flood basin was aggraded by a crevasse splay that originated from the meandering stream as a result of breached

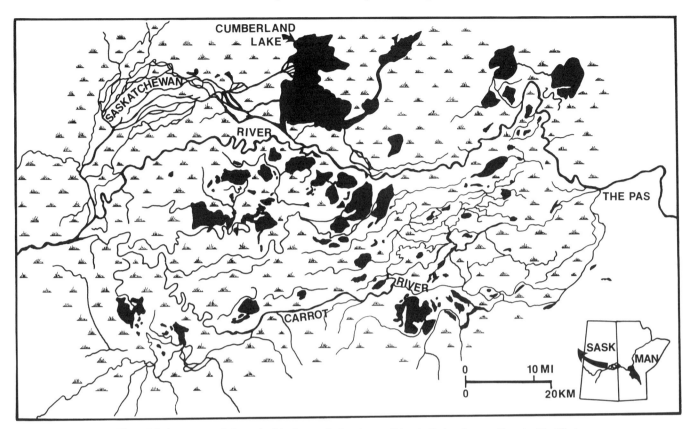

Figure 24. Anastomosed channel of the Lower Saskatchewan River in Saskatchewan, Canada. Modified from Smith, 1983.

levee. The crevasse splay prograded toward the floodbasin, establishing a system of multiple crevasse splays. The crevasse channels of this system were widened and stabilized by vegetation at the proximal area (nearest the meandering stream) and bifurcated at the distal area as progradation ensued. The crevasse channel at the area of breached levee was transformed into a major conduit as the meandering stream was gradually abandoned and finally served as the avulsion route permitting diversion of major flow into the floodbasin (Fig. 25B). The crevasse channels diverged and converged creating embryonic anastomosis as the crevasse system enlarged by progradation. Thus, the floodbasin was aggraded vertically by a crevasse splay system that eventually debouched into floodplain lakes. This mode of filling was succeeded by anastomosed streams as the diverging and converging crevasse channels matured and developed small intervening floodbasins (Fig. 25C). The filling of the floodbasin by anastomosed streams continued until the base level was reached. At this time, an anastomosed stream developed high sinuosity and assumed characteristics of a meandering stream (Fig. 25D). As major flow was concentrated along this meandering stream, associated anastomosed streams were abandoned. Lateral migration accompanied by vertical aggradation of the meandering stream transformed the old anastomosed belt into a meanderbelt. Deposition along the meanderbelt created an alluvial ridge and an adjoining topo-

graphic low or a floodbasin. The succeeding cycle of anastomosis occurred during the next stream avulsion via a crevasse splay system into this floodbasin.

The diversion of detritus into the floodbasin produced a dichotomy of intra-floodbasin and extra-floodbasin backswamps in the alluvial plain. The intra-floodbasin backswamps, which formed within the belt of anastomosis, were generally low-lying, well-drained, frequently choked by detrital influx. This resulted in the accumulation of relatively thin coal beds and abundant carbonaceous shale beds. In contrast, an extrafloodbasin backswamp formed as a result of stream avulsion that abandoned meanderbelt deposits and developed away from the belt of anastomosis (Fig. 25C). This backswamp was poorly drained and free of water-borne sediments. Detrital incursion was probably prevented by development of a raised swamp (Fig. 25D), which was proposed originally by Flores (1981) for the Tertiary coals of the Powder River Basin. Raised swamps are common in modern alluvial plain environments in Borneo (Wilford, 1961; Anderson, 1964). The raised swamps are densely forested and are found in high rainfall areas that exceed annual evaporation (ombrotrophic swamp). The raised swamps are maintained by a groundwater table developed near the surface resulting from high rate of precipitation. The key to the accumulation of thick coal deposits in this swamp is probably controlled by the growth of forest vegeta-

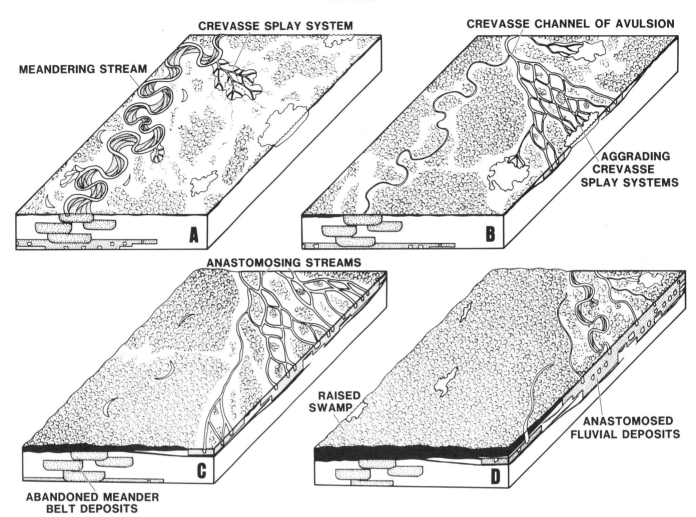

Figure 25. Hybrid fluvial model of coal deposition showing stages of development of anastomosing and meandering streams and backswamp formation. A) floodplain bounded by a meandering stream from which originates a crevasse-splay system. B) abandonment of meandering stream due to crevasse channel of avulsion, which causes major flow into the floodbasin. C) development of anastomosing streams due to crevasse channel maturity. D) development of meandering stream due to high sinuosity of anastomosed stream.

tion. The forested swamps are interpreted to generate mainly woody peat deposits that are relatively less compactible than nonwoody peat deposits. Under this condition, it is not difficult to visualize the accumulation of unusually thick coals in the Powder River Basin. Petrographic analysis of the Felix coal by Warwick and others (1984) indicates as much as 95 percent vitrinite or huminite (average 85 percent), which supports the woody origin of the coals.

CONCLUSIONS

The most fruitful method of determining the styles of coal deposition is the study of coal-bearing intervals as individual or multiple packages over regional areas, which in turn are utilized for deductive interpretation of basin depositional models. In order

for this investigative approach to be successful, stratigraphic data should be derived primarily from continuous surface outcrops supplemented by stratigically placed drill holes. This research approach led to a series of detailed investigations of several coal zones that include minable coal beds in the Tertiary deposits in the Powder River Basin and to the determination of interrelationships between the depositional facies and areal distribution of associated coal deposits. Among the minable coal beds studied, the most common relationship is lateral juxtaposition of channel-levee complexes with anomalously thick coal beds. In addition, these channel-levee complexes, which are bounded by minor floodplain facies, constituted the principal depositional facies involved in coal bed splits. The paleogeographic distribution of temporal channel-levee, floodplain, and backswamp facies shows channel deposits consistently oriented in south-north and west-east directions. The orientations of these fluvial axes are parallel to the direction of elongation of coal beds formed in related backswamps. The south-north and west-east paleodepositional slopes are supported by basinwide sand distribution patterns and by a general northeastward direction of crossbeds of the channel deposits. These channel complexes are interpreted to have been deposited by braided, meandering, and anastomosing fluvial systems. However, the most representative fluvial system with bordering backswamps in which thick peat developed in the Powder River Basin is a trunk-tributary system composed of meandering rivers. The anastomosed fluvial system usually has backswamps with thin peat beds.

The fluvial systems described for the coal-bearing Tertiary deposits in the Powder River Basin are analogous to those that drain modern peat-forming alluvial plains in both intermontane and plains settings. The intermontane Kutai Basin of Borneo, drained by the Mahakam River and its tributaries, is the best modern analog to the depositional setting of the Tertiary deposits of the Powder River Basin. In the Kutai Basin the alluvial plain consists of vast and continuous peat-forming backswamps that equal if not exceed those in the Powder River Basin. Most importantly, the alluvial plain of the Mahakam River, as well as those of the Rio Paraiba do Sul in Brazil and the Upper Columbia and Lower Saskatchewan rivers in Canada, duplicates all the depositional facies recognized in the Tertiary rocks. Thus, these modern analogs indicate that the accumulation of thick coal beds in ancient rocks has little bearing on site-specific environment (e.g., deltaic environment) and dispel the idea that an alluvial environment is not ideal for the accumulation of economic coal deposits.

REFERENCES CITED

Allen, J.R.L., 1970, Studies in fluviatile sedimentation: A comparison of fining-upwards cyclothems, with special reference to coarse-member composition and interpretation: Journal of Sedimentary Petrology, v. 40, p. 298–323.

—— , 1978, Studies in fluviatile sedimentation: An exploratory quantitative model for the architecture of avulsion-controlled alluvial suites: Sedimentary Geology, v. 21, p. 129–147.

Anderson, J.A.R., 1964, The structure and development of the peat swamps of Sarawak and Brunei: Journal of Tropical Geography, v. 18, p. 7–16.

Ansyahari, T., Bower, R., Hoffman, R., Nitsch, M., Poerwanto, A., Speller, D., Syaif, E., and Woods, T., 1983, Land capability classification, Tenggarong—Part 2, The environment: Transmigration Area Development Project, Samarinda, Indonesia, p. 3–20.

Ayers, W. B., Jr., and Kaiser, W. R., 1984, Lacustrine-interdeltaic coal in the Fort Union Formation (Paleocene), Powder River Basin, Wyoming and Montana, *in* Rahamani, R. A., and Flores, R. M., eds., Sedimentology of Coal Deposits: International Association of Sedimentologists, Special Publication No. 7, p. 61–84.

Blackstone, D. L., Jr., 1981, Compression as an agent in deformation of the east-central flank of the Bighorn Mountains, Sheridan and Johnson Counties, Wyoming, *in* Boyd, D. W., and Lillegraven, J. A., eds., Rocky Mountain Foreland Basement Tectonics: Contributions to Geology, University of Wyoming, Laramie, v. 19, p. 105–122.

Bridge, J. S., and Leeder, M. R., 1979, A simulation model of alluvial stratigraphy: Sedimentology, v. 26, p. 617–644.

Brown, R. W., 1958, Fort Union Formation in the Powder River Basin, Wyoming: Wyoming Geological Association, 13th Annual Field Conference, Guidebook, p. 111–113.

Canavello, D. A., 1980, Geology of some Paleocene coal bearing strata of the Powder River Basin, Wyoming and Montana [M.S. thesis]: Raleigh, North Carolina, North Carolina State University, 63 p.

Childers, M. O., 1970, Uranium geology of the Kaycee area, Johnson County, Wyoming, *in* Wagner, R. L., Renfro, A. R., and Laraway, W. H., eds., Symposium on Wyoming Sandstones: Wyoming Geological Association, 22nd Field Conference, Guidebook, p. 13–20.

Clough, S. R., and Smith, N. D., 1983, Evolution of fluvial style in a wetland environment: Cumberland marshes, Saskatchewan: Geological Society of America Abstracts with Programs, v. 15, no. 4, p. 227.

Coss, J. M., 1984, Paleoenvironments of the Upper Fort Union Formation at Pine Ridge, western Powder River Basin, Wyoming [M.S. thesis]: Boulder, Colorado, University of Colorado, 84 p.

Culbertson, W. C., and Mapel, W. J., 1976, Coal in the Wasatch Formation, northwest part of the Powder River Basin near Sheridan, Sheridan County, Wyoming, *in* Landon, R. B., Curry, W. H., and Runge, J. S., eds., Geology and Energy Resources of the Powder River: Wyoming Geological Association, 28th Annual Field Conference, Guidebook, p. 193–201.

Curry, W. H., 1971, Laramide structural history of the Powder River Basin, Wyoming, *in* Renfro, A. R., Madison, L. W., and Jarree, G. A., eds., Symposium on Wyoming Tectonics and their Economic Significance: Wyoming Geological Association, 23rd Field Conference, Guidebook, p. 49–60.

Davis, J. A., Wegemann, C. H., and Winchester, D. E., 1912, Coal fields in eastern Wyoming: U.S. Geological Survey Bulletin 471-F, 95 p.

Dufficy, J. P., and Smith, N. D., 1983, Facies relations in avulsion-controlled fluvial systems: Cumberland marshes, Saskatchewan: Geological Society of America Abstracts with Programs, v. 15, no. 4, p. 225.

Emery, P. A., Boettcher, A. J., Snipes, R. J., McIntyre, H. J., Jr., 1971, Hydrology of the San Luis Valley, south-central Colorado: U.S. Geological Survey Hydrology Atlas HA-381.

Ethridge, F. G., Jackson, T. J., and Youngberg, A. V., 1981, Floodbasin sequence of a fine-grained meander belt subsystem: The coal-bearing Lower Wasatch and Upper Fort Union Formations, southern Powder River Basin, Wyoming, *in* Ethridge, F. G., and Flores, R. M., eds., Recent and Ancient Nonmarine Depositional Environments—Models for Exploration: Society of Economic Paleontologists and Mineralogists Special Publication No. 31, p. 191–209.

Flores, R. M., 1981, Coal deposition in fluvial paleoenvironments of the Paleocene Tongue River Member of the Fort Union Formation, Powder River area, Powder River Basin, Wyoming and Montana, *in* Ethridge, F. G., and Flores, R. M., eds., Recent and Ancient Nonmarine Depositional Environments—Models for Exploration: Society of Economic Paleontologists and Mineralogists, Special Publication No. 31, p. 169–190.

—— 1983, Basin facies analysis of coal-rich Tertiary fluvial deposits, northern Powder River Basin, Montana and Wyoming, *in* Collinson, J. D., and J. Lewin, eds., Modern and Ancient Fluvial Systems: International Association of Sedimentologists Special Publication no. 6, p. 501–515.

Flores, R. M., and Ethridge, F. G., 1985, Evolution of intermontane fluvial systems of Tertiary Powder River Basin, *in* Flores, R. M., and Kaplan, S., eds., Cenozoic Paleogeography of west-central United States: Society of Economic Paleontologists and Mineralogists, Rocky Mountain Section, p. 107–126.

Flores, R. M., and Hanley, J. H., 1984, Anastomosed and associated coal-bearing fluvial deposits: Upper Tongue River Member, Paleocene Fort Union Formation, northern Powder River Basin, Wyoming, U.S.A., *in* Rahmani, R. A., and Flores, R. M., eds., Sedimentology of Coal Deposits: International Association of Sedimentologists Special Publication No. 7, p. 85–103.

Flores, R. M., Hardie, J. K., Coss, J. M., Weaver, J. N., and Van Gosen, B. S.,

1984, Upper Fort Union coals in western Powder River Basin, Wyoming [abs.]—Alluvial-plain deposits: American Association of Petroleum Geologists Bulletin, v. 68, no. 4, p. 477.

Flores, R. M., and Warwick, P. D., 1984, Dynamics of coal deposition in inter-montane alluvial paleoenvironments, Eocene Wasatch Formation, Powder River Basin, Wyoming, *in* Houghton, R. L., ed., Proceedings of the Sixth Symposium on the Geology of Rocky Mountain Coal: North Dakota Geological Society Publication 84-1, p. 184–199.

Galloway, W. E., 1979, Early Tertiary-Wyoming intermontane basins, *in* Galloway, W. E., Kreitler, C. W., and McGowen, J. H., eds., Depositional and Ground-water Flow Systems in the Exploration for Uranium: Bureau of Economic Geology, University of Texas, Austin, Research Colloquim Notes, p. 197–228.

Galloway, W. E., and Hobday, D. K., 1983, Terrigenous Clastic Depositional Systems-Applications to Petroleum, Coal and Uranium Exploration: New York, Springer-Verlag, 423 pp.

Glass, G. B., 1980, Coal resources of the Powder River coal basin, *in* Glass, G. B., eds., Guidebook to the Coal Geology of the Powder River Coal Basin, Wyoming: Geological Survey of Wyoming, Public Information Circular No. 14, p. 97–131.

Hamilton, W. B., 1979, Tectonics of the Indonesian region: U.S. Geological Survey Professional Paper 1078, 345 pp.

Hanley, J. H., 1976, Paleosynecology of nomarine Mollusca from the Green River and Wasatch Formations (Eocene), southwestern Wyoming and northwestern Colorado, *in* Scott, R. W., and West, R. R., eds., Structure and classification of Paleocommunities: Dowden, Hutchinson, and Ross, Inc., p. 235–261/

Hanley, J. H., and Flores, R. M., 1983, Depositional environments in an alluvial-lacustrine system: Molluscan paleoecology and lithofacies relations in upper part of Tongue River Member of Fort Union Formation, Powder River Basin, Wyoming: American Association of Petroleum Geologists Bulletin, Abstracts with Programs, v. 67, no. 3, p. 478–479.

Hansen, W. B., 1983, Channeling in Paleocene coals, northern Powder River Basin, Montana: American Association of Petroleum Geologists Bulletin, Abstracts with Programs, v. 67, no. 8, p. 1340.

Hardie, J. K., and Van Gosen, B. S., 1986, Coal bed correlations within the Sussex coal zone of the Upper Fort Union Formation in the eastern part of the Kaycee quadrangle, Johnson and Campbell Counties, Wyoming: U.S. Geological Survey Coal Investigation Series C-107.

Horn, G. H., and Richardson, E. E., 1958, Areal geology of the West Sussex oil field, Johnson County, Wyoming: U.S. Geological Survey Open-file Report 124 K.

Hose, R. K., 1955, Geology of the Crazy Woman Creek area, Johnson County, Wyoming: U.S. Geological Survey Bulletin 1027-B, 118 pp.

Instituto de Pesquisas Tecnologica, 1981, Prospecção regional de turfa do Estado de São Paulo, Brasil: Minas e Geologia Applicada, Relatorio no. 15, 318, 41 pp.

Kent, B. H., Weaver, J. N., Roberts, S. B., Ming, L. S., and Mao, B., in preparation, Geology and resource appraisal of the Felix coal deposit, Powder River Basin, Wyoming: U.S. Geological Survey Bulletin.

Lappalainen, E., 1981, A study of the useful fuel peat resources of the SJ-II peatland in São Jose dos Campos, São Paulo: Instituto de Pesquisas Tecnologica, contrato AJ-DES-325/14.986180, 39 pp.

Law, B. E., Barnum, B. E., and Wollenzien, T. P., 1979, Coal bed correlations in the Tongue River Members of the Fort Union Formation, Monarch, Wyoming, and Decker, Montana, areas: U.S. Geological Survey Miscellaneous Investigations Series Map I-1128.

Lewis, B. D., and Hotchkiss, W. R., 1981, Thickness, percent sand, and configuration of shallow hydrologic units in the Powder River Basin, Montana and Wyoming: United States Geological Survey Miscellaneous Investigations Series, Map I-1317.

Lynn, L. R., Jr., 1980, Stratigraphic framework of some Tertiary coal-bearing alluvial strata, Powder River Basin, Wyoming and Montana [M.S. thesis]: Raleigh, North Carolina, North Carolina State University, 44 p.

Mapel, W. J., 1959, Geology and coal resources of the Buffalo-Lake de Smet area, Johnson and Sheridan Counties, Wyoming: U.S. Geological Survey Bulletin 1078, 148 pp.

Matson, R. E., and Blumer, J. W., 1973, Quality and reserves of strippable coal, selected deposits, southeastern Montana: Montana Bureau of Mines and Geology, Bulletin 91, 135 p.

Miall, A. D., 1978, Lithofacies types and vertical profile models in braided river deposits—A summary, *in* Miall, A. D., ed., Fluvial Sedimentology: Canadian Society of Petroleum Geologists, Memoir 5, p. 597–604.

Obernyer, S., 1978, Basin-margin depositional environments of the Wasatch Formation in the Buffalo-Lake de Smet area, Johnson County, Wyoming, *in* Hodgson, H. E., ed., Proceedings of the Second Symposium on the Geology of Rocky Mountain Coal: Colorado Geological Survey, Resource Series 4, p. 49–65.

Pait, E. D., 1982, The stratigraphy and facies relationships of some coal-bearing alluvial plain strata, Powder River Basin, Montana and Wyoming [M.S. thesis]: Raleigh, North Carolina, North Carolina State University, 66 p.

Pierce, F. W., Kent, B. H., and Grundy, W. D., 1982, Geostatistical analysis of a 113-billion-ton coal deposit in the Paleocene Fort Union Formation, central part of the Powder River Basin, *in* Gurgel, K. D., ed., Proceedings of the fifth symposium on the Geology of Rocky Mountain Coal: Utah Geological and Mineral Survey Bulletin 118, p. 262–272.

Rust, B. R., 1972, Structure and process in a braided river: Sedimentology, v. 18, p. 221–246.

Samuel, L., and Muchsin, S., 1975, Stratigraphy and sedimentation in the Kutai Basin, Kalimantan, *in* Proceedings of the Fourth Annual Convention: Indonesian Petroleum Association, p. 27–39.

Seeland, D. A., 1976, Relationship between early Tertiary sedimentation patterns and uranium mineralization in the Powder River Basin, *in* Laudon, R. B., Curry, W. H., and Runge, J. S., eds., Geology and Energy Resources of the Powder River: Wyoming Geological Association, 28th Annual Field Conference Guidebook, p. 221–230.

Smith, D. G., 1983, Anastomosed fluvial deposits: Modern examples from western Canada, *in* Collinson, J. D., and Lewin, J., eds., Modern and Ancient Fluvial Systems: International Association of Sedimentologists Special Publication No. 6, p. 155–168.

Smith, D. G., and Smith, N. D., 1980, Sedimentation in anastomosed river systems—Examples from alluvial valleys near Banff, Aberta: Journal of Sedimentary Petrology, v. 50, p. 157–164.

Swanson, V. E., Medlin, J. H., Hatch, J. R., Coleman, S. L., Wood, G. H., Woodruff, S. D., and Hildebrand, R. T., 1976, Collection, chemical analysis, and evaluation of coal samples in 1975: U.S. Geological Survey Open-file Report 76-468, 503 p.

Tewalt, S. J., Bauer, M. A., Mathew, D., Roberts, M. P., Ayers, W. B., Jr., Barnes, J. W., and Kaiser, W. R., 1983, Estimation of coal resources in Texas Gulf Coast, Ohio northern Appalachian and Wyoming Powder Basins—A comparison of statistical approaches: Bureau of Economic Geology, University of Texas, Report of Investigations 136, 157 pp.

Toth, J. C., 1982, Facies of Paleocene alluvial plains, Powder River Basin, Montana [M.S. thesis]: Raleigh, North Carolina, North Carolina State University, 69 p.

Transmigration Area Development Project, 1983, Muara Munta Sheet 18155, Tenggaroung Sheet 18156, and Muara Acalong Sheet 18163: Kalimantan, Timur, scale 1:100,000.

Voss, F., 1982, Atlas, East Kalimantan Indonesia: HWWA-Institut fur Wirtschafts Forschung, Hamburg, 52 pp.

Warwick, P. D., Flores, R. M., and Ferm, J. C., 1984, Alluvial model for Eocene Wasatch Formation coal, Powder River Basin, Wyoming [abs.]: American Association of Petroleum Geologists Bulletin, v. 68, no. 7, p. 953.

Weaver, J. N., and Flores, R. M., 1984, Paleotectonic influence on sedimentation of upper Fort Union Formation (Paleocene) at TA Hills, western Powder River Basin, Wyoming: Geological Society of America Abstracts with Programs, v. 16, no. 4, p. 259.

Wilford, G. E., 1961, The geology and mineral resources of Brunei and adjacent parts of Sarawak with descriptions of Seria and Miri oilfields: Geological Survey of the Department of British Territorial Borneo, Memoir 10, 112 p.

Williams, P. F., and Rust, B. R., 1969, The sedimentology of a braided river: Journal of Sedimentary Petrology, v. 39, p. 649–679.

Wolfe, J., 1985, Distribution of major vegetational types during the Tertiary, *in* Sundquist, E. T., and Broker, W. S., Natural Variations in Carbon Dioxide and Carbon Cycle: American Geophysical Union Monograph 32, p. 357–375.

MANUSCRIPT ACCEPTED BY THE SOCIETY APRIL 16, 1986

Discussion of Paper by Romeo Flores. Responses by Flores.

Jim Fassett

Question: Can you explain how fluvial channels could remain geographically stable long enough for 200-ft thick coal beds to have formed between or adjacent to these channels?

Response: It is not a matter of fluvial channels becoming stable long enough to permit an accumulation of a very thick coal bed in an adjoining poorly drained backswamp. The key to the accumulation of thick coal beds in a fluvial setting is the process of avulsion of streams and subsequent abandonment of that part of the alluvial plain. Abandonment provides an ideal setting for development of poorly drained backswamps that are relatively free of detrital influxes for a long period of time. The clue to the accumulation of a 200-ft thick coal bed lies, perhaps, in the composition of the organic deposits. That is, a forested backswamp may generate thick peat consisting mainly of relatively incompactible woody organic matter. Forested backswamps are commonly developed in alluvial plain environments in Borneo and Malaysia, where they generate domed peats that are perched above drainage level.

Jim Fassett

Question: Are you suggesting that coal "swamps" in the Powder River Basin were physiographically higher than adjacent stream channels? If so, why wasn't the peat oxidized?

Response: Yes, the coal "swamps" probably were physiographically higher than adjacent streams. Alluvial-plain raised peat swamps in Sarawak and Brunei in Borneo and Malaysia record a rise in elevation of as much as 200 ft. These tropical raised swamps are densely forested and are found in high rainfall areas that exceed annual evaporation. Raised swamps maintain a ground water table near the surface due to a high rate of precipitation. The work of Fisk on the Mississippi River floodplain has shown that topographic highs as much as 10 ft are sufficient to control peat accumulation.

W. R. Kaiser (Bureau of Economic Geology)

Question: How do you reconcile your model of an axial fluvial system with Ayers and Kaiser's model of a lake at the center of the Powder River Basin?

Response: Ayers and Kaiser's coal model for the Tongue River Member of the Fort Union Formation in the Powder River Basin proposed deposition in lacustrine-interdeltaic environments. The model calls for major deltas to prograde to the west from the Black Hills through Moorhead, Gillette, and Wright, Wyoming, and minor deltas prograding from the south and northwest. These deltas were presumed to have filled a large "Lebo Lake" that was centrally located along the structural basin axis, which covers the western part of the basin extending from Montana across the Montana-Wyoming state line to the southern tip of the basin. Ayers and Kaiser suggested only a minimum input of sediments from the west. The lithofacies and environmental interpretations of Ayers and Kaiser are based mainly on subsurface data and sand percent maps of sandstones greater than 40 ft thick.

There are numerous arguments against their lacustrine-interdeltaic model. Our outcrop and subsurface investigations of the Upper Fort Union Formation in the Sussex and Kaycee areas at the southwestern part of the basin demonstrated that the Sussex coal at the basin axis is as much as 178 ft thick. In addition, the Sussex coal was mapped across the basin axis and is split into numerous coal beds, as much as 20 ft thick, towards the west and southwest by channel and floodplain deposits. Proximal to the line of split, the channel deposits consist of multistory sandstone bodies, each as much as 25 ft thick and 1500 ft wide, which display lateral accretion or point bar units. These channel sandstones represent deposits of a meandering fluvial system. Distal to the line of split, the channel deposits contain framework-supported conglomerates which are interpreted as braided stream deposits. These conglomeratic channel sandstones occur in an interval of as much as 1,000 ft thick and along a 12-mile outcrop belt. The isolith map of the channel sandstones shows north-southwest orientation and bifurcation to the southwest. The channel sandstone complex is mapped from the outcrop to the subsurface across the basin axis for 30 mi. This channel sandstone complex is interpreted as a trunk-tributary fluvial system laterally juxtaposed west of a poorly drained backswamp of the Sussex coal. That the stream channels transported sediments to the northeast is indicated by 311 measurements of trough crossbed directions.

The presence of framework-supported conglomerates of braided stream deposits in the upper part of the Fort Union Formation is also documented in the western part of the basin. Our work in the TA Hills, 18 mi south of Buffalo, records occurrence of pebble and cobble size conglomerates derived from Mesozoic and Paleozoic sedimentary rocks in channel sandstones. These conglomeratic channel sandstones average 20 ft in thickness and extend as much as 1.25 mi laterally. The conglomeratic channel sandstones occur in a 350-ft-thick interval that extends for about a 3-mi belt. Trough crossbed measurements of the channel sandstones show east-northeast direction of transport of sediments.

In the Mowry Basin, about 9 mi northwest of Buffalo, Mapel and Obernyer mapped framework-supported conglomerates for 5 mi along the western part of the basin. The conglomerates consist of pebble to boulder sizes and were derived from Mesozoic and Paleozoic sedimentary rocks. Crossbed measurement by Obernyer shows east-northeast and east-southeast directions of transport of sediments. These conglomerates are interpreted to be basin-margin tributary alluvial fan deposits.

Thus, thick conglomeratic units commonly occur in the upper part of the Fort Union Formation in the southwestern and western parts of the Powder River Basin. The presence of these very coarse clastics was ignored by Ayers and Kaiser. Sedimentation of pebble- to boulder-size clastics at the western margin of the basin does not support their interpretation that the sediments and associated finer-grained detritus were either lacustrine, delta front or prodelta deposits. In addition, the contention of Ayers and Kaiser—that the Black Hills served as the major uplift and source area of Tongue River sediments accompanied by only minimum input of sediments from the west—does not account for the uplifts developed at the southwest and west of the basin which supplied pebble-to boulder-size sediments.

Studies of basin-wide sandstone belts in the Tongue River Member by Warwick, Budai, and Ethridge and his students support the idea of a major north-northeast trending and subordinate east-west trending channel sandstone orientations. That the channel sandstone complexes were interconnected and that a prominent north-south oriented channel complex is found along the shallow axis of the basin is supported by a sand percent map of the combined Tongue River Member and Wasatch Formation by Lewis and Hotchkiss. Basinwide crossbed measurements of the channel sandstones show sediments input from bounding uplifts during deposition of the Tongue River and Wasatch sediments. Net direction of transport of these sediments was to the northeast. Thus, these arguments indicate a weakness in the hypothesis of lake sedimentation along the western margin of the Powder River Basin.

Printed in U.S.A.

Geological Society of America
Special Paper 210
1986

Evolution of thick coal deposits in the Powder River Basin, northeastern Wyoming

Bion H. Kent
U.S. Geological Survey
Denver Federal Center
Denver, Colorado 80225

ABSTRACT

Wyodak, Big George, and Felix are multibillion-ton coal deposits in Paleocene and Eocene rocks along the eastern flank of the Powder River Basin; they contain beds of subbituminous coal as much as 61 m (200 ft) thick, and average thicknesses are 30.5, 34, and 7.6 m (100, 113, and 25 ft), respectively. These thick coal deposits are elongate north-south; they split to the east and to the west. Laramide structural movements (subsidence and uplift) provided the necessary tectonic control for establishing and prolonging optimal depositional environments and conditions in early Tertiary time.

During Paleocene and Eocene time, quiescent periods of thick coal deposition on the eastern flank of the subsiding basin were interspersed with episodes of clastic influx from uplifted eastern source areas. Pivotal effects of western (basin) subsidence and eastern (Black Hills) uplifts produced linear fulcrum areas, in dynamic equilibrium, on the eastern flank of the basin. The fulcrum areas were elongate north-south, parallel to the strike of west-tilted paleoslopes: they were centers for swamp development and coal deposition. Optimal conditions prevailed just west of the fulcrum, where subsidence compensated for upward-building peat accumulation. During prolonged periods of thick coal deposition, those ecosystems were shifted west by eastern uplifts and east by western subsidence. The geometries of the Wyodak, Big George, and Felix coal deposits reflect those processes and indicate how thick coal deposits evolved as products of basin evolution.

INTRODUCTION

Some of the largest coal deposits in the world are found in Paleocene and Eocene rocks along the eastern flank of the Powder River Basin in northeastern Wyoming. This paper describes the Wyodak (55 billion tons), Big George (113 billion tons), and Felix (5 billion tons) coal deposits: they contain beds of subbituminous coal as much as 61 m (200 ft) thick, with average thicknesses of 30.5, 34, and 7.6 m (100, 113, and 25 ft), respectively.

Deposits of such magnitude indicate that early Tertiary climates and depositional environments were ideal for thick coal deposition and that some form of active paleoenvironmental control established and prolonged such favorable conditions. This paper reviews some aspects of thick coal deposition and peat-to-coal transformation with active paleoenvironmental control and provides some insight as to how these thick coal deposits were formed.

The Powder River Basin and surrounding uplifts were formed by Laramide structural movements during Paleocene and Eocene times. These movements (subsidence and uplift) probably provided the active paleoenvironmental control required for thick coal deposition. Accordingly, this paper presents a hypothesis of how thick coal deposits in the Powder River Basin were conditioned by Laramide structural movements during early Tertiary time.

THICK COAL DEPOSITS

Coal occurrences in the Powder River Basin are usually

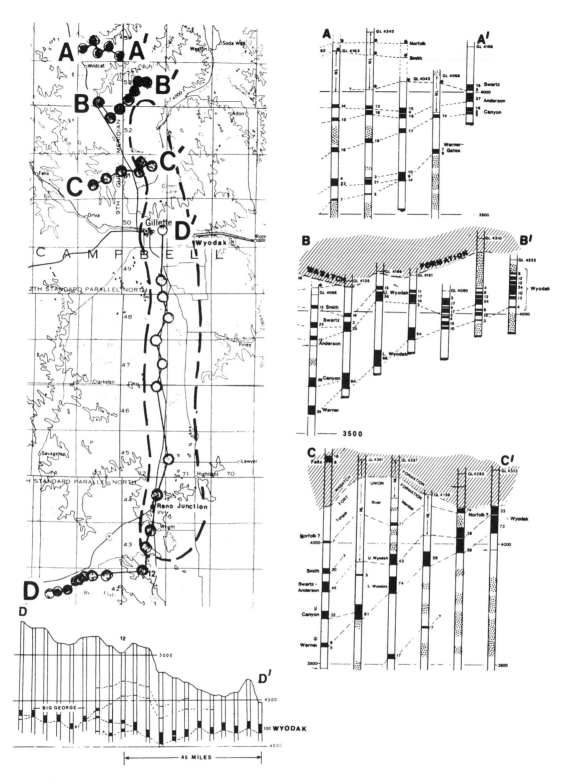

Figure 1. Lines of sections illustrating how individual coal beds merge locally to form the Wyodak deposit of combined coal near Gillette, Wyoming. The index map of the area shows the approximate outline of the deposit. Lines A–A′, B–B′, and C–C′ modified from lines F–F′, G–G′, and H–H′ of Kent and others (1980); coal bed nomenclature is that used by Kent and others (1980). The east-west segment of line D–D′ indicates how the Wyodak deposit connects westward to the Big George coal deposit.

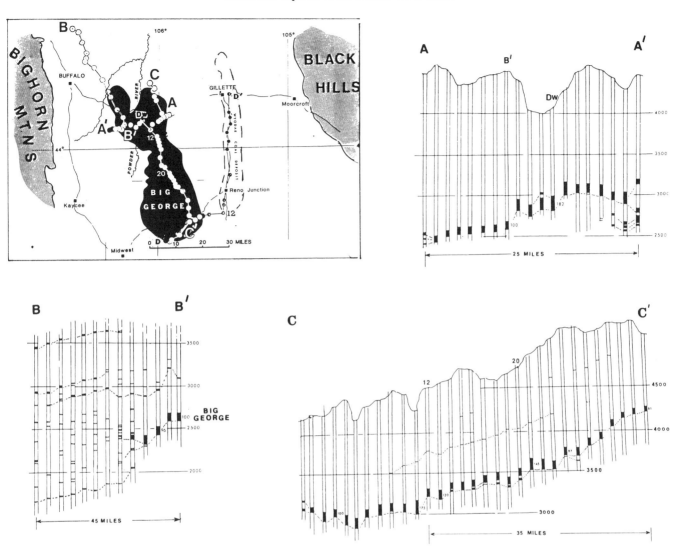

Figure 2. Lines of sections illustrating how individual coal beds merge to form the Big George deposit of combined coal in the central part of the Powder River Basin, northeastern Wyoming. The index map shows the location of the "discovery" well (Dw) indicated on line A–A'. Line D–D' is shown in Figure 1.

treated as local, individual beds, which are named and correlated on a coal-bed basis. At a regional scale, however, individual beds merge and split, and closely associated coal beds merge locally to form thick "deposits" of combined coal. For example, the Smith, Swartz, Anderson, Canyon, and Werner coal beds merge locally to form the Wyodak coal deposit (Fig. 1, lines B–B' and C–C'), as many as eight individual coal beds merge to form the Big George coal deposit (Fig. 2, line B–B'), and the east-west profile of Felix coal occurrences (Fig. 3) illustrates how individual beds merge locally to form a Felix deposit of combined coal. Names such as "Wyodak," "Big George," and "Felix" are used in a collective sense to identify deposits of combined coal and to avoid awkward expressions of coal-bed nomenclature. The Wyodak, Big George, and Felix deposits of combined coal are outlined on an index map of the Wyoming part of the Powder River Basin (Fig. 4).

Wyodak Coal Deposit

An open-pit mine near Wyodak (Fig. 1) is in a 30.5-m- (100-ft-) thick coal bed known locally as the Wyodak; the bed is strip-mined extensively along its north-south trend east of Gillette. The coal bed was mapped as "bed D" by Dobbin and Barnett (1928) who placed it at the top of the Tongue River Member of the Fort Union Formation of Paleocene age; bed D was correlated regionally with the Roland coal bed of Taff (1909) in the Sheridan area (Fig. 4), where the Smith coal bed of Taff (1909) is 38.1 m (125 ft) lower stratigraphically.

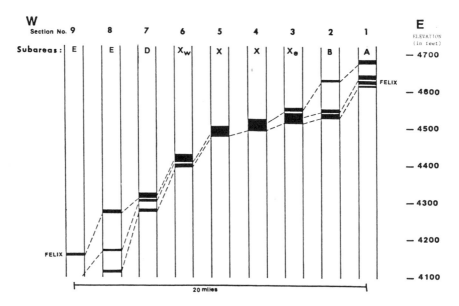

Figure 3. East-west line of sections illustrating how individual coal beds merge locally to form the Felix deposit of combined coal. The location of the line is indicated in Figure 7.

The current mine near Wyodak is the site of an old "Peerless" mine that was active in 1925. According to Dobbin and Barnett (1928, p. 59) the maximum observed thickness of "bed D (100 ft) or the Roland" occurs at the Peerless mine. Thom (1928, p. 59) indicated that the coal occurrence at the Peerless mine is a deposit of combined coal, describing it as a 16- to 20-m- (52- to 66-ft-) thick "upper bench of coal (Roland bed)" separated by a 20-cm- (8-in-) thick clay parting from a 12-m- (38-ft-) thick lower bench of coal "believed to correspond to the Smith coal bed." Thom observed that the lower bench "diverges from the Roland bed both eastward and westward" (1928, p. 57).

Olive (1957) mapped an Anderson coal bed 61 m (200 ft) below a Smith bed in the Wildcat area north of Gillette (Fig. 1); the Anderson was correlated with bed D or the Roland of Dobbin and Barnett (1928); and Olive (1957, p. 13) thought that Tongue River rocks above bed D (or the Anderson) "probably have been removed by pre-Wasatch erosion in the Gillette coal field."

East-west lines of sections in the Wildcat-Gillette area (Fig. 1) indicate that five individual coal beds merge eastward to form the Wyodak deposit of combined coal and Tongue River rocks above the Wyodak have been removed by pre-Wasatch erosion. The Wyodak deposit of combined coal, 97 km (60 mi) long, 9.7 to 16 km (6 to 10 mi) wide and 30.5 m (100 ft) thick (Fig. 1), is continuous along a strike line from Gillette to a point 13 km (8 mi) south of Reno Junction (Fig. 1, line D–D'). The east-west segment of line D–D' (Fig. 1) connects the Wyodak west to the Big George deposit.

Big George Coal Deposit

The Big George coal deposit was "discovered" in 1981,

when a gamma ray log of a 1974 oil and gas test hole indicated the presence of a single bed of coal 55 m (182 ft) thick and 335 m (1,100 ft) below the level of the Powder River (Fig. 4). However, the existence of the deposit has been known for some time because nearly all of the several hundred test holes drilled since 1974 have a gamma ray log of the interval that might contain it.

In 1983, U.S. Geological Survey (USGS) coal exploratory drilling 1.6 km (1 mi) west of the discovery well (Fig. 4) confirmed a single bed of subbituminous coal 61 m (200 ft) thick. Natural gamma ray and density logs of the cored coal are shown in Figure 5; analytical data on the cores taken are presented in Table 1.

The Big George deposit of combined coal underlies an elongate north-south area of 2,460 km^2 (950 mi^2) (Fig. 2). Lines A–A', B–B', and C–C' (Fig. 2) indicate how individual coal beds merge to form the deposit. Pierce and others (1982) made a geostatistical analysis of the deposit, using computer Kriging techniques to generate structure contour and thickness maps and to estimate that the deposit contains 113 billion tons of coal. The structure contour map of the base of the deposit (Fig. 6a) indicates that it is tilted north and west; the thickness map (Fig. 6b) indicates that the two depocenters of thickest coal are on the eastern flank of the structure.

Felix Coal Deposit

As a coal bed, the Felix is virtually a landmark on the eastern flank of the Powder River Basin where parts of it have been mapped and studied for the past 75 years. The outcrop trace of the Felix (Fig. 7) indicates the general structure of the basin. The trace is at lowest elevation, 1,158 m (3,800 ft) above sea level, near the Powder River. It rises to 1,524 m (5,000 ft) near

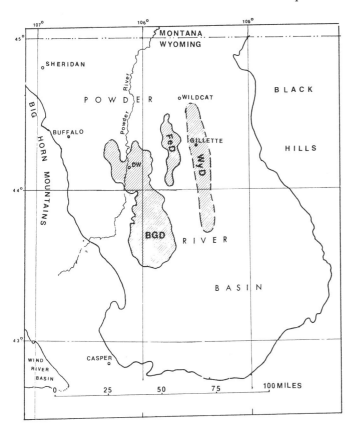

Figure 4. Index map of the Wyoming part of the Powder River Basin, showing the size, shape, and location of the Wyodak (WyD), Big George (BGD), and Felix (FeD) deposits of combined coal. The "discovery" well (DW) for the Big George deposit is shown in Figure 2.

Reno Junction, and the 122-m (400-ft) rise of the Felix from Gillette south to Reno Junction is in marked contrast to that of the Wyodak along the same trend (Fig. 1, line D–D′). The outcrop trace encompasses a 6,475 km² (2,500 mi²) area (Fig. 7).

Data on subsurface Felix coal were obtained from 300 logged drill holes distributed throughout the 6,475 km² (2,500 mi²) area encompassed by the outcrop trace (Fig. 7). In the subsurface, parts of the Felix coal bed merge and split, and various combinations merge locally to form thick deposits of combined coal (Fig. 3); a diagrammatic east-west profile (Fig. 8a) illustrates the areal pattern of Felix coal occurrence.

The subareas shown on Figures 3 and 8 had been used to separate Felix coal occurrences into resource units for area resource assessment at regional (1:100,000) scale. Assessments are made on a "resource unit" basis; resource units are established according to guidelines as follows. Closely associated coal beds are combined (as one resource unit) where partings between them are thinner than the coals, and parts of an individual coal bed are assessed separately (as separate resource units) where rock units are thicker than the coal. To facilitate assessment, the guidelines had been used in constructing a combined resource

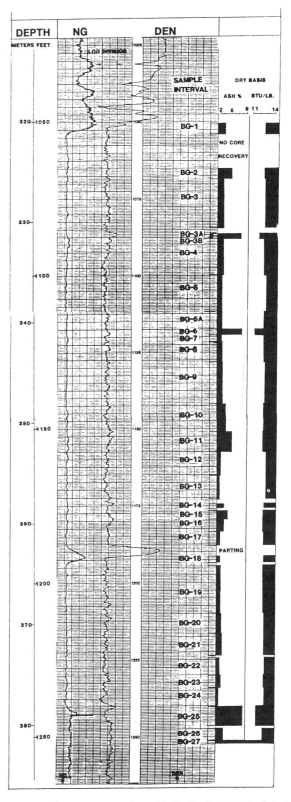

Figure 5. Natural gamma ray (NG) and bulk density (DEN) of the Big George bed of subbituminous coal penetrated by a 1983 U.S. Geological Survey coal exploratory hole drilled 1 mi west of the "discovery" well location shown on Figure 4 of this report. The sample intervals (BG-1 through BG-27) are keyed to analytical data presented in Table 1.

TABLE 1. ANALYTICAL DATA FROM 27 CORE SAMPLES OF THE BIG GEORGE DEPOSIT OF COMBINED COAL IN A 1983 USGS COAL EXPLORATORY HOLE DRILLED IN T. 48N., R. 77W., POWDER RIVER BASIN, NORTHEASTERN WYOMING

Sample No.	Depth (ft)	Thickness (ft)	Form of analysis	Moisture	Ash	Volatile matter	Fixed carbon	Btu/lb	Hydrogen	Carbon	Nitrogen	Oxygen	Sulfur	Forms of sulfur			Ash-fusion temperature (°F)		
														Sulfate	Sulfide	Organic	Initial deformation	Softening	Fluid
BG-1	1051.00-1054.35	3.35	1	21.15	2.59	34.92	41.34	10041	6.30	58.29	0.85	31.75	0.22	0.02	0.01	0.19	2120	2130	2240
			2		3.29	44.29	52.42	12734	4.99	73.92	1.08	16.44	.28	.02	.01	.25			
			3			45.79	54.21	13167	5.16	76.43	1.12	17.00	.29	.02	.01	.26			
BG-2	1065.85-1068.85	3.00	1	25.41	3.88	31.86	38.85	9399	6.54	54.40	.72	34.30	.16	.01	.01	.14	2100	2220	2310
			2		5.21	42.71	52.08	12601	4.96	72.93	.96	15.72	.22	.01	.01	.20			
			3			45.06	54.94	13293	5.23	76.94	1.01	16.59	.23	.01	.01	.21			
BG-3	1068.85-1085.85	17.00	1	22.48	2.38	32.39	42.75	9889	6.28	57.79	.71	32.70	.14	.01	.00	.13	2130	2240	2290
			2		3.07	41.78	55.15	12757	4.86	74.55	.91	16.43	.18	.01	.00	.17			
			3			43.10	56.90	13161	5.01	76.91	.94	16.95	.19	.01	.00	.18*			
BG-3A	1086.55-1087.15	.60	1	21.78	5.98	31.51	40.73	9420	6.18	54.43	.82	31.43	1.16	.04	.35	.77	2260	2340	2370
			2		7.65	40.28	52.07	12043	4.78	69.59	1.05	15.45	1.48	.05	.45	.98			
			3			43.62	56.38	13040	5.18	75.35	1.14	16.73	1.60	.05	.49	1.06			
BG-3B	1087.30-1087.55	.55	1	21.09	6.01	29.93	42.97	9412	6.07	55.13	.67	30.64	1.48	.07	.83	.58	2270	2340	2370
			2		7.62	37.92	54.46	11928	4.71	69.86	.84	15.09	1.88	.08	1.05	.75			
			3			41.05	58.95	12912	5.10	75.62	.91	16.33	2.04	.09	1.14	.81			
BG-4	1087.85-1099.85	12.00	1	23.81	2.36	31.87	41.96	9691	6.31	56.32	.66	34.09	.26	.02	.02	.22	2130	2210	2280
			2		3.09	41.83	55.08	12719	4.79	73.92	.86	17.00	.34	.03	.03	.29			
			3			43.16	56.84	13125	4.94	76.28	.89	17.54	.35	.02	.03	.30			
BG-5	1099.85-1111.65	11.80	1	22.01	2.03	34.27	41.69	10127	6.39	58.47	.70	32.26	.15	.01	.00	.14	2050	2180	2230
			2		2.60	43.94	53.46	12985	5.03	74.97	.89	16.32	.19	.01	.00	.18			
			3			45.11	54.89	13331	5.16	79.97	.91	16.76	.20	.01	.00	.19			
BG-5A	1111.65-1117.65	6.00	1	24.65	1.99	30.37	42.99	9583	6.38	56.42	.59	34.50	.12	.00	.00	.12	2210	2350	2390
			2		2.64	40.31	57.05	12718	4.81	74.87	.78	16.74	.16	.00	.00	.16			
			3			41.40	58.60	13063	4.94	76.90	.80	17.20	.16	.00	.00	.16			
BG-6	1117.65-1119.65	2.00	1	25.32	5.90	28.77	40.01	8637	5.91	51.96	.52	35.59	.12	.00	.01	.11	2240	2280	2330
			2		7.91	38.52	53.57	11565	4.12	69.57	.69	17.55	.16	.01	.01	.14			
			3			41.83	58.17	12558	4.47	75.54	.75	19.07	.17	.01	.01	.15			
BG-7	1119.65-1121.65	2.00	1	26.84	1.86	28.24	43.06	9332	6.38	55.28	.61	35.71	.16	.00	.00	.16	2200	2320	2400
			2		2.54	38.61	58.85	12756	4.62	75.56	.83	16.23	.22	.01	.00	.21			
			3			39.62	60.38	13088	4.74	77.53	.85	16.65	.23	.01	.00	.22			
BG-8	1121.65-1127.65	6.00	1	25.20	2.03	28.36	44.41	9536	6.23	56.66	.64	34.33	.11	.01	.01	.09	2140	2280	2310
			2		2.72	37.92	59.36	12749	4.56	75.75	.85	15.97	.15	.01	.01	.13			
			3			38.98	61.02	13105	4.69	77.86	.87	16.43	.15	.01	.01	.13			
BG-9	1127.65-1141.65	14.00	1	23.75	2.03	28.24	45.98	9777	6.11	57.62	.67	33.48	.09	.02	.01	.06	2130	2250	2290
			2		2.66	37.04	60.30	12822	4.53	75.57	.87	16.26	.11	.03	.01	.07			
			3			38.05	61.95	13172	4.65	77.63	.89	16.72	.11	.03	.01	.07			
BG-10	1141.65-1150.65	9.00	1	25.40	2.83	27.44	44.33	9426	6.19	55.78	.69	34.44	.07	.01	.00	.06	2040	2120	2180
			2		3.79	36.78	59.43	12636	4.48	74.78	.92	15.94	.09	.01	.00	.08			
			3			38.23	61.77	13133	4.66	77.72	.96	16.57	.09	.01	.00	.08			
BG-11	1150.65-1157.65	7.00	1	21.95	4.17	30.42	43.46	9780	6.01	57.70	.83	31.18	.11	.01	.01	.09	2050	2200	2250
			2		5.35	38.97	55.68	12531	4.55	73.93	1.06	14.97	.14	.01	.01	.12			
			3			41.17	58.83	13239	4.81	78.11	1.12	15.81	.15	.01	.01	.13			
BG-12	1157.65-1165.65	8.00	1	22.00	1.80	32.92	43.28	10174	6.43	58.80	.89	31.96	.12	.02	.00	.10	2090	2200	2240
			2		2.30	45.20	55.50	13043	5.09	75.38	1.14	15.93	.16	.03	.00	.13			
			3			43.19	56.81	13350	5.21	77.16	1.17	16.30	.16	.03	.00	.13			
BG-13	1165.65-1173.65	8.00	1	22.86	1.69	32.30	43.15	10071	6.47	58.31	.86	32.55	.12	.01	.00	.11	2110	2240	2270
			2		2.19	41.87	55.94	13056	5.07	75.59	1.12	15.87	.16	.01	.00	.15			
			3			42.81	57.19	13348	5.18	77.28	1.15	16.23	.16	.01	.00	.15			

TABLE 1. (CONTINUED)

Sample No.	Depth (ft)	Thickness (ft)	Form of analysis	Moisture	Ash	Volatile matter	Fixed Carbon	Btu/lb	Hydrogen	Carbon	Nitrogen	Oxygen	Sulfur	Forms of sulfur			Ash-fusion temperature (°F)		
														Sulfate	Sulfide	Organic	Initial deformation	Softening	Fluid
BG-14	1173.85-1175.45	1.60	1	21.44	2.56	30.57	45.43	10089	6.27	58.91	.92	31.26	.08	.02	.00	.06	2060	2170	2220
			2		3.26	38.92	57.82	12843	4.93	74.98	1.17	15.55	.11	.03	.00	.08			
			3			40.23	59.77	13276	5.10	77.51	1.21	16.07	.11	.03	.00	.08			
BG-15	1176.40-1179.65	3.25	1	21.32	3.36	31.78	43.54	10068	6.08	58.74	.95	30.79	.08	.01	.00	.07	2130	2230	2280
			2		4.27	40.39	55.34	12796	4.69	74.65	1.20	15.08	.11	.01	.00	.10			
			3			42.19	57.81	13366	4.90	77.98	1.25	15.76	.11	.01	.00	.10			
BG-16	1179.65-1183.65	4.00	1	23.17	2.62	31.29	42.92	9829	6.31	57.69	.82	32.45	.11	.02	.00	.09	2120	2160	2210
			2		3.41	40.73	55.86	12793	4.84	75.08	1.07	15.46	.14	.02	.00	.12			
			3			42.17	57.83	13245	5.01	77.73	1.11	16.01	.14	.02	.00	.12			
BG-17	1183.65-1188.45	4.80	1	24.47	1.84	28.19	45.50	9693	6.18	57.43	.87	33.58	.10	.02	.01	.08	2090	2150	2170
			2		2.44	37.32	60.24	12833	4.55	76.04	1.15	15.69	.13	.03	.01	.09			
			3			38.25	61.75	13154	4.66	77.94	1.18	16.09	.13	.03	.01	.09			
BG-18	1191.85-1193.45	1.60	1	21.26	1.82	29.64	47.28	10088	6.02	59.29	.90	31.83	.14	.01	.00	.13	2090	2150	2180
			2		2.32	37.64	60.04	12812	4.63	75.30	1.14	16.44	.17	.03	.00	.16			
			3			38.53	61.47	13116	4.74	77.08	1.17	16.84	.17	.01	.00	.16			
BG-19	1194.25-1210.25	16.00	1	23.36	1.90	28.13	46.61	9821	6.08	57.75	.88	33.27	.12	.01	.00	.10	2140	2180	2220
			2		2.47	36.71	60.82	12815	4.52	75.35	1.15	16.35	.16	.01	.00	.14			
			3			37.64	62.36	13140	4.63	77.26	1.18	16.77	.16	.01	.00	.14			
BG-20	1210.25-1216.25	6.00	1	21.18	2.06	31.14	45.62	10232	6.04	59.73	.99	31.07	.11	.02	.00	.09	2090	2140	2170
			2		2.62	39.51	57.87	12982	4.66	75.78	1.26	15.54	.14	.02	.00	.12			
			3			40.57	59.43	13331	4.79	77.82	1.29	15.96	.14	.02	.00	.12			
BG-21	1216.25-1224.25	8.00	1	21.32	2.51	29.56	46.61	10195	6.10	59.12	1.00	31.15	.12	.01	.00	.11	2100	2170	2240
			2		3.19	37.57	59.24	12958	4.72	75.14	1.27	15.53	.15	.02	.01	.12			
			3			38.81	61.19	13385	4.88	77.62	1.31	16.04	.15	.02	.01	.12			
BG-22	1224.25-1230.25	6.00	1	22.85	1.78	31.10	44.27	10118	6.34	58.55	.96	32.26	.11	.01	.00	.10	2150	2210	2240
			2		2.31	40.31	57.38	13115	4.90	75.89	1.24	15.52	.14	.02	.01	.12			
			3			41.26	58.74	13425	5.02	77.68	1.27	15.89	.14	.01	.01	.12			
BG-23	1230.25-1234.25	4.00	1	21.93	2.03	29.46	46.58	10145	6.19	59.13	1.01	31.56	.08	.00	.00	.08	2060	2160	2230
			2		2.60	37.74	59.66	12995	4.78	75.74	1.29	15.48	.11	.00	.00	.11			
			3			38.75	61.25	13342	4.91	77.76	1.32	15.90	.11	.00	.00	.11			
BG-24	1234.25-1240.25	6.00	1	21.79	1.56	31.77	44.88	10215	6.30	59.59	1.03	31.38	.14	.00	.00	.14	2000	2080	2140
			2		2.00	40.62	57.38	13061	4.94	76.20	1.32	15.37	.17	.00	.00	.17			
			3			41.45	58.55	13328	5.04	77.75	1.35	15.69	.17	.00	.00	.17			
BG-25	1240.25-1246.60	6.35	1	20.77	6.98	29.47	42.78	9550	5.70	56.12	.93	30.05	.22	.00	.00	.22	2350	2440	2470
			2		8.81	37.19	54.00	12053	4.26	70.83	1.18	14.65	.27	.00	.00	.27			
			3			40.78	59.22	13217	4.67	77.67	1.29	16.07	.30	.00	.00	.30			
BG-26	1247.45-1252.25	4.80	1	20.21	2.79	31.81	45.19	10300	6.16	59.19	1.09	30.55	.22	.01	.00	.21	1990	2230	2360
			2		3.49	39.86	56.65	12908	4.89	74.18	1.37	15.79	.28	.01	.01	.26			
			3			41.30	58.70	13375	5.07	76.86	1.42	16.36	.29	.01	.01	.27			
BG-27	1252.25-1252.85	.60	1	17.20	22.22	28.64	31.94	7883	5.40	44.82	.83	25.36	1.37	.03	.55	.79	2680	2790	2800
			2		26.84	34.59	38.57	9521	4.20	54.13	1.00	12.17	1.66	.04	.66	.96			
			3			47.28	52.72	13013	5.74	73.99	1.37	16.63	2.27	.05	.90	1.32			

Note: All analyses except Btu/lb and ash-fusion temperatures in percent.

Forms of analysis: 1. as received; 2. moisture free; 3. moisture and ash free.

All analyses by Geochemical Testing, Somerset, Pa.

N.D. indicates no data.

Free-swelling index determinations were made on all samples; all were 0.0.

Metric conversion factors:
  1 ft = 0.305 m
  degrees Centigrade =
    (degrees Farenheit x 0.555)-32
  Kcal/Kg = (Btu/lb)x 0.5556

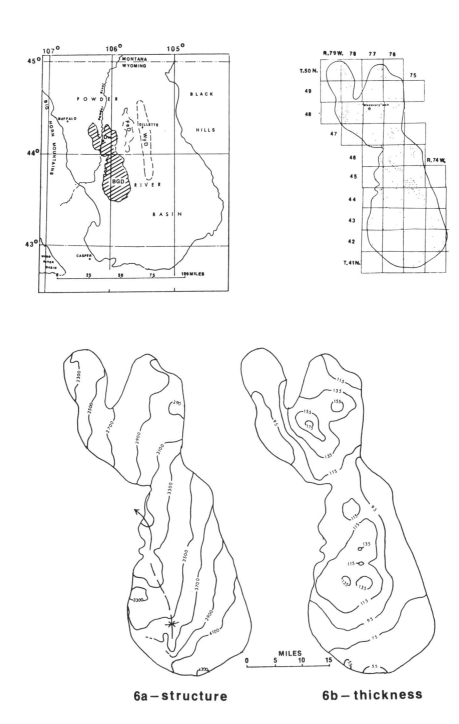

6a—structure   **6b—thickness**

Figure 6. a) Structure contour and b) thickness maps of the Big George (BGD) coal deposit, Powder River Basin, northeastern Wyoming. Structure contours, in feet above sea level, drawn on the base of the deposit; contour interval, 200 ft. Thickness in feet; contour interval, 20 ft. Townships covering the Big George deposit are indicated in Figure 7. Structure contour and thickness maps modified from Pierce and others (1982).

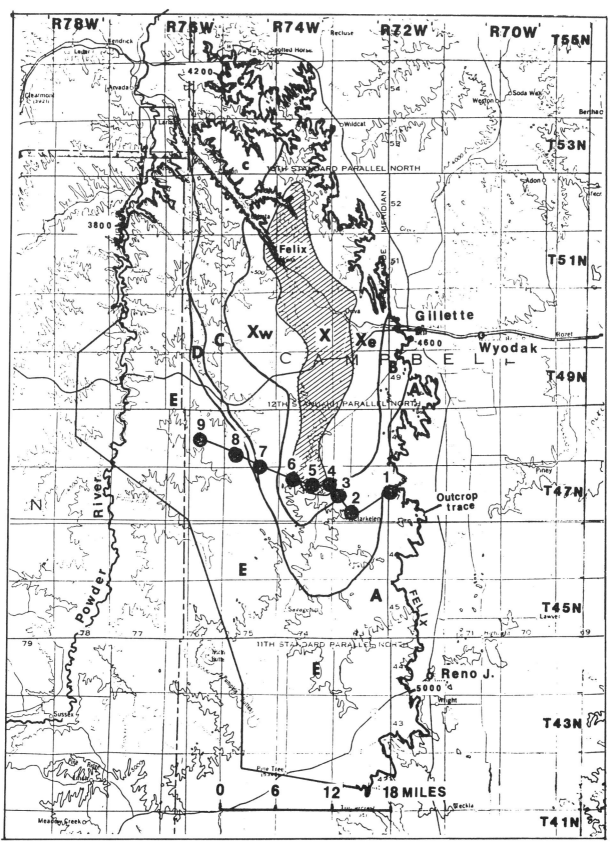

Figure 7. Index map of part of the eastern flank of the Powder River Basin, showing the outcrop trace of the Felix coal bed, subareas of Felix coal occurrence in the subsurface, and the east-west line of sections (1–9) illustrated in Figure 3 of this report. The subareas (A, B, Xe, X, Xw, D and E) are also shown in Figure 3; subarea X is the Felix deposit of combined coal that is outlined in Figure 4.

unit of Felix coal including all or part of every subarea of Felix coal occurrence. A diagrammatic east-west profile of the combined resource unit of Felix coal (Fig. 8b) emphasizes the transitional nature of Felix coal deposition. (The combined resource unit contains 33 billion tons of subbituminous coal.)

Figure 7 includes a subarea map of the combined resource unit of Felix coal occurrence. Subarea X forms an elongate north-south, central core of the resource unit (Fig. 7). East of the central core the lower bench of coal is thicker than the upper bench, whereas west of the central core the upper bench is thicker than the lower (Figs. 3 and 8).

Subarea X (containing 5 billion tons of coal) is the Felix deposit of combined coal outlined on Figure 4. The Wyodak (55 billion tons) and Big George (113 billion tons) deposits of combined coal are also elongate north-south cores of larger resource units (Figs. 1 and 2). It seems apparent that the mechanics of thick coal deposition were influenced in some consistent evolutionary way.

MECHANICS OF THICK COAL DEPOSITION

Coal originates from accumulation and partial decomposition of organic materials in a subaqueous environment, controlled and restricted by water levels, water depths, and subsidence. The thickness a peat bed attains is determined by (a) a settling coefficient, (b) the degree of balance maintained between incremental subsidence and incremental peat accumulation, and (c) the length of time those processes were operative before some event upsets either the depositional environment or the balance.

Accumulation involves settling: as organic materials settle and decompose, the lower parts of the developing peat bed become more dense and compacted than upper parts. The scope of that peat-forming process has been expressed by a 5 to 1 "settling coefficient" (Stutzer and Noe, 1940, p. 175–178; Raistrick and Marshall, 1939, p. 53–54). The coefficient implies, for example, that a cumulative thickness of 15 m (50 ft) of water-saturated organic materials settled, accumulated, decomposed, and compacted to form a peat bed 3 m (10 ft) thick; however, the coefficient would be influenced by the nature of the organic materials involved.

The incremental, upward-building process of accumulating organic materials to form peat beds generally takes place below water level; such systems may not be more than 3 m (10 ft) thick at any given time. Thus, depositional environments might accommodate accumulations of peat beds 3 m (10 ft) thick or so in a static way, but accumulation must be balanced by subsidence for much thicker peat to form. However, peat accumulation could continue indefinitely for as long as that balance is maintained and the cumulative amount of incremental balancing subsidence involved should be about the same as the thickness of the peat bed at the time of burial.

A peat bed continues to compact from the time of burial to some present stage of coalification. The scope of the compactional process can be expressed by a "compaction coefficient"

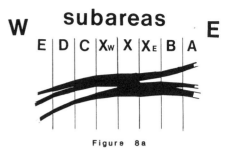

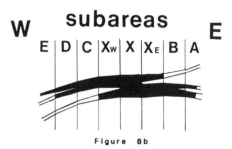

Figure 8. Diagrammatic east-west profiles showing areal variations of Felix coal occurrence in the subsurface: a) subareas of Felix coal occurrence and b) profile of a combined resource unit of Felix coal that includes all or part of every subarea of Felix coal occurrence, as indicated by the shaded areas.

based on water loss; for example, the bed moisture content of peat has been estimated as 75% and that of "subbituminous B" coal 25% (Teichmuller and Teichmuller, 1978, p. 169), expressing a compaction coefficient of 3 to 1. The ratio varies inversely with the specific moisture content of the coal involved. Compaction ratios are not appreciably affected by a 75–90% range of peat moisture content, but they vary dramatically with the moisture content of coal; for example, if the moisture content of the peat was 75% and a bituminous coal has a moisture content of 5%, the compaction coefficient is 15 to 1.

A compaction coefficient of 3 to 1 is a specific expression of the thickness change of a peat bed to a correlative bed of subbituminous coal; the coefficient relates coal thickness back to peat thickness at the time of burial, and the cumulative amount of subsidence involved (or required) during peat accumulation should be about equal to peat thickness attained to that time. The Big George deposit of subbitumous coal has an average moisture content of 25% (Table 1), where it is 61 m (200 ft) thick (Fig. 5). If the moisture content of the peat was 75%, the compaction coefficient (3 to 1) indicates that the Big George peat bed was as much as 183 m (600 ft) thick at the time of burial. The Wyodak and Felix are also subbituminous coals; the 3 to 1 coefficient indicates a peat bed 91 m (300 ft) thick compacted to form 30.5-m- (100-ft-) thick Wyodak coal and a 27-m- (90-ft-) thick peat bed formed 9-m- (30-ft-) thick Felix coal. Cumulative amounts of subsidence involved during Big George, Wyodak and

Felix coal deposition would be 183, 91, and 27 m (600, 300, and 90 ft), respectively.

Subsidence and flooding may kill forest and vegetation, thereby activating the peat-forming process. New growth on that organic debris may be killed in the same way, and an episode of pronounced subsidence may cause sediments to be deposited over those peat beds. Uplift of source area may cause an influx of clastics over a subsiding coal swamp, thereby arresting peat accumulation and burying the peat beds, and continuing subsidence would increase depths of burial. A new cycle of peat accumulation may develop on those clastics causing the development of vertical sequences of coal and clastics.

The Powder River Basin was subsiding before, during, and after thick coal deposition on the eastern flank, and rates of subsidence probably increased progressively westward toward the basin axis where drainage base levels developed; conversely, rates of uplift probably increased eastward toward uplifted (Black Hills) source areas (Fig. 4). Swamp development and coal deposition across west-tilted paleoslopes may have been limited westward by flooding and eastward by high ground; but eastern uplift would have caused those systems to shift westward and western subsidence would have shifted them east. Several eastern and western migrations could be involved during a prolonged period of thick coal deposition.

Although the migratory response of coal deposition to subsidence and uplift is reminiscent of strandline response to transgression and regression, coal is not a clastic material and is rarely reworked and redeposited as such; rather, coal is formed in situ from buried peat at some later time. The migration was by environments favorable to peat accumulation, either to maintain or to re-establish optimum conditions.

LARAMIDE STRUCTURAL MOVEMENTS

Figure 9 shows the geologic setting of the Wyodak, Big George, and Felix coal deposits. The Powder River Basin and surrounding uplifts (Fig. 9) are products of the Laramide Orogeny, and Laramide tectonics and associated sedimentation formed and filled the basin during latest Cretaceous and early Tertiary time. However, the matter of Laramide structural movements controlling thick coal deposition on the eastern flank of the basin during Paleocene and Eocene time depends on a critical issue: what was the nature of Black Hills uplifts and when did they occur?

Evolution of the Powder River Basin

During much of Late Cretaceous time an epicontinental sea covered most of interior North America and an offshore deposit of marine shale (Pierre Shale) on the western margin of the seaway covered the area shown in Figure 9. West of the area, however, regressive strandline deposits prograded eastward, to intertongue with the Pierre.

The Bearpaw Shale of Montana is equivalent to the upper part of the Pierre. According to Gill and Cobban (1976, p. 21), during a "Bearpaw transgression":

> While the sea advanced into western Montana, it retreated across eastern Wyoming, clearly showing the importance of local crustal instability in effecting transgression or regression. Stratigraphic data show that while Montana was subsiding, central Wyoming was being uplifted and eroded (Gill and Cobban, 1966; Reynolds, 1966; Zapp and Cobban, 1962).

The Fox Hills Sandstone forms the clastic floor of the Powder River Basin (Fig. 9). Gill and Cobban (1976, p. 36) suggested that during a "Fox Hills regression" strands of marine sandstone moved rapidly eastward across northern Wyoming to form extensive lobes that spread laterally into the retreating sea in which subsidence was less than sedimentation. A culminating lobe of Fox Hills Sandstone covered southeastern Montana where it is represented by the light-gray, cliff-forming Colgate Sandstone Member.

The Lance Formation of Wyoming overlies the Fox Hills Sandstone. The Lance is comprised of nonmarine sandstone, sandy shale, and claystone; it is equivalent to the nonmarine Hell Creek Formation of Montana (Fig. 9). Robinson and others (1964) reported that the Lance Formation, 488 m (1,600 ft) thick in east-central Wyoming, thins northward to 152 m (500 ft) near the Wyoming-Montana border. In Wyoming the contact between the Lance and the Fox Hills Sandstone is gradational from nonmarine to marine rocks; in Montana the contact is placed at the top of the distinctive Colgate Sandstone Member of the Fox Hills Sandstone.

The overlying Fort Union Formation, of Paleocene age, comprises nonmarine sandstone, sandy or silty shale, carbonaceous shale, and coal. The formation has been divided into lower, middle, and upper units that are the Tullock, Lebo Shale, and Tongue River Members, respectively. The Tullock Member, 305 m (1,000 ft) thick east of Gillette (Fig. 9), thins northward to 152 m (500 ft) near the Wyoming-Montana border (Robinson and others, 1964, p. 99). The Lebo Shale Member is 91 m (300 ft) thick in exposures along the east margin of the basin; it thickens westward in the subsurface. The Tongue River Member (Fig. 9) contains the Wyodak and Big George coal deposits; the member is 244 m (800 ft) thick in the Gillette area and 366 to 396 m (1,200 to 1,300 ft) thick in the Wildcat area (Fig. 5) of the Spotted Horse coal field (Olive, 1957).

The Wasatch Formation overlies the Fort Union Formation. Wasatch rocks are of Eocene age; they contain the Felix coal deposit (Fig. 9).

According to Curry (1971) the first evidence of Laramide deformation in the basin is marked by deposition of nonmarine (Tullock) rocks, and prominent subsidence along the axis of the basin did not begin until sediments of the Lebo were deposited. Curry (1971) thought basin subsidence (rather than uplift of adjacent mountains) was the first stage of structural deformation, because the Lebo Shale Member thickens westward toward the basin axis where thickest sections have the lowest sandstone con-

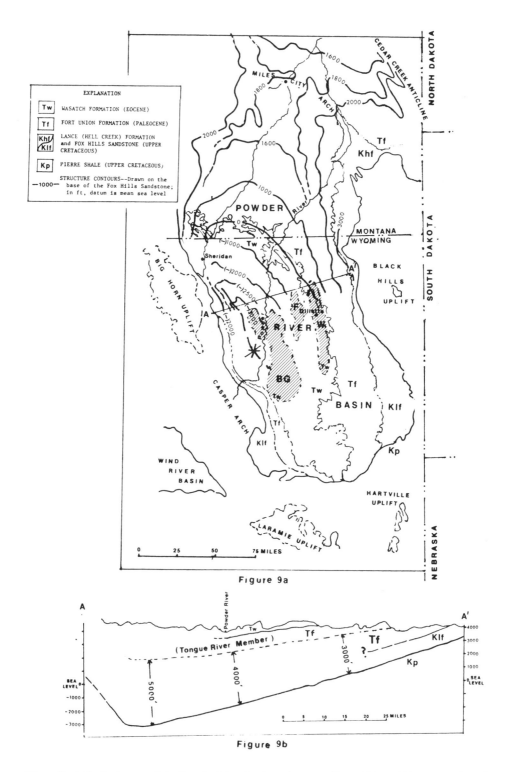

Figure 9. a) Geologic map of the Powder River Basin and surrounding uplifts and b) cross section of basin structure and clastic fill, showing the geologic settings of the Wyodak (W) and Big George (BG) coal deposits in the Tongue River Member of the Fort Union Formation (Paleocene age), and the Felix (F) coal deposit in the Wasatch Formation (Eocene age). The deposits are also outlined on Figure 4 of this report.

tent; a unit of combined Tongue River and Wasatch rocks also thickens westward, and sandstone content is least in the area of greatest subsidence. According to Curry (1971, p. 60), strong subsidence continued along the axis of the basin through late Paleocene time, influx of sandstone was the first evidence of adjacent mountains being uplifted and eroded, and uplift continued through Eocene time when the mountains were eroded to their Precambrian cores.

Black Hills Uplifts

According to McGrew (1971), both the Bighorn and Black Hills uplifts (Fig. 9) were in evidence by the beginning of Tertiary time, following deposition of nonmarine (Lance) rocks in the Powder River Basin. Shapiro (1971) thought that the Black Hills uplift was completed during late Paleocene and early Eocene time. Robinson and others (1964, p. 116) reported that "the major structural deformation and uplift of the Black Hills began in early Tertiary time—or possibly latest Cretaceous time—and ended before deposition of the Oligocene White River Formation." The igneous plugs and domes in the northern part of the Black Hills, intruded at a time of uplift before deposition of White River rocks, provide supporting evidence that dominantly vertical forces formed the main structural features of the Black Hills (Robinson and others, 1964, p. 116).

Late Paleocene and Eocene History

The base map for the Felix coal deposit (Fig. 7) locates some features of late Paleocene and Eocene history, which Olive (1957, p. 13–14) described as follows:

> Eastward and southeastward of the NW¼sec.12,T.55N.,R.75W., strata of the Tongue River member above the Smith coal bed wedge out and the Wasatch formation overlies the Smith coal bed. East of the Powder River–Little Powder River divide the interval between the Smith coal bed of Tongue River age and the Felix coal bed of Wasatch age is occupied by 160 ft [49 m] of cross-bedded, coarse-grained sandstone. In places to the west the interval between those two beds is occupied by 670 ft [204 m] of interbedded sandstone, shale, and coal—225 ft [69 m] belonging to the Tongue River member and 445 ft [36 m] to the Wasatch Formation (see plate 3). This relationship suggests that the southern part of the mapped area was uplifted slightly at the close of the Paleocene, with a resulting change from deposition to nondeposition or erosion. The sandstone between the Smith and Felix coal beds is assigned to the Wasatch formation and is interpreted as an aeolian deposit that accumulated above the eroded Tongue River member near the eastern margin of a basin in which the Wasatch formation was deposited. While the sandstone was being laid down, shale, sandstone, and coal, indicative of swampy conditions, were accumulating in the west in other parts of the basin during Wasatch time. As the basin filled, swamps encroached eastward and the material of the Felix coal bed accumulated on the sandstone. Owing to this transgression of the basin margin, the Felix bed is about 100 ft [30.5 m] higher stratigraphically near the eastern margin of the basin than in areas to the west.

A schematic profile of Tongue River and Wasatch coal-bearing rocks from the Gillette area northwest to the Powder River (Fig. 10) charts a sequence of events as follows: 1) Tongue River rocks on the east flank of the Powder River Basin were uplifted and tilted westward during late Paleocene time and they were truncated by erosion at the close of the Paleocene; 2) the eroded Paleocene clastic materials and coals were reworked, transported westward, and redeposited as Eocene rocks of the lower part of the Wasatch Formation; 3) uplifts of source area to the east stimulated Eocene influx of clastic materials that spread westward over the erosion surface; and 4) Felix coal was deposited across that sandstone platform. The interval between the Felix and the Smith coal beds is the least where it consists almost entirely of sandstone (Fig. 10); the anomaly of interval increasing northwestward as sandstone content decreases is easily explained by the sequence of events involved. The events were activated by uplift.

Figure 11 shows sections of Eocene (Wasatch) coal-bearing rocks along an east-west line northwest of Gillette. The Felix coal bed is tilted west about ½° (9 m/km [30 ft/mi]), but the west-tilt of strata above the Felix decreases upward and westward, causing coal beds to converge eastward; the interval between the Felix coal bed and the "Truman-Parnell" increases from 67 m (220 ft) at the east end of the line to 119 m (390 ft) at the west end (Fig. 10). Although no specific data are available on sandstone content, the matter of interval increasing westward might be caused by uplift. During episodes of basin filling between times of coal deposition, minor periodic uplifts of eastern source areas would have stimulated tilting, erosion, channeling, and sediment bypass westward, followed by deposition of channel-fill sandstone.

The phenomena of eastward converging coal beds and the seemingly anomalous relation of rock intervals between them increasing westward as sandstone content decreases are directly related to uplift. Events of late Paleocene and Eocene history strongly indicate that Black Hills uplifts occurred periodically throughout late Paleocene and Eocene time.

EVOLUTION OF THICK COAL DEPOSITS

Basin subsidence and (Black Hills) uplifts were active during late Paleocene and Eocene time when thick coal deposits were formed on the east flank of the Powder River Basin; those Laramide structure movements probably interacted to establish and prolong optimum conditions for thick coal deposition. The nature of such active environmental control is described in context with a "teeterboard" hypothesis based on a simple assumption: if a western area is subsiding while an eastern area is uplifted, an intervening fulcrum area is in dynamic equilibrium. Fulcrum areas were pivots for westward (basin) subsidence and eastward (Black Hills) uplifts during early Tertiary time.

Conceivably, effects of subsidence and uplift were minimal during quiescent periods of coal deposition, and linear fulcrum areas developed north-south across west-tilted paleoslopes. Fulcrum areas were most favorable to coal swamp development and the thickest peat accumulated in them. Optimum conditions prevailed just west of the fulcrum where subsidence was in balance

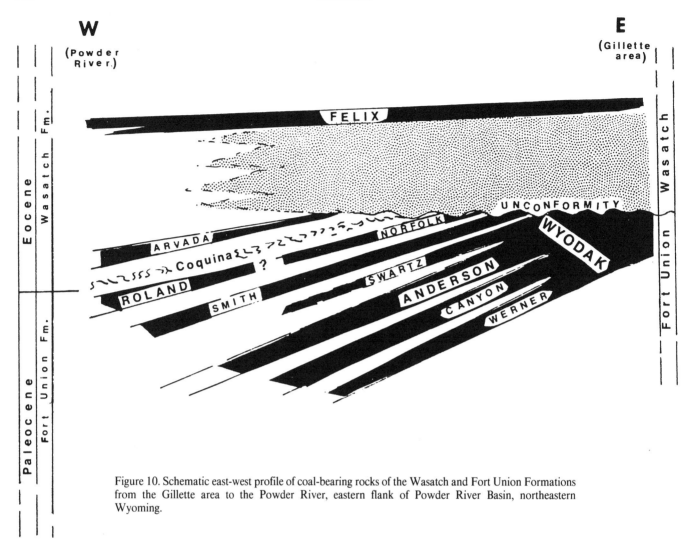

Figure 10. Schematic east-west profile of coal-bearing rocks of the Wasatch and Fort Union Formations from the Gillette area to the Powder River, eastern flank of Powder River Basin, northeastern Wyoming.

with peat accumulation. A succeeding event of pronounced subsidence would cause a fulcrum area to shift eastward; an event of pronounced uplift would cause it to shift westward. Coal deposition would be arrested eastward either by high ground or by clastic influx from uplifted source areas to the east, but the fulcrum area would shift westward ahead of clastic influx to some western point where flooding may arrest further coal deposition. Fulcrum-area migrations may occur several times over a prolonged period of coal deposition until a new episode of basin filling by clastic influx covers those peat beds and buries them; the overall fulcrum-area migration would be westward, as a "build-up" to that climax.

Geometries of the Wyodak and the Felix coal deposits illustrate the "fulcrum area" concept. The Wyodak core in the Gillette area is thought to represent a locus of linear north-south fulcrum areas that were most favorable to coal deposition; any eastward extensions from the Wyodak core in the Gillette area were removed by pre-Wasatch erosion (Fig. 10), but Felix coal "deposits" (Fig. 4) are more complete. Subarea X (Figs. 3 and 4) forms an elongate north-south, central core comprising a single

bed of combined Felix coal; eastward extensions from that central core are characterized by a thick lower bench of coal whereas westward extensions are characterized by a thick upper bench. That areal pattern is accentuated in the east-west profile of the Felix coal deposit as a resource unit (Fig. 8b), and the distribution of thickest coal indicates an overall westward migration of fulcrum areas during the prolonged period of Felix coal deposition.

Evolution of the Big George Deposit

Although the Big George deposit is also an elongate north-south core of combined coal, some aspects of Big George distinguish it from the Felix and the Wyodak deposits. A structure contour map on the base of the Big George deposit (Fig. 7) indicates that the core is tilted to the northwest, but a synclinal structure in the southern half of the core area has a northwest-plunging axis that appears to be a southern segment of the axis of the basin itself (Fig. 9). The thickness map of the deposit (Fig. 7b) shows a northeast-trending area of thickest coal within the northern half of the core, and a northeast-trending area of relatively

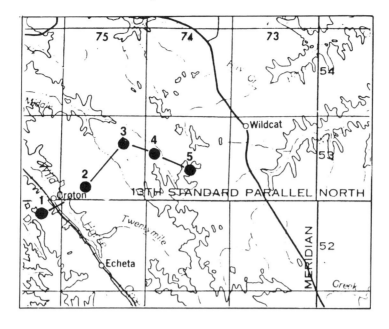

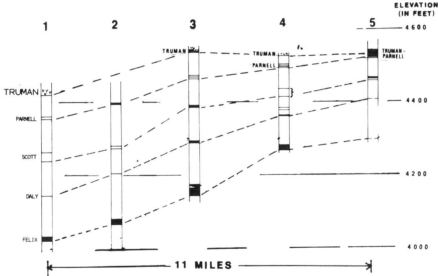

Figure 11. West-east line of sections showing the vertical sequence of coal beds in the lower part of the Wasatch Formation in the Wildcat area northwest of Gillette, Wyoming. Sections 1 and 2 modified from Haddock and others (1976); sections 3, 4, and 5 modified from Kent and others (1977). Coal-bed nomenclature is that of Haddock and others (1976).

thick coal within the southern half. Positions of those thickest coal areas on the east flank of the core structure (Fig. 7) indicate control associated with Black Hills uplifts; however, the overall thickness and structure patterns of the Big George deposit, and its position within the basin, suggest that the Laramie and Hartville uplifts (Fig. 9) also provided control during the prolonged period of coal deposition (Big George) in late Paleocene time.

Phenomena such as 61-m- (200-ft-) thick beds of subbituminous coal, peat beds 183 m (600 ft) thick, and 183 m (600 ft) of subsidence during peat accumulation might be explained by (a)

the establishment of a coal swamp in a topographic depression, (b) achievement of some subsidence by differential compaction of underlying sediments, (c) the presence of high-energy stream transport to raft in large quantities of massive organic material (logs, etc.), thereby adding bulk to peat accumulations, and ultimately (d) the formation of a very thick bed of allochthonous coal. In the Powder River Basin, however, thick coal deposition was concentrated in linear, elongate north-south areas that developed across west-tilted paleoslopes during quiescent periods when rates of (tectonic) subsidence increased progressively westward toward the basin axis; predictably, west-flowing, low-energy stream transport of organic material would bypass those centers of thick coal deposition, and north- or south-flowing components of drainage would be shifted westward away from them.

Thick coals of allochthonous origin would be expected to have high ash content because influx of drift material would be accompanied by a considerable amount of clay and silt that would be mixed with the peat. Big George coal is thick (Fig. 6). But ash content is notably low (less than 7% except at the base, see Table 1). With basal sample 27 excluded, the average content of ash (3.4%) in the 61-m- (200-ft-) thick coal bed indicates an inferred content of 1% ash in the 183-m- (600-ft-) thick peat bed; a content of 1% does not indicate much detrital sediment. My interpretation of the data at hand, then, indicates that Big George coal is of autochthonous origin, from generations of in situ plants and trees periodically killed by flooding and decaying in a subsiding coal swamp. In that respect, the Felix and Wyodak coals should also be autochthonous.

Keefer (1969) charted a Tertiary history of the Wind River Basin (Fig. 9). He concluded that fluvial conditions had been re-established near the close of the Paleocene Epoch, and by earliest Eocene time, streams flowed northeastward into the (Powder River) basin, across the site of the (Casper) arch, which had not yet begun to rise. Surrounding uplifts (Bighorn, Laramie, Hartville, and Black Hills) had been rising since early Paleocene time, and the Powder River Basin is thought to have been intermontane since middle Paleocene time. The basin remained open to the north and northeast, however, and during late Paleocene and Eocene times drainage was to the north across the (Miles City) arch (Fig. 9) that may have been rising during that period. If so, north-flowing drainage would have been locally and periodically ponded along its course through the subsiding basin to the south. Such ponding effects would have added considerable lateral extent to the coal swamps where the Big George deposit was forming. The irregular shape of the Big George core (Fig. 9) may reflect those possibilities.

REFERENCES CITED

Curry, W. H., III, 1971, Laramide structural history of the Powder River basin, Wyoming: Wyoming Geological Association, 23rd Annual Field Conference, Guidebook, Wyoming Tectonics Symposium, p. 46–60.

Dobbin, C. E., and Barnett, V. H., 1928, The Gillette coal field, northeastern Wyoming: U.S. Geological Survey Bulletin 796A, p. 1–50.

Gill, J. R., and Cobban, W. A., 1966, Regional unconformity in Late Cretaceous, Wyoming, in Geological Survey Research 1966: U.S. Geological Survey Professional Paper 550-B, p. B20–B27.

—— , 1976, Stratigraphy and geologic history of the Montana Group and equivalent rocks, Montana, Wyoming, and North and South Dakota: U.S. Geological Survey Professional Paper 776, 37 p.

Haddock, D. R., Kent, B. H., and Bohor, B. F., 1976, Geologic map and coal sections of the Croton quadrangle, Campbell County, Wyoming: U.S. Geological Survey Miscellaneous Field Studies Map MF-826, scale 1:24,000.

Keefer, W. R., 1969, General stratigraphy and depositional history of the Fort Union, Indian Meadows, and Wind River Formations, Wind River Basin, Wyoming: Wyoming Geological Association, 21st Annual Field Conference, Guidebook, Symposium on Tertiary rocks of Wyoming, p. 19–28.

Kent, B. H., Haddock, D. R., and Bohor, B. F., 1977, Geologic map and coal sections of the Truman Draw Quadrangle, Campbell County, Wyoming: U.S. Geological Survey Miscellaneous Field Studies Map MF-917.

Kent, B. H., Berlage, L. J., and Boucher, E. M., 1980, Stratigraphic framework of coal beds underlying the western part of the Recluse 1° × ½° quadrangle, Campbell County, Wyoming: U.S. Geological Survey Coal Investigations Map C-81-C.

McGrew, P. O., 1971, The Tertiary history of Wyoming: Wyoming Geological Association, 23rd Annual Field Conference, Guidebook, Wyoming Tectonics Symposium, p. 29–33.

Olive, W. W., 1957, The Spotted Horse coal field, Sheridan and Campbell Counties, Wyoming: U.S. Geological Survey Bulletin 1050, 83 p.

Pierce, F. W., Kent, B. H., and Grundy, W. D., 1982, Geostatistical analysis of a 113-billion-ton coal deposit, central part of the Powder River Basin, northeastern Wyoming, in Proceedings of the fifth symposium on the geology of Rocky Mountain coal: Utah Geological and Mineral Survey Bulletin 118, p. 262–272.

Raistrick, A., and Marshall, C. E., 1939, The nature and origin of coal and coal seams: London, The English Universities Press Ltd., 282 p.

Reynolds, M. W., 1966, Stratigraphic relations of Upper Cretaceous rocks, Lamont-Bairoil area, south-central Wyoming, in Geological Survey Research 1966: U.S. Geological Survey Professional Paper 550-B, p. B69–B76.

Robinson, C. S., Mapel, W. J., and Bergendahl, M. H., 1964, Stratigraphy and structure of the northern and western flanks of the Black Hills uplift, Wyoming, Montana, and South Dakota: U.S. Geological Survey Professional Paper 404, 134 p.

Shapiro, L. H., 1971, Structural geology of the Fanny Peak lineament, Black Hills, Wyoming-South Dakota: in Wyoming Geological Association, 23rd Annual Field Conference, Guidebook, Wyoming Tectonics Symposium, p. 61–64.

Stutzer, O., and Noe, A. C., 1940, Geology of coal: Chicago, University of Chicago Press, 461 p.

Taff, T. A., 1909, The Sheridan coal field, Wyoming: U.S. Geological Survey Bulletin 341-B, p. 123–150.

Teichmuller, M., and Teichmuller, R., 1978, Coal-diagenesis and metamorphism, in The Encyclopedia of Sedimentology: Stroudsburg, Pennsylvania, Dowden, Hutchinson and Ross, Inc., p. 167–173.

Thom, W. T., Jr., 1928, The Minturn District and the northwestern part of the Gillette field: U.S. Geological Survey Bulletin 796A, p. 50–64.

Zapp, A. D., and Cobban, W. A., 1962, Some Late Cretaceous strand lines in southern Wyoming, in Short papers in geology, hydrology, and topography: U.S. Geological Survey Professional Paper 450-D, p. D52–D55.

Manuscript Accepted by the Society April 16, 1986

Discussion of paper by Kent. Responses by Kent

Alvis L. Lisenbee (South Dakota School of Mines)
Question: Is there a weathering zone beneath the clastic wedge (Laramide) built outward from the Black Hills uplift?
Response: I don't know of any. If there is one, it would not be associated with the Black Hills uplift. The K/T boundary between the Lance and the overlying Fort Union might be represented locally by a weathering zone. Many weathering zones occur at all levels in upper Paleocene (Fort Union) and lower Eocene (Wasatch) rocks along the eastern margin of the Powder River Basin, where they develop on erosion surfaces associated with Black Hills uplift.

Joe Sarnecki (Exxon Coal Resources)
Question: We assume Big George is the Anderson coal bed(?). As such, by your model, do you need 2 "fulcrums" for different stages of the Anderson?
Response: Yes. We probably do need a western "fulcrum" for the Big George depositional stage.

Jim Skehan, S. J. (Boston College)
Question: It appears that there are many similarities between the intermontane Narragansett basin's paleoenvironments and that of the Powder River Basin. If some of our anthracitic coals, 30–40 ft thick, represent approximate true thicknesses (apart from tectonic thickening), what do you estimate as the original thicknesses of the peat deposits?
Response: For lignite and subbituminous and bituminous coals, reasonable estimates of original thicknesses of peat beds can be obtained by applying "compaction coefficients" based on water loss; the coefficients are derived from estimates of the bed moisture content of peat (75–90 percent) and the "as-received" moisture content of a coal sample for analysis.

However, for semianthracites and anthracites, the "compaction coefficient" method would not produce reliable estimates of original peat thicknesses, because the bed moisture content of anthracites is not a factor. A reasonable estimate might be obtained by assuming that, (a) at some stage of coalification prior to regional metamorphism, the 30–40-ft bed of anthracite was a bed of mature bituminous coal containing 2 percent moisture, and (b) applying a coefficient on the order of 40 to 1, the original peat thicknesses probably did not exceed 1600 ft.

Wayne Sigleo (U.S. Geological Survey, Reston, VA)
Question: What was the maximum thickness of peat that formed the Big George coal bed and was the peat allochthonous?
Response: After a peat bed is buried, the process of compaction continues to some present stage of coalification, and the amount of compaction involves can be expressed by a coefficient based on water loss. Teichmuller and Teichmuller (1978, p. 169) provided a way to determine compaction coefficients by estimating that the average bed moisture content of peat is 75 percent. The average bed moisture content of the peat that formed Big George coal probably was within a range of 75–90 percent; the average moisture content of Big George coal is 24.6 percent; and the coefficients (3–3.6 to 1) provide a measure of the thickness-change of a peat bed to the correlative bed of subbituminous coal. Big George is defined as a single bed of subbituminous coal as much as 200 ft thick. According to the applicable compaction coefficients (3–3.6 to 1), Big George peat could have been as much as 720 ft thick. If we prefer to rely on a published peat-to-coal ratio such as 10 to 1 or 15 to 1, we face the problem of explaining how a peat bed 2000 to 3000 ft thick could form. That problem is more than just a challenge to creative geology. The thickness of a peat bed is also a measure of the cumulative amount of subsidence involved (or required) during peat accumulation.

Mechanisms capable of producing 3000 ft of subsidence, during a relatively brief period of coal deposition, should also produce a catastrophic event.

I think that the depositional environment for Big George was an extensive Tertiary coal swamp, where incremental subsidence of the swamp floor was in balance with peat accumulations for a prolonged period of time. So long as a balance with autochthonous peat accumulations and subsidence was maintained, there would be no limit to the thickness of peat that could accumulate, and that process could have involved several generations of in situ plants and forests.

Paul C. Lyons
Question: Could you further comment on your teeter-totter hypothesis on the origin of the extremely thick coal beds such as "Big George" in the Powder River Basin? More specifically, what are the geological structural elements comparable to a teeter-totter?
Response: "Teeterboard" theory is just a simplistic depiction of regional subsidence and uplift interacting to produce relatively stable areas of coal deposition within an otherwise mobile environment. The theory is based on a simple assumption: if a western area is subsiding and an eastern area is uplifted, some (fulcrum) area in between must be in dynamic equilibrium. Although west-tilted strata beneath potential sites for swamp development would seem as the teeterboard, subsidence at one level may not have been accompanied by uplift at the others. Nevertheless, the theory is that linear fulcrum areas that developed north-south across west-tilted slopes were favorable sites for swamp development and coal deposition, and that optimum conditions would prevail in areas just west of the fulcrum, where progressive subsidence could be in balance with peat accumulations. The theory accommodates and utilizes continuing tectonic activity before, during, and after a period of coal deposition, and it proposes that the thick coal deposits evolved as products of that activity.

Jim Fassett
Question: Have you used time datums to correlate coals?
Response: Several Powder River Basin coal beds contain thin layers of altered volcanic ash (tonsteins). Although those time datums have been used as an aid in correlating coal beds that contain them, we have not been able to establish regional coal-bed correlations on that basis alone. Coal deposits tend to cross time units and a coal bed containing a tonstein may correlate with one that does not. A number of different tonsteins are involved and there is no immediate guarantee that two coal beds correlate because they both contain a tonstein. So the first step is to correlate the tonsteins.

Five or six years ago, the USGS did some experimental work on paleomagnetic zonations of upper Paleocene and lower Eocene coal-bearing rocks in the Powder River Basin. That work was instrumental in establishing some regional coal-bed correlations. At the time, we were in the process of tracing Eocene coal beds from east to west across the basin in order to check some regional coal-bed correlations of long standing. The experimental paleomagnetic work indicated that on the west side of the basin, the Eocene coal beds in question were in a zone of different polarity from those on the east side and those on the west side were younger. Subsequently, those Eocene coal beds were traced westward to levels stratigraphically 200 ft below those coal beds on the west side.

Christine M. Budai (Portland State University)
Question: Dr. Chao, of the USGS, presented a paper on the Big George Coal deposit at the 1984 Rocky Mountain Coal Symposium in Bismark,

ND. He proposed that the thickest portion of the Big George Deposit was formed by rafting of organic debris into the basin. What are your thoughts on this idea? Do you agree with it? Why or why not?

Response: The question has to do with whether Big George coal is allochthonous or autochthonous. I think Big George coal is predominantly autochthonous, formed from in situ plants and trees, because the thickest part of the deposit (200 ft) was cored and analyzed and the average ash content (3.6%) is notably low; the ash content of the peat was probably less than one percent. Allochthonous coals, formed from drifted or rafted organic debris, commonly have high ash content, probably because the drift material was associated with large quantities of fine clay or silt brought in by streams.

Presumably, the (Big George) peat bed was as much as 700 ft thick. Although a peat thickness of that magnitude may imply that the peat forming environment was flooded periodically by great quantities of bulky organic debris, it may also indicate that the environment was subsiding while the peat was accumulating. Theoretically, if progressive subsidence is kept in balance with peat accumulation, there would be no limit to the thickness of peat that could form. Progressive subsidence also suggests that in situ plants and forests were killed by flooding, peat formed, and succeeding generations of plants and trees developed and died on that base. As long as subsidence of the peat-forming environment is in balance with peat accumulation, there would be no limit to the thickness.

Geological Society of America
Special Paper 210
1986

Deposition of deltaic and intermontane Cretaceous and Tertiary coal-bearing strata in the Wind River Basin, Wyoming

John F. Windolph, Jr.
Ralph C. Warlow
Nelson L. Hickling
U.S. Geological Survey
National Center
Reston, Virginia 22092

ABSTRACT

Coal-bearing strata of Late Cretaceous age in the western part of the Wind River Basin show transitions in depositional environment from coastal marine deltaic (neritic and paralic) to nonmarine intermontane (limnic). Earliest peat accumulation in the Frontier Formation coincided with several extensive marine regressive cycles. Deposition of terrestrial strata in this deltaic environment ended with encroachment by the sea from the east, which resulted in an extensive period of marine-dominated deposition of the thick Cody Shale.

The overlying Mesaverde Formation was initially deposited as a prograding delta shoreline complex of sand bodies on which coastal swamps were established. Peat accumulation in the Mesaverde was terminated by deposition of the widespread marine transgressive white sandstone member of Troyer and Keefer (1955). During deposition of the overlying Meeteetse Formation, local emergence to the north and subsidence to the east transformed this area into a developing intermontane basin. Extensive airfalls of volcanic ash also accompanied sedimentation throughout Cretaceous and Tertiary time. Many of these events and changes in the environment during these periods are recorded in the coal geochemistry.

Analysis of coal samples from two thick ($\leqslant$305 cm [120 in]) coal beds, the Signor in the Mesaverde Formation and the Welton in the Meeteetse Formation, shows significant differences in trace element content and coal quality, which are interpreted to reflect contrasting paleodepositional environments. Higher iron and sulfur content in the Signor coal bed is attributed to marine and brackish influences on syn- and post-depositional sedimentation. Elevated ash values and silica content in the Welton coal bed resulted from the increased influx of volcaniclastic sediment in a developing intermontane basin undergoing rapid subsidence and structural deformation. The depositional history of coal-bearing rocks in this basin is linked to a series of tectonic events and sedimentary cycles that began during deposition of the Frontier Formation within or west of the Green River Basin. This pattern of sedimentation and deformation continued to evolve in an eastward direction through the present area of the Wind River Basin and culminated in the development of enormous coal deposits in the Powder River Basin.

INTRODUCTION

Stratigraphic investigations of coal-bearing rocks in the Wind River Basin (Fig. 1) record both a gradual and abrupt change in sedimentary environments from a dominantly coastal regime subject to marine influences to a completely restricted or closed basin. Major changes in paleoenvironment occurred between the beginning of Mesaverde Formation and the close of Meeteetse Formation deposition. The evolution of the basin to its present configuration is detailed in later rock sequences and peri-

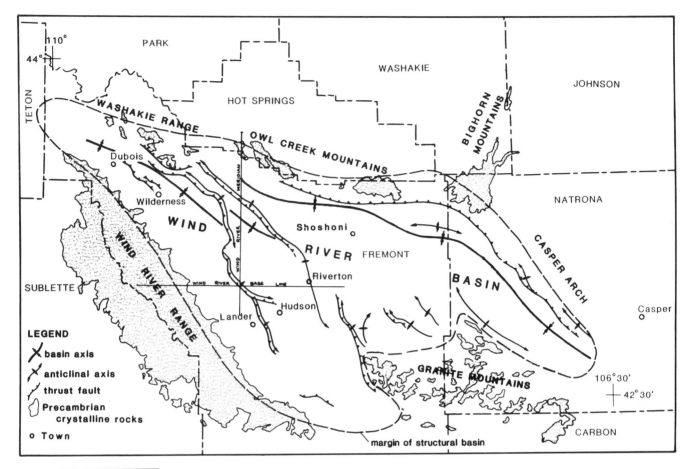

Figure 1. Index map of the Wind River Basin.

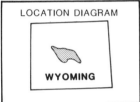

ods of tectonic deformation in Cretaceous, Paleocene, Eocene, and Holocene time, verifying basin restrictions and the limiting of marine influences.

Field investigations were conducted from June 1978 to September 1982, including the measurement and description of more than 12,801 m (42,000 ft) of measured section, geologic mapping of nine and parts of three 7.5-minute quadrangles (Fig. 2), and drilling and logging of 61 stratigraphic and coal exploration holes. Core samples of coal beds were analyzed for trace element content, proximate and ultimate content, heat-value content, free-swelling index, and ash-fusion temperature.

Two coal beds, up to 305 cm (120 in) thick—the Signor in the Mesaverde Formation and the Welton in the Meeteetse Formation—from contrasting paleodepositional environments were compared for significant variations in trace element content and coal quality. The Signor coal bed is interpreted to have

formed in a paralic or prograding coastal and deltaic environment behind a protective marine barrier bar system, whereas the Welton coal bed was formed in a predominantly limnic or freshwater terrestrial environment during the early stages of a developing intermontane basin.

PREVIOUS INVESTIGATIONS

The Wind River Basin was included in the early geologic investigations of the western United States. The earliest investigations are those of Hayden (1869), Comstock (1874), and Eldridge (1894). Knight (1895) prepared a summary of coal fields in Wyoming, and Woodruff (1906) prepared a detailed report on the Lander coal field. A stratigraphic study of the Paleozoic and Mesozoic strata of central Wyoming was made by Darton (1906). Woodruff and Winchester (1912) completed an investigation of the coal resources of Cretaceous and Tertiary strata in the Wind River Basin. Mesozoic and Cenozoic stratigraphy and geology were investigated by Love (1939, 1948, 1970). The coal resources of Wyoming were estimated by Berryhill and others

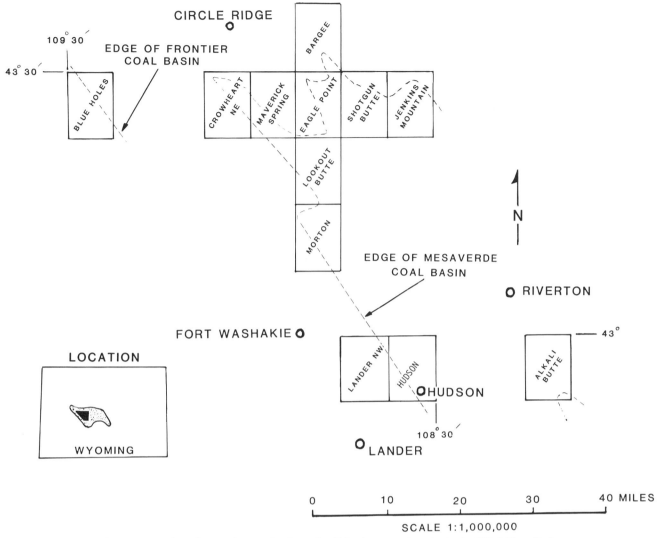

Figure 2. Location of geologic mapping in twelve 7.5 minute quadrangles in the Wind River Basin, Wyoming.

(1950). Thompson and White (1952) described the geology and coal resources of the Alkali Butte, Big Sand Draw, and Beaver Creek coal fields.

Keefer (1961, 1970, 1972) and Keefer and Rich (1957) and Keefer and Troyer (1964) published several detailed geologic reports on the stratigraphy and structure of the Wind River Basin, as well as geologic maps and oil and gas investigations. Seeland and Brauch (1975) compiled a mineral resource investigation for the Bureau of Indian Affairs. A new Wind River Basin coal resource report was prepared by Glass and Roberts (1978), and Windolph, Hickling and Warlow (1982) compiled a coal resource assessment for the Bureau of Indian Affairs.

GEOGRAPHIC AND GEOLOGIC SETTING

The Wind River Basin (Fig. 1) covers approximately 13,677 km² (5,280 mi²) in west-central Wyoming and is largely in Fremont, Natrona, and Hot Springs Counties. Keefer (1970, p. D2) stated "the Wind River Basin in central Wyoming is typical of the large sedimentary and structural basins that formed in the Rocky Mountain region during Laramide deformation."

The Wind River Basin is bounded along the north (from east to west) by the southern Bighorn Mountains, the Owl Creek Mountains, and the Washakie Range; on the southwest by the Wind River Range; on the south by the Granite Mountains (Sweetwater Arch); and on the east by the Casper Arch. Except for the Casper Arch, the surrounding structural uplifts have exposed cores of Precambrian crystalline rocks. In the deepest part of the basin, crystalline and metamorphic rocks are overlain by sedimentary rocks comprising an aggregate thickness of 7,925 m (26,000 ft) or more. This sequence represents a nearly complete record of the geologic history of Paleozoic, Mesozoic, Tertiary, and Quaternary time.

The Mesaverde and Meeteetse Formations of Late Cretaceous age are the major coal-bearing strata in the west-central part of the Wind River Basin and underlie approximately 8,850 km² (3,417 mi²). Exposures of the formations are limited to isolated outcrops of gently dipping strata in the south and southwest and steeply dipping to overturned, folded and faulted strata to the north and northwest.

SEDIMENTARY ROCKS AND STRATIGRAPHY

Cretaceous Period

Upper Cretaceous Series. **Frontier Formation.** The Frontier Formation consists of 183 to 305 m (600 to 1,000 ft) of sandstone, siltstone, shale, bentonite, volcanic tuff, coal, underclay, and limestone. The sandstone is medium gray to medium light gray, fine to coarse grained with occasional zones of well rounded pebbles, thin bedded to massive, porous, friable, and contains a high percentage of dark mineral grains, coal fragments, and glauconite. Locally this formation is very calcareous and contains abundant fossilized marine shells. The uppermost sandstone may be correlative with the Wall Creek Sandstone member of Wegemann (1911).

The shale is medium gray to grayish black and light greenish gray, poorly bedded to very fissile, silty to sandy, and locally is smectitic and carbonaceous. In places the coal is in zones with multiple beds. The Wilderness coal bed, named for the nearby town site, (Windolph and others, 1982), is as much as 107 cm (42 in) thick, is approximately 61 m (200 ft) below the top of the formation, and overlies a sandstone that may be correlative with the Torchlite Sandstone Member of Hintze (1915). The Frontier Formation is both marine and nonmarine and crops out in three to five prominent sandstone ridges and in two to four less resistant intervening shale troughs. These ridges are conspicuous along the basin margins and on the flanks of many of the anticlinal folds parallel and subparallel to the anticlinal axes. In the Blue Holes quadrangle, coal-bearing strata of the Frontier Formation have been thrust over variegated rocks of the Indian Meadows Formation of Eocene age. Here the coal-bearing rocks have been truncated downdip by the fault.

Sedimentologic data (Windolph, 1984) indicate that during and after the deposition of the Frontier Formation, the northwestern part of the present-day basin was the locus for minor sediment transport in a deltaic system that prograded eastward. This system provided a depositional platform and swamp environment favorable for the accumulation of plant matter that was later coalified.

In the subsurface, the base and top of the Frontier Formation are indicated on electric logs by distinct response signatures probably resulting from thin volcanic ash beds in the upper part of the underlying Mowry Shale, by sandstone beds in the upper part of the Frontier, and by thin chalk beds in the lower part of the overlying Cody Shale.

Cody Shale. The Cody Shale is 914 to 1524 m (3,000 to 5,000 ft) thick and consists of marine shale, siltstone, sandstone, and thin limestone beds. The shale is medium gray to grayish black, silty, soft, thin-bedded, poorly fissile to fissile, and commonly smectitic and calcareous. The sandstone is medium gray to medium light gray, very fine to medium grained, very calcareous, porous, thin bedded to massive, and commonly contains marine fossils such as ammonites and marine bivalves. In some of the more structurally complex areas of the basin, the Cody Shale has been tectonically thinned by as much as 305 m (1000 ft) and contains horizontal faults (décollements) where large-scale movements may have taken place without recognizable vertical block movement or thrusting. This indicates that such adjustments probably were accommodated by plastic flow within the Cody Shale. Areas of large-scale adjustment may occur between the Owl Creek Mountains and overturned beds of the Mesaverde Formation in an area extending from south of Jenkins Mountain to Eagle Point, and between Maverick Spring Dome and Coal Draw (T.5 and 6 N., R.1 and 2 W.).

The Cody Shale includes the Shannon Sandstone Member (Wegemann, 1911) and the Beaver Creek sandstone member. These blanket sandstones are very calcareous and contain fossil marine mollusks. The uppermost sandstone beds in the Cody Shale intertongue to the west with and are regressive precursors of the overlying Mesaverde Formation. These successive sandstone units increase upward in thickness from a few inches to tens of feet and include characteristic successive packets of low-angle, contorted, and parallel beds that are suggestive of a prodelta paleodepositional environment. Thin coal, or carbonaceous shale beds with fossil root zones associated with predominantly marine strata, that are indicative of neritic deposits, overlie the thicker sandstone tongues. This prograding marine delta-front model is similar in depositional evolution to those discussed in Ryer (1981), Roehler (1984), and Kaiser and Ayers (1984).

Mesaverde Formation. The Mesaverde Formation consists of a 457 to 671 m (1,500 to 2,200 ft) thick sequence of sandstone, siltstone, shale, coal, underclay, and thin silty limestone beds. In most places the base of the formation is characterized by a massive sandstone that may exceed 61 m (200 ft) in thickness. The lower part of this sandstone unit is medium gray, very fine grained, silty, calcareous, and often contains fossil marine molluscan shell fragments. The upper part is white to light gray, fine to medium grained, friable, noncalcareous, and characteristically contains more quartz. This high-quartz content may have been caused by winnowing of nonquartz grains in a high-energy, nearshore environment.

Strata overlying the basal sandstone consist of numerous lenticular coal beds and interspersed beds of carbonaceous shale, siltstone, thin silty limestone, and lenticular sandstone, and are indicative of swamp and bay-fill sediments. These strata were named the Maverick Spring coal zone by Warlow (1981). This coal zone ranges from 23 to 61 m (75 to 200 ft) in thickness and is of widespread distribution. The coal in this zone is of subbituminous rank and commonly contains tonsteins recording episodes of volcanic ash fall.

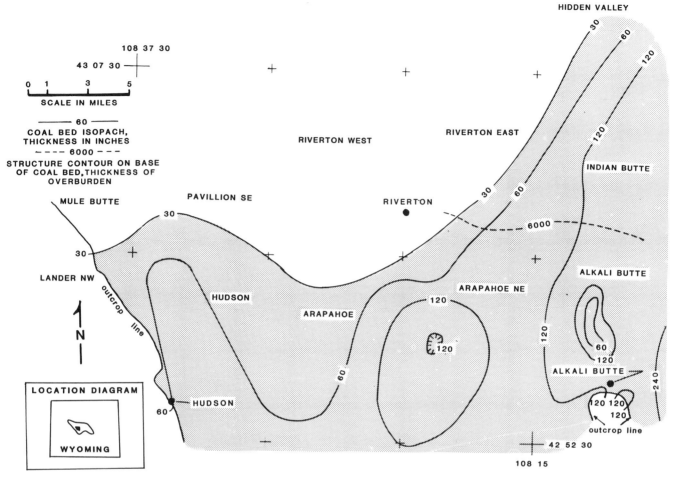

Figure 3. Extent of the Signor coal bed in the Alkali Butte and Hudson coal fields. Shaded pattern indicates resources of subbituminous coal greater than 30 in thick.

Approximately 69 m (225 ft) above the top of the Maverick Spring coal zone is the Signor coal bed (Fig. 3). It has a maximum thickness of 610 cm (240 in) in the Alkali Butte coal field (Fig. 4) and has been tentatively correlated with an 7.3 m (8 ft) coal bed westward for about 32 km (20 mi) to the Hudson coal field near the town of Hudson.

A discrete, linear east-trending channel-form or subareal alluvial fan sequence of grayish-red and greenish-gray smectitic shale and siltstone beds, containing rounded cobbles of Paleozoic and Mesozoic rocks crops out in the Maverick Spring quadrangle. This zone of red beds is as much as 518 m (1,700 ft) thick and includes several rooted zones. The local distribution of these strata and the lack of significant coal beds in the trend suggest that deposition may have taken place in an oxidizing environment conducive to biodegradation. This channel was a focal point of sediment transport into the basin and indicates a period of tectonic and volcanic activity in sediment source areas to the west (Windolph, 1984).

The uppermost rock unit in the Mesaverde Formation is the white sandstone member of Troyer and Keefer (1955). It ranges

from 15 to 133 m (50 to 435 ft) in thickness, and was reported by Keefer (1972) to be equivalent to the Teapot Sandstone Member, which occurs in the southeastern part of the basin. The white sandstone member is white to very light gray, fine to coarse grained, massive, and friable. This sandstone contains several carbonaceous shale units as much as 1.8 m (6 ft) thick and locally is unconformable on the underlying strata. Generally, the white sandstone member crops out in massive cliffs and hogbacks and characteristically supports a luxuriant growth of pine and juniper. The quartzose character, known distribution, relation to overlying marine strata to the east, and thickness variation of this blanket sandstone and underlying strata are indicative of a marine transgressive paleodepositional environment in which portions of the underlying strata were reworked and winnowed.

The Mesaverde Formation has been identified in logs of oil and gas wells in the deeper parts of the Wind River Basin between Shotgun Butte, Muddy Ridge, and Boysen Reservoir. Drilling in the Muddy Ridge gas field penetrated coal beds as much as 305 cm (120 in) thick at depths greater than 4420 m (14,500 ft).

Coal-bearing rocks of the Mesaverde Formation have also

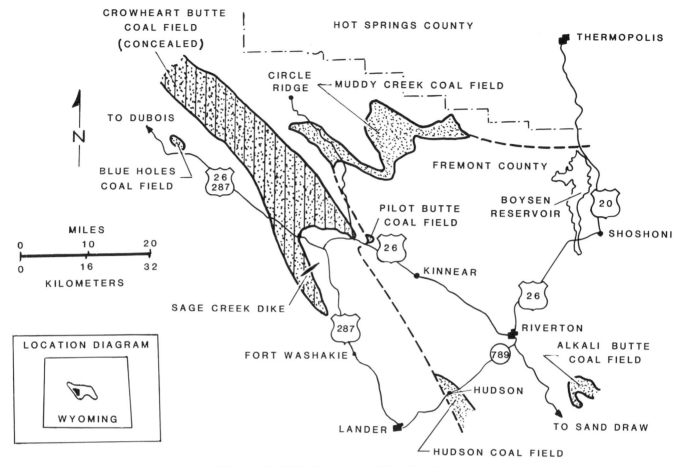

Figure 4. Coal fields in the western Wind River Basin.

been identified from cuttings and geophysical logs from oil and gas wells drilled from 1978 to 1980 in an area designated as the Crowheart Butte field (Windolph and others, 1982; Fig. 4). Sample and electric logs of these wells show coal beds as thick as 244 cm (96 in) at depths to 1524 m (5,000 ft). The beds are in an elongate, downfolded, northwest-trending concealed basin within the Wind River Basin and may extend from south of Winkelman Dome to northwest of the town of Wilderness. In the concealed basin, the Mesaverde Formation and other successive pre-Eocene formations are unconformably overlain by rocks of Eocene age, and are not exposed and have not been reported prior to their identification in recent oil and gas wells (Windolph and others, 1982).

The Mesaverde Formation crops out as numerous ridges near the outer edges of the basin in a discontinuously exposed narrow belt of folded, faulted, and overturned sandstone beds. The basal beds of the Mesaverde Formation, including the Maverick Spring coal zone, are exposed locally near Pilot Butte, Maverick Spring, Eagle Point, Jenkins Mountain, Hudson, and in the Alkali Butte coal field. At Alkali Butte all but the uppermost part of the formation is exposed around the flanks and nose of the northerly plunging Alkali Butte anticline.

Meeteetse Formation. The Meeteetse Formation overlies the white sandstone member of Troyer and Keefer (1955) in the Mesaverde Formation. Strata in the Meeteetse Formation consist of sandstone, siltstone, shale, coal, underclay, and bentonite beds. Most lithologic units are thin, lenticular, and discontinuous. Exceptions are several widespread dark-gray to black bentonite and coal beds.

A few thin grayish-red and greenish-gray calcareous shale and siltstone beds are in the basal part of the formation, and may be representative of marine transgressive tongues extending from the east. These beds were reported by Keefer (1972) to be equivalent to the Lewis Shale in central Wyoming. Exposures of the Meeteetse Formation attain their greatest outcrop thickness in the synclinal trough southeast of Shotgun Butte (Fig. 5) where they range in thickness from 0 to 287 m (0 to 940 ft). Thickness variations are due to truncation by overlying younger formations. Locally the formation is absent because of an erosional unconformity between the Meeteetse Formation and the overlying Lance Formation. Exposures of the Meeteetse Formation are limited to the northwestern part of the basin and are in the same outcrop belt as the Mesaverde Formation. At the southeast edge of the Muddy Creek coal field, exposures of the Meeteetse For-

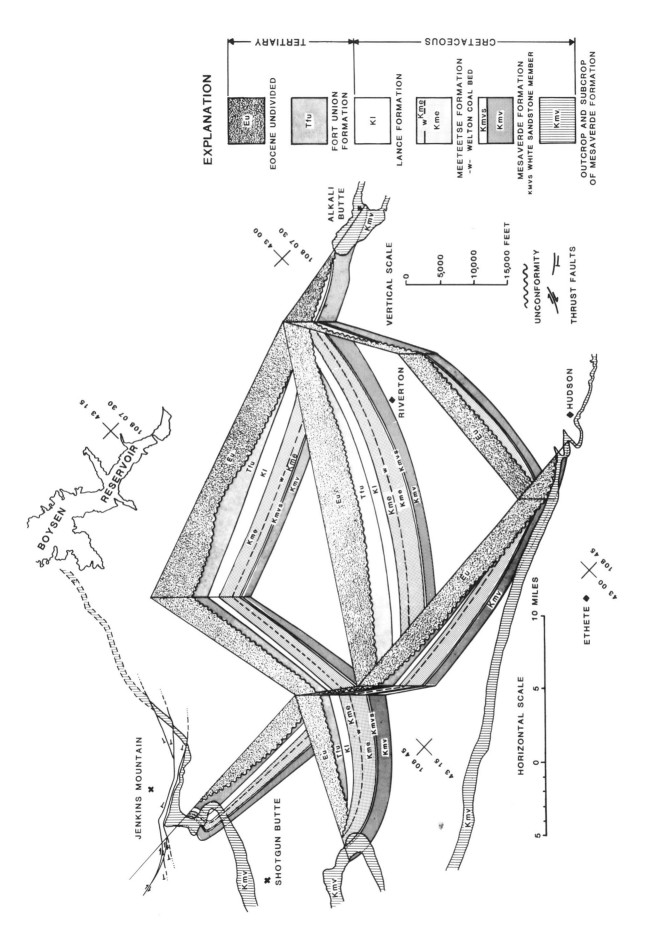

EXPLANATION

TERTIARY

EU — EOCENE UNDIVIDED

Tfu — FORT UNION FORMATION

CRETACEOUS

Kl — LANCE FORMATION

Kme — MEETEETSE FORMATION
w — WELTON COAL BED

Kmvs — MESAVERDE FORMATION
Kmv — kmvs WHITE SANDSTONE MEMBER

Kmv — OUTCROP AND SUBCROP
OF MESAVERDE FORMATION

VERTICAL SCALE

0
5,000
10,000
15,000 FEET

∿∿∿ UNCONFORMITY

⤜ THRUST FAULTS

HORIZONTAL SCALE

0   5   10 MILES

ETHETE ◆   108 45 / 43 00

ALKALI BUTTE

108 07 30 / 43 00

RIVERTON

HUDSON

BOYSEN RESERVOIR

108 07 30 / 43 15

JENKINS MOUNTAIN

SHOTGUN BUTTE

108 15 / 43 15

Figure 5. Fence diagram showing stratigraphic relationships between the Mesaverde and Meeteetse Formations in the west-central Wind River Basin, Wyoming.

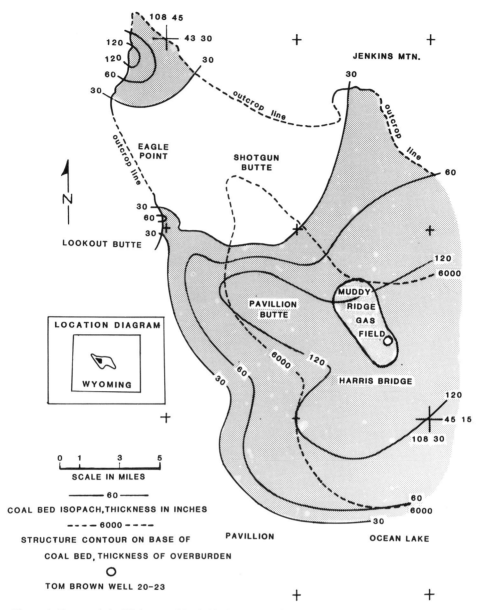

Figure 6. Extent of the Welton coal bed. Shaded pattern indicates resources of subbituminous coal greater than 30 in thick.

mation are terminated by the unconformity at the base of the Eocene strata. Subsurface data further eastward indicate that the Meeteetse is as much as 1,371 m (4,500 ft) thick and contains more than 100 coal beds in the west-central part of the Wind River Basin (Fig. 5). Depositional thinning of the formation northward from the center of the basin toward the Owl Creek Mountains indicates the existence of an emerging area during Meeteetse deposition. Sedimentary thickening in the central part of the basin indicates subsidence at a higher rate during deposition of Meeteetse sediments.

Several thick coal beds, 305 cm (120 in) or greater, occur in the Meeteetse Formation; notable among these is the Welton bed (Fig. 6), which crops out along Muddy Creek in the Eagle Point

quadrangle. This coal bed lies approximately 259 m (850 ft) above the base of the formation and is as much as 610 cm (240 in) thick in the Tom Brown well no. 20-23 (Fig. 6). Correlation of this coal bed has been extended tentatively to the southeast into the Muddy Ridge gas field (Fig. 6) where coal reported to be 610 cm (240 in) thick is overlain by more than 1829 m (6,000 ft) of younger rocks. A coal sample from the Welton(?) coal bed, 1829 m (6,000 ft) below the surface in the Tom Brown well no. 20-23, had a mean maximum vitrinite reflectance index of 0.66 percent, which indicates an apparent rank of high volatile bituminous B or C coal (R. G. Stanton, U.S. Geological Survey, personal communication, 1982).

In general, sediments of the Meeteetse Formation appear to

have accumulated rapidly in a subsiding trough, probably in response to accelerated erosion in the tectonically active source areas. However, many short periods of relatively local structural stability are indicated by numerous thin coal beds, and several long stable episodes are suggested by thicker coal beds occurring in the central part of the structural trough. Numerous episodes of volcanic activity are recorded in the Meeteetse Formation by bentonite, smectitic shale beds, and tonsteins. Variations in the thickness of coal beds and intervening rocks previously mentioned indicate the deposition of sediments in a rapidly shifting swamp environment with varying directions of sediment influx.

A period of minor structural deformation occurred at the end of Meeteetse deposition, accompanied by differential rates of uplift, subsidence, and erosion of the Meeteetse and older formations in locally emergent areas. These formations were deformed, tilted, and beveled, as evidenced by a decrease in their thicknesses, angularity of bedding, and the abundance of well-rounded siliceous chert pebbles in conglomeratic sandstone above an angular unconformity. This unconformity may have extended across as much as 3658 m (12,000 ft) of strata, but at the surface it is in contact with rocks no lower than the basal Mesaverde Formation, north of and on Alkali Butte.

Lance Formation. The Lance Formation, the youngest Cretaceous unit in the basin, is probably equivalent to the Hell Creek Formation in Montana (Brown, 1962). In the Wind River Basin, the Lance Formation consists of three unnamed members, a lower sandstone member, a middle ridge- and cliff-forming sandstone member, and a poorly exposed upper member containing smectitic sandstone, shale, and coal. The thickness of the formation in outcrop ranges up to 692 m (2,270 ft). Well logs from the deeper part of the Wind River Basin indicate that the Lance Formation is as much as 716 m (2,350 ft) thick in the subsurface. The basal contact of the Lance Formation undulates and in some places is marked by channels downcutting into the underlying Meeteetse units. This contact locally cross-cuts older strata at a low angle.

The Lance Formation crops out in the same belt as the underlying Meeteetse and Mesaverde Formations. However, it has a more restricted outcrop pattern due to the overlap of the Fort Union Formation of Paleocene age and the Indian Meadows and Aycross Formations of Eocene age.

The lower member of the Lance consists of lenticular sandstone beds from 0 to 61 m (0 to 200 ft) thick. This member is generally a distinct yellow brown and is fine- to coarse-grained, silty, and friable. In outcrops, the basal sandstone is thick-bedded and is commonly characterized by high-angle cross beds and slumped and contorted bedding. Abundant fragments of petrified wood, fossil dinosaur bone, and ironstone pebbles form lag-gravels with clasts up to 7.6 cm (3 in) in diameter at the base. Several lenticular beds of black, heavy-mineral concentrate, as much as 13 cm (5 in) thick, lie approximately 18 m (60 ft) below the top of the member.

The middle member of the Lance Formation resembles the white sandstone member of Troyer and Keefer (1955) of the Mesaverde Formation. Sandstone in this member is white to very light gray, moderately quartzose, fine to coarse grained, includes several thin shale beds, and is from 30 to 274 m (100 to 900 ft) thick. It is the best exposed part of the formation and generally crops out in linear ridges and massive cliffs. The middle member is tabular in form and widely distributed. The character and blanket tabular distribution pattern of this member indicates that it may also have partly originated as a marine transgressive deposit and may be a Fox Hills equivalent. Typically, the sandstone of the member has a high content of quartz grains, includes lenses of well-rounded chert pebbles, and contains scattered pyrite nodules, casts of animal burrows, and low-angle planar cross-beds.

The upper member of the Lance Formation is nonresistant and is generally poorly exposed. The lower part of the upper member consists mostly of smectitic shale that is medium gray to medium dark gray and slightly carbonaceous; it also includes several impure coal beds less than 30 cm (12 in) thick. This carbonaceous coal-bearing zone is as much as 51 m (170 ft) thick and is 195 to 247 m (640 to 810 ft) above the base of the upper member. The upper part of the upper member contains more sandstone and much less smectite than the lower part, is mostly light gray, and contains a higher percentage of quartz grains than the lower part. Shale in the upper part is generally medium gray to olive gray. The upper member of the Lance Formation is more than 320 m (1,050 ft) thick near Shotgun Butte.

Lance Formation–Fort Union Formation Unconformity. The top of the Lance Formation is marked by a major angular unconformity. An increase in tectonic activity and deformation is indicated by the high angularity of beds below the unconformity and by the development of high-amplitude folds. The hiatus between strata of the Lance and Fort Union Formations indicates an extensive period of uplift, folding, possible faulting, and erosion.

Tertiary Period

Paleocene Series. **Fort Union Formation.** Exposures of the Fort Union Formation are restricted to the northwestern part of the basin, principally in a southeast-trending structural trough. The formation ranges in thickness from 0 to 1219 m (0 to 4,000 ft) and consists of two members. The basal member is a sequence of coarse conglomerate and sandstone beds, approximately 304 m (1,000 ft) thick, and is exposed in outcrops west of Shotgun Butte. The conglomerate beds are medium gray to light yellow brown, lenticular, and contain rounded pebbles of quartz, chert, and petrified wood. Sandstone beds are medium light gray, fine to coarse grained, and thin to thick bedded. These conglomerate and sandstone beds wedge out and grade into finer-grained, thin-bedded sandstone and shale east of Shotgun Butte, and completely wedge out south of Jenkins Mountain. The contact between the Fort Union Formation and underlying strata, although unconformable, is commonly subtle and difficult to locate accurately because of lithologic similarities between the strata. This is particularly true where dipping beds of the Lance Formation and cross beds of the Fort Union Formation have similar dip angles and beds were deposited on areas of erosional topographic relief. In a few places east of Shotgun Bench, conglomerate included in the Fort Union Formation appears to have filled fractures in the steeply dipping Lance Formation. Locally, the conglomerates are cemented across the unconformity with the older, more resistant nonconglomeratic rocks of the Lance Formation. In other places, the Cretaceous-Tertiary boundary is very obvious because of the divergence and angularity of bedding between the two formations. East of Eagle Point the boundary is marked locally by a thick bed of conglomerate having dark brown to black manganiferous and ferruginous cement and thick bands of siderite. Another difference between conglomerates of the Lance and Fort Union Formations is the greater abundance of coarser, less-well-sorted, rounded quartz pebbles and cobbles in the Fort Union Formation.

The upper member of the Fort Union Formation is approximately 914 m (3,000 ft) thick. It is largely medium gray to light greenish gray shale with beds of slightly carbonaceous smectitic shale, a few thin beds of medium-gray calcareous sandstone and siltstone, and occasional thin beds of coal as much as 30.5 cm (12 in) thick. Several zones of grayish-red shale, at or near the top of the Fort Union Formation, may be indicative of subaerial weathering or oxidation and suggest the beginning of uplift and deformation responsible for the development of the basal Eocene unconformity between the Fort Union Formation and the overlying Indian Meadows Formation. Data from oil and gas wells indicate that the Fort Union strata in the subsurface of the Shotgun Butte quadrangle range in thickness from 259 to 488 m (850 to 1,600 ft). These drill hole data do not show the very thick coal beds present in the Fort Union Formation in the Powder River Basin. Coarse conglomerates in the lower part of the Fort Union Formation record a post-Lance–pre-Fort Union tectonic event that was followed by a long episode of crustal stability during the deposition of the upper shale member.

Eocene Series. **Indian Meadows Formation.** Following deposition of the Fort Union Formation, the area surrounding the Wind River Basin was subjected to an intense period of uplift with much folding, tilting, and thrust faulting of the Fort Union and underlying formations. The area then underwent a long period of erosion, after which the Indian Meadows Formation (Love, 1939) was deposited on this erosional surface (unconformity). The Indian Meadows is tentatively correlated with the basal Wasatch Formation (Keefer, 1972) and is here divided into lower and upper members. The lower member is comprised of coarse conglomerate wedges in facies relation with tuffaceous beds overlain by carbonaceous shale and thin coal beds, whereas the upper member consists predominantly of variegated shale with clastic interbeds and several dark gray to purple carbonaceous beds that occasionally include vertebrate fossils.

The Indian Meadows Formation was deposited on an erosional surface that forms a widespread, major unconformity. In most places throughout the basin, highly deformed rocks of the Mesaverde, Meeteetse, Lance, and Fort Union Formations dip steeply beneath the nearly flat-lying beds of the Indian Meadows Formation.

The conglomeratic facies of the lower member consists of a medium-gray and grayish-red to dark-reddish-brown conglomerate, arkosic sandstone, siltstone, shale, and white thin-bedded fresh-water limestone, and light- to medium-gray, smectitic shale beds. The lower member ranges in thickness from 0 to about 762 m (0 to 2,500 ft). In the northwest part of the basin, the lower member is massive and polymictic and contains rounded boulders of Precambrian crystalline and metamorphic rocks and Paleozoic, Mesozoic, and earliest Tertiary sedimentary rocks. The proximity of sources and high depositional gradients are indicated by boulders exceeding 4.5 m (15 ft) in diameter. The conglomerate wedges were deposited as fans and mudflows and probably distributed as a slurry of unsorted boulders, cobbles, arkosic sand, silt, and mud. Farther removed from source areas towards the basin center, these coarse wedges grade laterally into finer grained strata that include conglomerate lenses with interbeds of sandstone, siltstone, shale, and mudstone. Landslide deposits occur south of Jenkins Mountain and northeast of the town of Wilderness. Some of these landslide deposits contain individual blocks of internally cohesive stratified Paleozoic rock that are as much as 305 m (1,000 ft) long (Keefer, 1972). Northwest of the town of Wilderness, landslides and fans locally dammed drainages, resulting in ponds and lakes. This is indicated by thin beds of white fresh-water limestone deposited on underlying conglomerate, by intercalated beds of evenly stratified green shale, and by zones of calcareous shale nodules. These lake deposits were later overlain by wedge-shaped beds of conglomerate.

The basal units of the conglomeratic facies appear to have filled erosional or down-folded depressions; the units onlap across or wedge out against paleotopographic highs within the basin. In places, an entire formation is overlapped, and younger rocks rest directly on rocks older than the Indian Meadows Formation. This relationship omits the Indian Meadows from the local stratigraphic succession.

Generally, the conglomerate beds of the lower member consist of rock fragments deposited in an inverse order to their normal stratigraphic sequence. For example, fragments of the Pennsylvanian Tensleep Sandstone are most abundant near the base of the member and Cambrian Flathead Quartzite and Precambrian crystalline rocks are more abundant at the top. This relationship indicates a rapid layer-by-layer stripping of progressively older formations as the Owl Creek Mountains were uplifted and the Precambrian core was finally exposed and eroded.

In the tuffaceous facies of the lower member, early Eocene volcanic activity is recorded by numerous white to light-gray, thin- to thick-bedded tuff and smectitic shale beds. At least five tuffaceous units are exposed near Alkali Butte, and two near Hudson. The northwesternmost exposure of tuff is 5 km (3 mi) east of Little Dome. Simultaneous volcanism and tectonism is demonstrated by a basal conglomerate bed whose matrix consists of tuffaceous material in the lower member cropping out east of Hudson. At Alkali Butte, nontuffaceous conglomerate beds overlie the tuffaceous beds that record the earlier arrival of volcanic ash in the central part of the basin.

Most of the tuffaceous beds are very siliceous and form resistant outcrops containing fossil root traces and penetrations. They are overlain in many places by light grayish-brown carbonaceous shale beds containing abundant, well-preserved fossil plant impressions and lenses of coal 2.5 to 8 cm (1 to 3 in) thick, which are of probable lignite rank.

Thickness of the tuffaceous conglomerate beds of the lower member ranges from a few feet at the surface along the southern edge of the basin to more than 1829 m (6,000 ft) in depositional troughs. Conglomerate beds of the lower members appear to have been deposited on a topographic surface of considerable relief. Deposition was initially rapid and chaotic and decreased in energy and intensity as irregularities in the topographic surface were filled or were eroded away. Periods of relative local crustal stability are recorded by widespread carbonaceous shale beds, thin lignite beds, and thin lacustrine limestone units. The upper member of the Indian Meadows Formation is predominantly grayish red to variegated and consists of distinct layers of silty shale, mudstone, bentonite, and tuff; thin, dark-gray to purple shale beds that may represent paleosols; lignitic carbonaceous shale; and several thin lenses of conglomerate and arkosic sandstone. The carbonaceous shale beds commonly contain well-preserved fossil fish, turtle and crocodile bones, and thin lenses of lignite as much as 30 cm (12 in) thick, which are indicative of an open-water lake or distributary channels in which swampy depositional environments developed.

The rocks of the upper members are poorly consolidated and generally erode into spectacular, steeply sloping badlands. The most extensive exposures are north of the town of Wilderness (Fig. 1) along the north side of the Wind River. Outcrops of the upper member range in thickness from zero to tens of meters along the flanks of anticlines and synclines in the basin to more than 213 m (700 ft) in the Blue Holes quadrangle. In the subsurface, particularly in depositional troughs, the thickness of the upper member locally may exceed 1,768 m (5,800 ft). The overall total thickness of the Indian Meadows Formation may be greater than 2,133 m (7,000 ft). This great disparity in thickness is interpreted to indicate a substantial amount of differential subsidence, uplift, and accompanying erosion and deposition on a deeply dissected paleotopographic surface.

The origin of the varicolored sediments is debatable but is interpreted here to be indicative of deposition in an oxidizing environment in and across a broad alluvial flood plain that was subject to a subtropical climate. Tectonism in the basin at this time appears to have been minor, and volcanic activity more frequent. This is indicated by both the lack of coarse sediments and the abundance of tuff and smectitic shale beds.

Aycross Formation. The Aycross Formation (Love, 1939) consists predominantly of light-greenish-gray arkosic sandstone, and minor interbeds of greenish-gray to olive-green siltstone, shale, mudstone, and coal. The arkosic sandstone is fine to very coarse grained, massive to lenticular bedded, smectitic, and fria-

ble, and includes thin, varicolored siltstone and shale interbeds and conglomerate lenses. The arkosic sandstone beds include abundant feldspar granules derived from the weathering and disintegration of granite and gneiss in nearby mountains. The shale and siltstone units are nonbedded to thin evenly bedded, and contain numerous layers of light greenish gray limestone nodules. The mudstones are mostly smectitic and contain very fine to coarse sand grains. Coal beds as much as 5 m (18 ft) thick associated with stacked arkosic channel-fill sandstones are reported 8 km (5 mi) east of Boyson Reservoir (Thaden, 1978). These lignite-bearing strata may be correlatives of the Aycross Formation. In places, the Aycross Formation intertongues with the underlying variegated upper member of the Indian Meadows and at others rests unconformably on it at a low angle. Exposures of the Aycross Formation range from 0 to more than 274 m (0 to 900 ft) in thickness near Crowheart Butte.

Numerous large fossil tree trunks, as much as 1 m (3 ft) in diameter, are preserved in the Aycross Formation on a ridge on the southeastern flank of Sheldon Dome in Maverick Spring Quadrangle. The tree trunks, several feet in length, include complete root systems and are in an upright position, indicating rapid sedimentation and burial. The lenticular distributary and channel-fill character of these sandstone beds indicates deposition of coalescing fans on an alluvial plain that was crossed by moderately flowing streams, with a predominant source to the west.

The dominant greenish-gray color of Aycross rocks was caused by chemical reduction of iron in the sediments and may have been the result either of a climatic change occurring after deposition of the Indian Meadows Formation or, more likely, where intertonguing with variegated beds was due to chemical-reducing conditions controlled by higher precipitation or raised ground water levels during sedimentation.

Quaternary Period

Quaternary Deposits. The Wind River Basin had attained its present structural development as an intermontane basin by the beginning of the Quaternary Period. It was being modified by faulting, dissection, and redistribution of sediments during the Oligocene, Miocene, and Pliocene Epochs. Except in the southeastern part of the basin, very little evidence of these sediments now exists.

Pleistocene Deposits. Pleistocene deposits are widespread in the basin and consist of several glacial moraines, numerous high-level lake and river terraces, channel deposits, pediments, alluvial fans, sand dunes, and loess deposits. The glacial moraines, river terraces, alluvial fans, and some channel deposits are largely boulder-gravels, composed of boulders, cobbles, pebbles, and granules. Other Pleistocene deposits are composed mostly of sand, silt, and clay. Clasts in boulder-gravel deposits consist essentially of Precambrian crystalline rocks and the more resistant Paleozoic and Mesozoic rocks, such as quartzite, chert, and agate. South of and proximal to the Owl Creek Mountains, many Pleistocene deposits contain abundant fragments of dark gray to black igneous rocks that were derived from mafic dike swarms intruded into the crystalline core.

Throughout the basin, river and stream channel deposits are preserved on, and locally form, the tops of mesas and ridges. These "high-level" gravel deposits generally consist of boulder- to granule-sized clasts that have provided "armor," protecting easily eroded pre-Quaternary sedimentary rocks from erosion.

In the western part of the basin, the ancestral Wind River was temporarily dammed and diverted from its channel by terminal moraines. Remnants of these glacial moraines are conspicuous on the north bank of the river. High-level river terraces and deposits are common along the Wind River Valley, and accumulation of alluvium and loess more than 91 m (30 ft) thick is exposed in the banks of many river and stream channels and tributaries. The remains of an extinct Pleistocene bison (*Bison occidentalis*), a predecessor to the modern bison, was discovered in a layer of gravel under approximately 3 m (10 ft) of sediments in a narrow ravine northeast of Alkali Butte.

High-level gravel lake terraces of probable Pleistocene age are also present along the margins of the Wind River Basin. Sand dune fields associated with these marginal terraces suggest that a large lake and drainage system may have extended from the Wind River Basin into the Powder River Basin and filled the basins to an altitude greater than 1,829 m (6,000 ft) above sea level. Outcrops of Paleozoic limestone and dolomite on the northern shore of the lake were encountered as the lake level rose and the initial downcutting of the Wind River Canyon through the Owl Creek Mountains commenced along solution cavities, fractures, and joint planes developed in the northeast-dipping beds. During the downcutting, the lake level gradually fell, as indicated by elevated river channel gravels capping mesas and by pediment slope angle, until resistant crystalline Precambrian rocks were exposed in the core of the Owl Creeks at an altitude of approximately 1,524 m (5,000 ft) above sea level. Sand dunes and loess deposits were then formed at this level as sediments in the lake were exposed and eroded.

Holocene Deposits. Holocene deposits consist of unconsolidated accumulations of boulders, cobbles, sand, silt, and clay. These accumulations are preserved on river terraces, in alluvial floodplains, as slope wash, on pediments, and as colluvial, landslide, lake, and dune deposits.

Numerous Holocene landslides have occurred in the Blue Holes quadrangle south of and adjacent to a thrust fault and also on a coal zone and smectitic underclay in the Frontier Formation. A large active southeastwardly migrating sand dune is located 13 km (8 mi) southeast of the town of Wilderness. Colluvial deposits are most numerous at the base of the massive cliff-forming sandstones in the Mesaverde, Lance, and Aycross Formations.

Igneous and Volcanic Rocks. Several types of intrusive and extrusive igneous rocks occur in the Wind River Basin, including dikes, airborne volcanic debris (tuff, bentonite, volcaniclastic sandstone, siltstone, and shale), ash beds, and tonsteins. The oldest dikes occur in swarms in the Owl Creek Mountains Precambrian metamorphic crystalline complex. Erosion of these

dikes contributed a significant component to coarse clastics in the Eocene, Pleistocene, and Holocene rocks overlying the coal-bearing Cretaceous and Paleocene Formations adjacent to the Owl Creek Mountains.

The Sage Creek dike (Fig. 4) is the only igneous body that may have intruded coal-bearing rocks in the Crowheart Butte coalfield. The mafic syenite dike is medium gray to light grayish green, very finely to coarsely crystalline, and contains numerous xenoliths of Precambrian granulites and gneisses. It is approximately 3 km (2 mi) long and forms a prominent erosionally resistant wall about 8 m (25 ft) high and 6 m (20 ft) wide, where it crosses Sage Creek. The dike intrudes rocks as young as the Aycross Formation and is truncated by Pleistocene terrace gravels. A potassium-argon age (Early Miocene) of 22.2 ± 0.8 Ma (Windolph and others, 1982) was determined from a biotite concentrate and is the youngest date known for intrusive igneous rock in the Wind River Basin. Based on this age, the dike may be related to volcanism that occurred 22 to 25 Ma in the Yellowstone Park area.

Tuff beds accumulated over much of the basin during the deposition of the Indian Meadows Formation of Eocene age. They are white to medium light gray, and light grayish brown to greenish gray, medium to very finely crystalline, dense, and contain angular quartz fragments, skeletal shards of volcanic glass, biotite, and other dark mineral grains.

In most places the upper part of the tuff beds is very hard, siliceous, and resembles silcretes or ganisters; these beds are excellent isochrons. They also contain sparse to abundant fossil root impressions and pyritic zones, and in most areas are overlain by carbonaceous shale beds. A tuff bed with flattened volcanic lapilli agglomerate including individual lapilli up to 2.5 cm (1 in) in diameter crops out on the southwestern flank of Alkali Butte. The large size of the lapilli and their distribution associated with the increase of as many as five individual tuff beds to the southeast, indicates a nearby volcanic source.

The most common type of volcanic rock associated with coal beds in the Wind River Basin is tonstein, a distinct stratigraphic unit consisting of tephra, or wind blown volcanic ash, which was deposited in and preserved in peat swamps. On outcrops tonsteins weather light grayish brown to white, and in the basin range from a few millimeters to more than 20 cm (8 in) thick. Tonsteins are widely distributed geographically. In the western United States they occur in coal beds of early Late Cretaceous to Eocene age.

Some tonsteins in coal beds of the Mesaverde Formation contain well-preserved fossil plant impressions, such as *Metasequoia* fronds; also present are cones, leaves, and seed pods from deciduous trees. Coal beds associated with tonsteins commonly contain abundant fusain at the coal-tonstein contact. This fusain may result from charring or burning of vegetation by hot volcanic ash. The basal part of most tonsteins is characterized by coarse flattened lapilli fragments and granular to fine-grained feldspathic phenocrysts. X-ray diffraction examination of 7 tonstein samples revealed abundant kaolinite and quartz.

Tonsteins are useful for stratigraphic correlations over short distances (of several kilometers), but at greater distances become less dependable because of the abundance of tonsteins in various stratigraphic horizons, their variable thicknesses, and lack of a distinctive mineralogical, chemical, or geophysical signature. The variation in number and thickness of beds may be a function of such factors as prevailing winds, frequency of volcanic events, and nearness to volcanic sources.

The most abundant rock types related to volcanic activity are bentonite and smectitic sandstone, siltstone, and shale. These rocks contain admixed volcanic ash that fell during deposition of the clastic sediments and commonly were bioturbated during and after sedimentation. Most smectitic sandstone and shale beds vary widely in color. The beds are characterized by a crumbly surface layer that resulted from swelling and shrinking of the smectite, which was caused by changes in moisture content. Weathered exposures of bentonite or smectitic beds are commonly subdued and rounded.

DEPOSITIONAL ENVIRONMENTS OF COAL BEDS AND RELATED ROCKS

Most coal beds in the Wind River Basin are subbituminous in rank. Ultimate and proximate analysis and heating values show that some of the older coal beds, such as those in the Frontier Formation, and coal buried at depths greater than 1,829 m (6,000 ft) in the basin or coal subjected to intense tectonic deformation have undergone more advanced diagenesis or coalification and are raised to bituminous rank.

Coal beds are indicators of relative local crustal stability over extensive periods of time. For example, the compaction ratio of most peat to coal for the Cretaceous has been shown by Ryer and Langer (1980) to be approximately 11:1, implying that a 3 m (10 ft) coal represents about 34 m (110 ft) of peat accumulation. This implies an extensive amount of time, far greater than that necessary to deposit an equivalent amount of clastic material. Coal beds and associated rocks also record variations and changes in plant types, climate, and volcanic activity and are sensitive indicators of water levels in swamps. Peat depositional rate, oxidation, and biodegradation in the swamp control peat accumulation, and are directly indicated by the amount of plant material preserved at or beneath the water table. Peat that accumulated near the landward edge of the swamp and adjacent to distributary or stream channels commonly includes numerous impurities and partings, notably in a limnic or intermontane environment. The resultant coals are generally higher in ash.

Deposition of the Frontier Formation

Initial peat development in the Wind River Basin occurred during deposition of the Cretaceous Frontier Formation. Thin, impure peat beds grading laterally into carbonaceous clay were deposited on sand bodies whose depositional geometry and distribution are largely unknown, but which appear to be partly neritic and paralic, related to shallow coastal or nearshore barrier

and swampy sand islands. In this model, it is suggested that peats and clays were deposited in a coastal and brackish-water backswamp formed on a seaward prograding deltaic system.

The coal beds of the middle and upper parts of the Frontier Formation in the basin are thin but very widespread; most average about 25 cm (10 in) in thickness, but range from several inches to about 102 cm (40 in) in thickness. These coal beds occur in a shaly zone about 61 m (200 ft) below the top of the formation and attain their greatest thickness northwest of the historic town site of Wilderness (Fig. 1). This coal zone includes a thin sandstone that contains sparse, well-rounded pebbles of quartz, andesite, and chert. This zone directly overlies a thick sandstone unit correlative with the Torchlight Sandstone Member of Hintze (1915) in the Bighorn Basin to the north. The lobate geometry of the sandstone and its relation to coal beds in the Frontier Formation indicate that sand platforms developed as stacked distributary channels during the seaward progradation of a deltaic system in which the main distributaries in this depocenter flowed eastward. Coastal swamps developed on these sand platforms and persisted long enough for multibedded peat to accumulate before transgression by the sea. A part of this stacked sequence of rocks was eroded, as indicated by numerous large, detrital fragments of coal in the overlying Wall Creek Sandstone Member of the Frontier Formation (Wegemann, 1911).

Deposition of the Cody Shale

An extensive marine transgression persisted during deposition of the Cody Shale. The Cody Shale is a thick cyclical deposit recording numerous periods of volcanic ash fall and carbonate precipitation. It consists predominantly of black pyritic shale, indicative of anaerobic conditions. Several regressive cycles are indicated by widespread blanket fossiliferous marine sands. The uppermost sands in the Cody Shale are characteristic of the neritic zone, indicating near-coastal shallow marine conditions. Locally, they were above sea level long enough to support plant growth and minor accumulations of peat. The uppermost shale beds of the Cody Shale are in an intertonguing relationship with the basal sandstone beds of the Mesaverde Formation, are thinner to the west, and are consistent with a paleodepositional model with peat accumulation in the upper part of the Cody Shale and the lower part of the Mesaverde Formation. The peat accumulation is contemporaneous with a widespread and long-lasting prograding shoreline environment.

Deposition of the Mesaverde Formation

Initial peat development in the Mesaverde Formation occurred in paralic coastal swamps that formed landward of and above thick sandstone bodies. The sandstones underlying the Maverick Spring coal zone were deposited by a system of distributary channels that formed coastal barrier bars and prograding delta fronts. This depositional model is similar to the Early Pennsylvanian marine deltaic environment of the Appalachian basin in which the Pocahontas Formation developed (Englund and others, 1984). Data from oil and gas well logs (Windolph and others, 1982) indicate that coal in the Maverick Spring coal zone, in both the Crowheart Butte and Alkali Butte coal fields, is thickest and most extensive over the thickest part of the basal sand bodies. Both of these coal fields are large and of widespread distribution. The Crowheart Butte lobe is associated with an east-trending distributary channel or alluvial fan system that crops out east of the Crowheart Butte coal field. The system contains cobble conglomerates in a bentonite matrix with interbedded variegated shale beds. The sparsity and thinning of coal beds in the red bed trend suggest a subaerial or oxidizing environment. The spatial relationship of these beds with fluviatile channel-fill sandstones, conglomerates, and bentonite indicates their formation was in a more limnic part of the swamp, landward of the upper delta plain, and was the result of a tectonic-volcanic event.

Outcrops of the Maverick Spring coal zone are extensive and contain numerous white weathering tonsteins as much as 18 cm (7 in) thick. This zone also includes several thin, lenticular, silty, finely crystalline dolomitic limestone beds that may be indicative of brief periods of shallow marine transgression or are the result of carbonate precipitation in interdistributary ponds or lakes on the upper part of the delta system.

The Signor coal bed is the thickest coal bed in the Mesaverde Formation, and is as much as 610 cm (240 in) in thickness. This coal bed is approximately 69 m (225 ft) above the Maverick Spring coal zone, and is widely distributed. It is absent where it has burned locally and is represented only by several inches of orange ash in outcrops on the east and west flanks of Alkali Butte. Thick, widespread coal beds of this type probably form more centrally in low energy, silt-free, back-bay barrier swamp environments during extensive periods of marine shoreline stillstand. The Signor coal bed at Alkali Butte is also displaced upwards and to the west by the north-trending Immigrant Trail thrust fault. To the south and east of Alkali Butte, the Signor coal splits into upper and lower beds that attain thicknesses of 305 cm (120 in) and are separated by as much as 15 m (50 ft) of intervening strata. Most of this coal bed north of Alkali Butte is buried under more than 1,829 m (6,000 ft) of overburden. Near Hudson, the Signor coal bed was exposed sometime prior to Eocene deposition, long enough to develop dessication cracks more than 61 cm (24 in) deep, which were later filled with sand and gravels of the Indian Meadows Formation.

The Beaver coal bed is approximately 69 m (225 ft) stratigraphically higher above the Signor, and on the south face of Alkali Butte has been truncated by an unconformity at the base of the Lance formation. This coal bed is much thinner, less widespread, and is overlain by the Shipton coal bed approximately 76 m (250 ft) higher in the section. Extensive volcanic activity is recorded in the Shipton coal bed, which contains numerous tonstein partings and abundant siliceous petrified tree stumps and fragments. Much of the fossil wood is concentrated near the middle of the coal bed and is partly fusinized, probably recording a fire with related biodegradation in the swamp.

The few remaining coal beds in the upper part of the Mesaverde Formation are thin, discontinuous, and typical of those found in a fluvial distributary environment of the upper delta plain. Additional coal beds may have formed during the deposition of the Mesaverde Formation, but all evidence of their existence was removed by the westward encroachment of the sea and with the reworking and deposition of the white sandstone member of Troyer and Keefer (1955).

Deposition of the Meeteetse Formation

The sea transgressed westward in the basin area for a very short period at the beginning of Meeteetse deposition and then regressed eastward. A totally different nonmarine limnic paleodepositional environment is interpreted to have now influenced the deposition and accumulation of peat. At this time, a somewhat restricted or intermontane basin was in the early stages of development. Well log data indicate that a positive area was forming at or north of the Owl Creek Mountains (Windolph and others, 1982). The central part of the basin subsided greatly as the depocenter moved eastward, and numerous peat deposits of variable thickness accumulated. Of the more than 100 coal beds identified in oil and gas well logs, as many as 30 of these beds reached resource thickness (greater than 76 cm [30 in]) in the deeper structural trough of the basin. Principal among these coal beds is the Welton coal bed, which is approximately 259 m (850 ft) stratigraphically above the base of the Meeteetse Formation and crops out in the Muddy Creek coal field. The Welton ranges from less than 76 cm (30 in) thick to a thickness of 531 cm (209 in) in outcrop and is as much as 610 cm (240 in) thick in the subsurface.

The large number of coal beds in the subsiding depocenter, the wide variations in thickness of the Welton and other coal beds, including partings, and interval changes between the other coal beds suggest a limnic depositional model; one with an unstable migrating swamp perimeter that was displaced by sediment inflow from several tectonically influenced highland or emerging areas. This paleodepositional model is similar to one proposed by Kent (1984) for the Paleocene coal-bearing sequence in the Powder River Basin. Volcanic eruptions from the west were common during Meeteetse deposition; their record is preserved by numerous smectitic sandstone and shale units and tonstein partings in coal beds.

Coal beds of resource thickness in the Meeteetse Formation above the Welton coal bed have not been identified in or proximally downdip of the outcrop. This lack of coal bed occurrences is due partly to truncation at overlying unconformities and may also be the result of increasing tectonic activity causing migration of the depocenter eastward. Oxygenation or biodegradation of plant remains, which inhibited peat accumulation, is characteristic of this part of the alluvial or upper delta plain fluvial distributary environment. The coarse composition, areal distribution, structural relations, and deformation of sediments succeeding the Meeteetse Formation are evidence of the continued development

TABLE 1. SELECTED ANALYTICAL DATA ON THE WELTON AND SIGNOR COAL BEDS

Welton Coal Bed
(Meeteetse Formation)

Sample Number	Ash[1]	Sulfur[2]	Calcium	Magnesium	Iron	Silica[3]
221650	15.8	0.3	13	2.5	3.2	47
221651	18.9	0.4	8.5	2.2	2.7	54
221657	11.5	0.6	9.7	2.0	3.6	54
Average	15.4	0.4	10.4	2.2	3.2	51.7

Signor Coal Bed
(Mesaverde Formation)

Sample Number	Ash[1]	Sulfur[2]	Calcium	Magnesium	Iron	Silica[3]
221644	8.5	0.7	8.8	3.6	3.3	45
221645	4.2	1	15	5.3	16	18
232809	9.4	2.4	--	--	--	--
232810	10	1.9	6.2	1.7	14	42
232811	11.3	0.7	8.7	1.7	12	47
232816	9.2	1	6	1.8	3.6	34
232817	5.2	0.7	7.3	2.5	2.7	43
Average	8.3	1.2	8.7	2.8	8.6	38.2

Averages for Sampled Western Coal Beds

	8.8	0.7	13	3.1	7.2	37

[1]From proximate or ultimate analysis, on as-received basis; expressed as % of coal sample.

[2]From ultimate analysis, on as-received basis, value in % of sample.

[3]Expressed as % of oxides in ash.

Note: Proximate and ultimate analyses performed by coal analysis section, U.S. Department of Energy. Chemical analyses performed by U.S. Geological Survey. Proximate analysis, in the case of coal and coke, refers to the determination, by prescribed methods, of moisture, volatile matter, fixed carbon (by difference) and ash. Ultimate analysis refers to the determination of carbon and hydrogen in the material as found in the gaseous products of its complete combustion, the determination of sulfur, nitrogen, and ash in the material as a whole, and the estimate of oxygen by difference. (A.S.T.M. D 121-30)

of the intermontane basin and its being further restricted by emergence and outlet closure.

COAL GEOCHEMICAL INDICATORS OF DEPOSITIONAL ENVIRONMENTS

Analytical data for the Signor and Welton coal beds (Table 1; Fig. 7, Warlow and others, 1986) were compared and evaluated for variations in composition and quality relating to contrasting paleodepositional environments. The most obvious difference between the two is an elevated ash content in the Welton coal bed. Ash values averaging 15.4% for three samples are nearly twice that of the 8.3% average for seven samples of the Signor coal bed. Silica content of ash values in the Welton coal bed averages 51.7%, compared to 38.2% for the Signor coal bed.

These data, when compared with the sampled western coal bed averages of 8.8% ash and 37% silica in ash, place the Signor coal bed close to the average for western coals (Swanson and others, 1976).

These higher percentages for the elevated ash value and silica content of the Welton coal bed are consistent with the model of a subsiding intermontane basin coupled with high levels of ongoing volcanic activity. As the basin became more isolated from marine influence, increasing amounts of sediment high in silicic volcanic ash were transported into the rapidly subsiding basin.

Trace element analyses from coal ash samples (Warlow and others, 1982; Windolph and others, in press, 1986) are also indicative of the Welton coal beds having been formed in a limnic environment that was modified by volcaniclastics. Of note is an

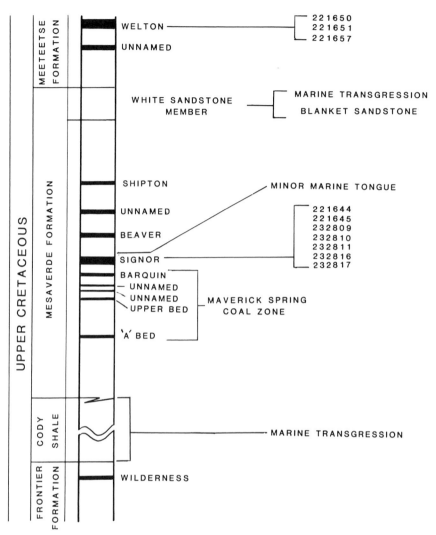

Figure 7. Generalized stratigraphic column showing locations of coal samples, Wind River Basin.

increase in the following tephra-, rare-earth- and chalcophile-related elements: Cr, Cu, La, Li, Nb, Pb, Sc, Th, U, V, Y, and Zr. The Signor coal bed, in contrast, shows an increase in elements such as B, Fe, Hg, Na, P, and S that are suggestive of a paralic environment.

Well log data from the Welton coal bed indicate that depocenters for peat accumulation were shifted laterally and eastward in the basin and continually displaced in various directions by the periodic encroachment of increasing amounts of tectonically induced sedimentation. An alternative model for thick peat accumulation is accounted for by a rise in base level and basin infilling brought on by restriction or closing of drainage outlets due to localized uplift. Both models for the deposition of the Meeteetse Formation are substantially validated by the immense sedimentary thickening and profusion of coal beds in the center of the basin and by geologic evidence for restriction and closing of the basin outlet in Eocene time.

Pyritic sulfur and iron content are much higher in the Signor coal bed than in the Welton coal bed. Iron and total sulfur in the Signor averages 8.6 and 1.2%, respectively, compared to 3.2 and 0.4% in the Welton, which is below the 0.7% average sulfur for sampled western coals. The origin of high-sulfur coal in other study areas has been attributed to the influence of overlying saline marine and brackish-water sedimentary successions (Williams and Keith, 1963; Ferm and others, 1976; Horne and others, 1978). The higher sulfur content of the Signor coal bed is consistent with the encroachment of a delta lobe periphery into a dominantly marine regime, as has been ascribed for the periphery of the Squire Jim and Pocahontas No. 3 coal beds by Englund and others (1984). The Signor coal bed at Alkali Butte is overlain by a white beach sand containing abundant pyritized burrow fillings. This beach sand is, in turn, overlain by thin fossiliferous dolomitic limestones that represent a brief marine incursion that advanced from the east. In contrast, low sulfur content in the Welton coal bed is attributed to peat accumulation in a nonmarine intermontaine lacustrine fluvial system.

SUMMARY

The geologic evolution of the Wind River Basin forms an important link in understanding the regional genesis and deposition of coal-bearing strata. This basin is the focal point of a major transition of depositional environments from marine deltaic (pa-

ralic) to nonmarine intermontane (limnic). Many cycles of prograding marine deltaic sedimentation accumulated as an advancing wave of tectonic events moved eastward through the present area of the Wind River Basin. The early stages of a developing intermontane basin are documented during deposition of the Meeteetse Formation. Numerous cycles of structural deformation were also imprinted on the successive formations, as the basin evolved eastward through geologic time into the area of the Powder River Basin, where these events ultimately determined the locus of numerous thick lignite and subbituminous coal deposits. These changes, observed in the stratigraphic record of the Wind River Basin, are supported by the geochemical analyses of representative coal samples from formations deposited before and after the transition of environments from deltaic to intermontane.

REFERENCES CITED

Averitt, Paul, 1975, Coal Resources of the United States, January 1, 1974: U.S. Geological Survey Bulletin 1412, 131 p.

Berryhill, H. L., Jr., Brown, D. M., Brown, A., Taylor, D. A., and others, 1950, Coal resources of Wyoming: U.S. Geological Survey Circular 81, 78 p.

Brown, R. W., 1962, Paleocene flora of the Rocky Mountains and Great Plains: U.S. Geological Survey Professional Paper 375, 119 p.

Comstock, T. B., in Jones, W. A., 1874, Report upon the reconnaissance of northwestern Wyoming in 1873: U.S. 43rd Congress, 1st Session, House of Representatives Executive Document 285, 210 p.

Darton, N. H., 1906, Geology of the Owl Creek Mountains: U.S. 59th Congress, 1st Session, Senate Executive Document 219, 48 p.

Eldridge, G. H., 1894, A geological reconnaissance in northwest Wyoming with special reference to its economic resources: U.S. Geological Survey Bulletin 119, 72 p.

Englund, K. J., Windolph, J. F., Jr., and Thomas, R. E., 1984, Deposition of low-sulfur coal in the Lower Pennsylvanian Pocahontas Formation, Virginia and West Virginia: Geological Society of America, 97th Annual Meeting Abstracts with Programs, p. 502.

Ferm, J. C., Horne, J. C., and Melton, R. A., 1976, Depositional models applied to coal exploration and development: American Institute of Mining Engineers Annual Meeting, Las Vegas, Nevada, February 1976, 12 p.

Glass, G. B., and Roberts, J. T., 1978, Update of the Wind River coal basin: Wyoming Geological Association 13th Annual Field Conference, Guidebook, p. 363–377.

Hayden, F. V., 1869, Geological report of the exploration of the Yellowstone and Missouri Rivers: U.S. 40th Congress 2nd Session, Senate Executive Document 77, 174 p.

Hintze, F. F., Jr., 1915, Basin and Greybull oil and gas fields: Wyoming Geological Survey Bulletin 10, 23 p.

Horne, J. C., Howell, D. J., Baganz, B. P., and Ferm, J. C., 1978, Splay deposits as an economic factor in coal mining, in Hodgson, H. E., ed., Proceedings of the second symposium on the geology at Rocky Mountain coal—1977: Colorado Geological Survey, Resources Series 4, p. 89–100.

Kaiser, W. R., and Ayers, W. B., Jr., 1984, Fluvial depositional architecture and lignite occurrences in the Wilcox Group (Eocene), Texas Gulf Coast Basin: Geological Society of America, 97th Annual Meeting, Abstracts with Programs, p. 553.

Keefer, W. R., and Rich, E. J., 1957, Stratigraphy of the Cody Shale and younger Cretaceous and Paleocene rocks in the western and southern parts of the Wind River Basin Wyoming: Wyoming Geological Association Guidebook, 12th Annual Field Conference, p. 71–78.

Keefer, W. R., 1961, The Meeteetse, Lance, and Fort Union Formations, southern

Wind River Basin, Wyoming: Wyoming Geological Association Guidebook, 16th Annual Field Conference, p. 180–186.

Keefer, W. R., and Troyer, M. L., 1964, Geology of the Shotgun Butte area, Fremont County, Wyoming: U.S. Geological Survey Bulletin 1157, 123 p.

Keefer, W. R., 1970, Structural geology of the Wind River Basin, Wyoming: U.S. Geological Survey Professional Paper 459-D, 35 p.

——, 1972, Frontier, Cody, and Mesaverde Formations in the Wind River and Southern Bighorn Basin, Wyoming: U.S. Geological Survey Professional Paper 495-E, p. E1–E23.

Kent, B. H., 1984, Evolution of thick coal deposits in the Powder River Basin, northeastern Wyoming: Geological Society of America, 97th Annual Meeting, Abstracts with Programs, p. 558.

Knight, W. C., 1895, Coal and coal measures of Wyoming: U.S. Geological Survey 16th Annual Report, part IV, 8 p.

Love, J. D., 1939, Geology along the South Margin of the Absaroka Range, Wyoming: Geological Society of America Special Paper 20, 134 p.

——, 1948, Mesozoic stratigraphy of the Wind River Basin, central Wyoming: Wyoming Geological Association Guidebook, 3rd Annual Field Conference, Wind River Basin, 15 p.

——, 1970, Cenozoic geology of the Granite Mountains area Central Wyoming: U.S. Geological Survey Professional Paper 495-C, p. C1–C154.

Roehler, H. W., 1984, The McCourt Sandstone tongue and the Glades coal bed—An Upper Cretaceous strand-plain coal-forming depositional environment, Rock Springs coal field, Wyoming-Utah: Geological Society of America, 97th Annual Meeting, Abstracts with Programs, p. 637.

Ryer, T. A., and Langer, A. W., 1980, Thickness change involved in the Peat-to-Coal Transformation for a Bituminous coal of Cretaceous age in Central Utah, Journal of Sedimentary Petrology, v. 50, p. 987–992.

Ryer, T. A., 1981, Deltaic coals of Ferron Sandstone Member of Mancos Shale: Predictive model for Cretaceous coal-bearing strata of western Interior: American Association of Petroleum Geologists Bulletin, v. 65, p. 2323–2340.

Seeland, D. A., and Brauch, E. F., 1975, Status of mineral resources information for the Wind River Indian Reservation, Wyoming: U.S. Geological Survey and U.S. Bureau of Mines Administrative report BIA-8, prepared for the U.S. Bureau of Indian Affairs, 66 p.

Swanson, V. E., Medlin, J. H., Hatch, J. R., Coleman, S. L., Wood, G. H., Jr., Woodruff, S. D., and Hildebrand, R. T., 1976, Collection, chemical analyses and evaluation of coal samples in 1975: U.S. Geological Survey Open-file Report OF-76-486, 503 p.

Thaden, R. E., 1978, Geologic Map of the Bonneville Quadrangle, Fremont County, Wyoming: U.S. Geological Survey, Geological Quadrangle Map

GQ-1439.

Thompson, R. M., and White, V. L., 1952, The coal deposits of the Alkali Butte, the Big Sand Draw, and the Beaver Creek Fields, Fremont County, Wyoming: U.S. Geological Survey Circular 152, 24 p.

Troyer, M. L., and Keefer, W. R., 1955, Geology of the Shotgun Butte area, Fremont County, Wyoming, U.S. Geological Survey Oil and Gas Inventory Map OM-172.

Warlow, R. C., 1981, Geophysical and lithologic logs from 3 coal test holes in the Maverick Spring Quadrangle, Fremont County, Wyoming: U.S. Geological Survey Open-file Report OF-81-727, 31 p.

Warlow, R. C., Bragg, L. J., Windolph, J. F., Jr., Hickling, N. L., Oman, J. K., and Kerr, P. T., 1986, Chemical Analysis and Evaluation of 40 samples from Upper Cretaceous coal beds from the Wind River Basin, Wyoming: U.S. Geological Survey Bulletin (in press).

Wegemann, C. H., 1911, The Salt Creek oil field, Natrona County: U.S. Geological Survey Bulletin 452, p. 43, 47.

Williams, E. G., and Keith, M. L., 1963, Relationship between sulfur in coal and the occurrence of marine roof beds: Economic Geology, v. 58, p. 720–729.

Windolph, J. F., Jr., Hickling, N. L., and Warlow, R. C., 1982, Coal resource Assessment of the Wind River Indian Reservation in Fremont and Hot Springs Counties, Wyoming: U.S. Geological Survey Administrative Report, prepared for the U.S. Bureau of Indian Affairs, 1150 p.

Windolph, J. F., Jr., 1984, A unique occurrence of Upper Cretaceous and Paleocene red beds in the Wind River Basin, Wyoming: Geological Society of America, 97th Annual Meeting, Abstracts with Programs, p. 698.

Windolph, J. F., Jr., Warlow, R. C., Hickling, N. L., and Bragg, L. J., 1986, Comparative Geochemistry of two Late Cretaceous coal beds from contrasting depositional environments in the western part of the Wind River Basin, Fremont and Hot Springs Counties, Wyoming: *in* U.S. Geological Survey Circular 979, Symposium Proceedings: a National Agenda for Coal-Quality Research, p. 263.

Woodruff, E. G., 1906, The Lander coal field, Wyoming: U.S. Geological Survey Bulletin 316.

Woodruff, E. G., and Winchester, D. E., 1912, Coal Fields of the Wind River Region, Fremont and Natrona Counties, Wyoming, *in* Contributions to Economic Geology, 1910, Part II: U.S. Geological Survey Bulletin 471, p. 516–564.

MANUSCRIPT ACCEPTED BY THE SOCIETY APRIL 16, 1986

Geological Society of America
Special Paper 210
1986

McCourt Sandstone Tongue and Glades coal bed of the Rock Springs Formation, Wyoming and Utah

Henry W. Roehler
U.S. Geological Survey
Denver Federal Center
Denver, Colorado 80225

ABSTRACT

A study of the McCourt Sandstone Tongue and the Glades coal bed of the Upper Cretaceous Rock Springs Formation in the Rock Springs coal field has provided valuable data for reconstructing an ancient coal-forming depositional environment. The sandstone and coal were deposited on a strand plain along the western shores of the Late Cretaceous interior seaway of North America. The McCourt Sandstone Tongue consists of a sequence of lenticular, eastward offlapping, north-northeast-trending, quartzose sandstone shoreline deposits. Lithofacies include lower and middle shoreface, surf, and forebeach, which are well preserved and are identifiable by their color, stratigraphic position, and sedimentary structures. The Glades coal bed formed in a narrow lagoon between two of the offlapping strand plain sandstones. Sedimentologic, palynologic, and maceral studies reveal that the coal was derived from organic debris that accumulated on the floor of a forest swamp that originally occupied the center of the lagoon and later expanded across the lagoon. The forest swamp was surrounded by a reed swamp. Landward of the reed swamp was an apron of sand that resulted from infilling of the western margin of the lagoon by detritus eroded from an older, abandoned strand-plain shoreline deposit. Initially, a large, open body of brackish water was situated at the eastern margin of the lagoon. The Snuggedy Swamp of the lower coastal plain of South Carolina is considered a modern analog of the depositional setting of the Glades coal bed.

INTRODUCTION

Purpose. The purpose of this paper is to present a depositional model for the McCourt Sandstone Tongue and Glades coal bed of the Rock Springs coal field, Wyoming. The model is considered in light of the stratigraphy, lithology, sedimentology, paleogeography, and palynology of the Rock Springs coal field. A modern analog will be suggested to support this model.

Location and accessibility of the study area. The McCourt Sandstone Tongue and the overlying Glades coal bed of the Upper Cretaceous Rock Springs Formation are located in the southwest part of the Rock Springs coal field. The sandstone and coal were investigated along a narrow, 13-km-long belt of outcrops that parallel the Wyoming-Utah State line 30 km west of the common boundary of Wyoming, Utah, and Colorado (Fig. 1). The area is located about 70 km southwest of Rock Springs,

Wyoming, and is accessible by Wyoming Highway 530 and U.S. Highway 191. The outcrops studied extend from the vicinity of Lucerne Campground on the west shore of Flaming Gorge Reservoir eastward to near Minnies Gap on U.S. 191. (Fig. 2).

Geologic setting. Outcrops of the McCourt Sandstone Tongue and the Glades coal bed are located within a series of prominent east-west trending ridges that dip 25 to 45° northward. The ridges comprise part of the northern foothills of the Uinta Mountains. From Flaming Gorge Reservoir eastward to Minnies Gap, the sandstone and coal are exposed in the lower part of south-facing slopes of a high-standing hogback ridge called "The Glades." The Glades ridge is capped by resistant sandstone of the Upper Cretaceous Ericson Sandstone that unconformably overlies the Rock Springs Formation. A valley that parallels the south

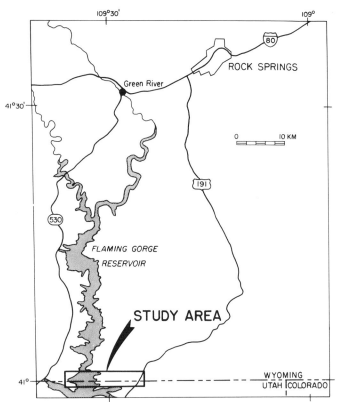

Figure 1. Map of the southwest part of the Rock Springs coal field showing the location of the study area.

margin of the Glades ridge is formed by deeply eroded shale of the Black Butte Tongue of the Rock Springs Formation. At the south edge of the shale valley is a topographically lower sandstone ridge that comprises the Minnies Gap Tongue of the Rock Springs Formation (Fig. 3). The structure in the Glades ridge consists of a broad, steeply dipping, north-plunging anticlinal nose. Steep northward dips across the nose of the anticline reflect deformation of the strata caused by movement of the Uinta Mountain fault of early Tertiary age located a few kilometers to the south. The Uinta Mountain fault is a reverse thrust fault that dips steeply southward and has several kilometers of displacement.

STRATIGRAPHY

Rock Springs Formation. The Rock Springs Formation was named by Schultz (1920) for coal-bearing rocks of the Montana Group in the Rock Springs coal field. The name McCourt Sandstone Tongue was assigned by Smith (1961) to a laterally continuous sandstone tongue that crops out in the upper part of the Rock Springs Formation near the McCourt Ranch in the southern part of the Rock Springs uplift. In this paper, the name Glades coal bed is applied to a previously unnamed coal bed in the study area.

The Rock Springs Formation has a maximum thickness of about 485 m in the study area. It consists of gray to tan, fine- to medium-grained sandstone, and interbedded gray siltstone and shale, gray and brown carbonaceous shale, and coal. The formation conformably overlies and intertongues with the Blair Formation, which is also of Late Cretaceous age. Both the Rock Springs and Blair Formations intertongue with and are replaced laterally eastward by two units that are in part equivalent—the Upper Cretaceous Baxter Shale of the Baxter basin near the Rock Springs uplift and the Hilliard Shale of the north slope of the Uinta Mountains and adjoining Wyoming.

Several sandstone and shale tongues are recognized within the Rock Springs Formation in the study area. In ascending sequence, these are the Chimney Rock Tongue (Hale, 1950), Minnies Gap Tongue (Roehler, 1965), Black Butte Tongue (Hale, 1950), Brooks Tongue (Smith, 1961), Coulson Tongue (Smith, 1961), McCourt Sandstone Tongue (Smith, 1961), and Gottsche Tongue (Smith, 1965). The stratigraphy and depositional environments of the Rock Springs Formation across the study area are shown in Figure 4 in generalized cross section A–A′.

The age of the upper part of the Rock Springs Formation is considered to be early Campanian (79–80 m.y.) based on the ammonite fossil, *Baculites* sp. (weakly ribbed), that was collected in 1967 at USGS Locality D6399 (J. R. Gill, unpublished data). Gill collected this specimen 23 m below the base of the Brooks Sandstone Tongue in NW¼sec.16,T.3N.,R.24E., in outcrops near Clay Basin, 17 km east of the study area (Fig. 2).

The Rock Springs Formation correlates regionally with the Blackhawk Formation in the vicinity of Price, Utah, with the Allen Ridge Formation in the vicinity of Rawlins, Wyoming, and with the Mesaverde Formation in the vicinity of Casper, Wyoming. The overlying Ericson Sandstone correlates with the Castlegate Sandstone (Price, Utah), the Pine Ridge Sandstone (Rawlins, Wyoming), and the Teapot Sandstone Member of the Mesaverde Formation (Casper, Wyoming).

McCourt Sandstone Tongue. The McCourt Sandstone Tongue ranges in thickness from 25 to 75 m and is composed mostly of sandstone, but it also contains thin interbedded siltstone and shale. The sandstone weathers to distinct benches along outcrops. The sandstone is normally tan or brown in the lower part and light-gray to white in the upper part. The sandstone is usually very fine-grained to fine-grained and intertongues with gray siltstone and shale for several meters at the base; it coarsens upward to medium-grained and has a sharp, clearly defined top. The sandstone benches offlap eastward (Fig. 4).

Glades Coal bed. The Glades coal bed is separated from the underlying McCourt Sandstone Tongue by 2 to 17 m of sandstone, siltstone, and shale. The coal bed is lenticular in cross section and has a maximum recorded thickness of 3.6 m near the middle of the outcrop belt. The coal bed contains carbonaceous shale, sandstone, and tonstein partings. It thins and wedges out as a single bed eastward. Westward, it thickens and splits into several thin, widely separated beds before wedging out.

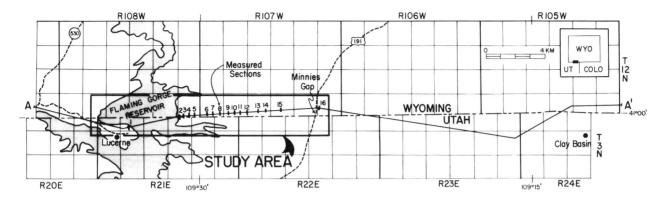

Figure 2. Map showing the location of Lucerne Campground, Minnies Gap, and measured sections in the study area. Cross section A–A' is illustrated in Figure 4.

SEDIMENTOLOGY

Depositional Environments and Lithofacies. The Mc-Court Sandstone Tongue and the Glades coal bed were deposited along the western shore of the Late Cretaceous interior seaway of North America in a subtropical to tropical paleoclimate (Norris and others, 1975; Kauffman, 1977). Temperature and precipitation ranges have not been determined, but palynomorphs collected from the Glades coal bed reveal that the paleoclimate was sufficiently warm and wet to favor the luxuriant growth of palms and cycads, as well as conifers, sphagnum peat moss, and freshwater green algae (E. I. Robbins, written communication, 1983).

The McCourt Sandstone Tongue is composed of a series of strand-plain sandstones that offlap eastward in imbricate fashion. The imbrication of the sandstones in the tongue occurs across the entire study area (Roehler and Phillips, 1980) and is evident in outcrops along facies strike northeast of the study area in the southern part of the Rock Springs uplift (Roehler, 1983). This offlapping relationship has also been interpreted on correlations of geophysical logs of oil and gas test wells (Roehler, 1984). Parts of four sandstone shoreline units are present within the McCourt Tongue in the study area. They weather to four distinct benches on outcrops; for that reason they are identified and discussed as benches A, B, C and D in this paper (Fig. 5).

Shoreline lithofacies in benches A through D are characterized by their color, stratigraphic position, and sedimentary structures. The lithofacies are interpreted as representing lower shoreface, middle shoreface, surf, and forebeach environments. They are illustrated on a restored cross section (Fig. 6). The lower shoreface is composed mostly of parallel laminated very fine grained sandstone and siltstone. Beds of this lithofacies weather to tan or brown ledges that contain numerous trace fossils (Figs. 7, 8). The middle shoreface overlies the lower shoreface and consists of tan, very fine- to medium-grained sandstone. The lithofacies consists of thick, parallel beds that are internally bioturbated (Fig. 9). The trace fossil *Ophiomorpha* is abundant in the middle shoreface. The surf and forebeach lithofacies cap the sandstone benches. These lithofacies weather light-gray to white and are

composed of fine- to medium-grained sandstone that exhibits thin, bidirectional, planar crossbeds and small-scale trough crossbeds in the lower part. The upper part exhibits thin, parallel, tabular beds at the top (Figs. 10, 11). Eolian dune sandstone that normally is present overlying the forebeach lithofacies was not recognized in the study area. It may not have been preserved. Washover fan deposits, however, are present along the landward margins of some of the sandstones of the McCourt Sandstone Tongue. These deposits are mostly composed of light-gray or white, fine- to medium-grained sandstone. They exhibit thin, tabular, current rippled bedding, and in places they show small-scale trough crossbeds.

The McCourt sandstone benches are composed of 92 to 96 percent clear to milky quartz grains, 1 to 3 percent rock fragments, and 1 to 5 percent feldspar, mica, and heavy mineral grains. The cementing materials are an unidentified white clay in

Figure 3. Outcrop of the upper part of the Rock Springs Formation. View is west from U.S. Highway 191 at Minnies Gap. 1) top of Minnies Gap Tongue, 2) valley formed by the Black Butte Shale Tongue, 3) McCourt Sandstone Tongue, and 4) the Glades ridge capped by Ericson Sandstone.

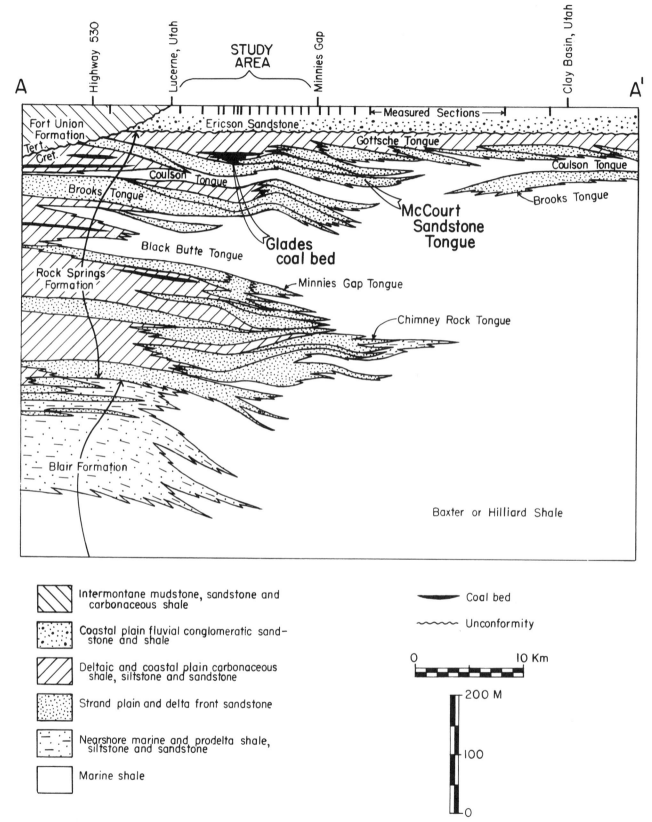

Figure 4. Cross section A–A′ showing the generalized stratigraphic relationships and depositional environments of the Rock Springs and associated formations across the study area. The location of cross section A–A′ is shown in Figure 2. (after Roehler and Phillips, 1980.)

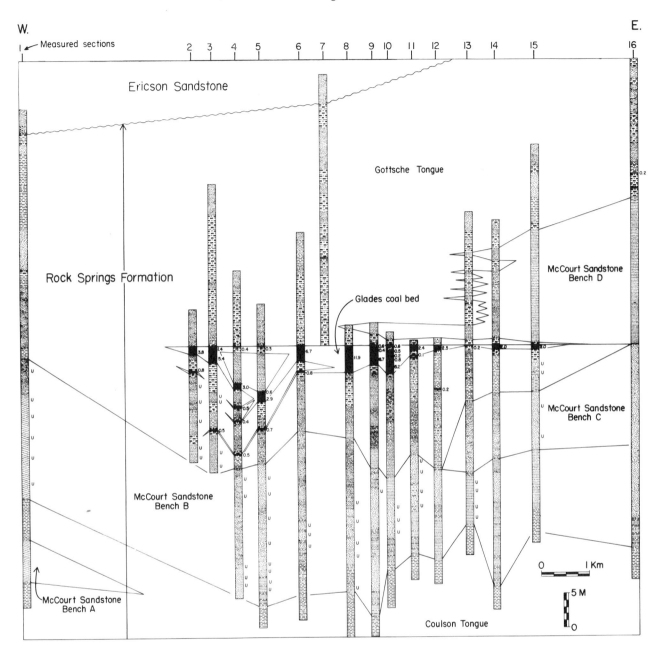

Figure 5. Stratigraphic cross section of the McCourt Sandstone Tongue, Glades coal bed, and associated rocks in the study area. The locations of 16 measured sections used to construct the cross section are indicated in Figure 2.

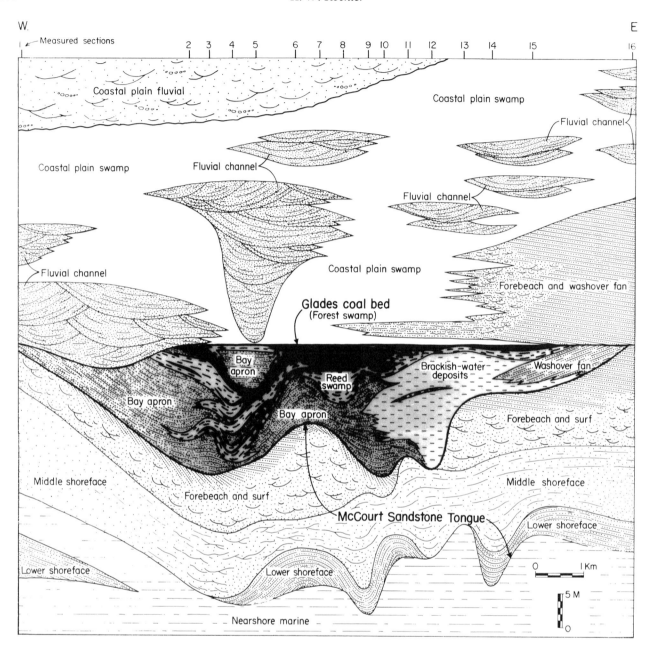

Figure 6. Restored cross section of rocks exposed in the study area showing depositional environments and lithofacies. Figure 6 has been constructed from the data shown in the measured sections in Figure 5. The lithofacies overlying the Glades coal bed are not discussed in this paper.

the forebeach and surf, whereas hematite cements are more common in the middle and lower shoreface. The heavy mineral assemblage consists dominantly of zircon and tourmaline and minor amounts of garnet and rutile (G. B. Schneider, written communication, 1984).

The Glades coal bed was deposited in a narrow, elongate lagoon that developed between and parallel to two offlapping strand-plain sandstones of the McCourt Sandstone Tongue. (The term lagoon in this paper includes swamps). The two sandstones are identified on Figure 5 as benches B and C. Marine shoreline

sedimentation, which deposited bench B, ended prior to the deposition of sediments in the lagoon. The shoreline at this time had shifted to the eastern edge of bench C, a barrier bar that had developed offshore. As the lagoon between benches B and C filled, bench B was mostly buried and preserved, but exposed parts of bench B were subjected to rapid subaerial erosion. An early stage of Glades coal deposition is illustrated in Figure 12.

The sediments that filled the lagoon between benches B and C are less than 20 m thick. They are lenticular in overall cross section, have an undulating lower surface, and rest upon the

Figure 7. Parallel-bedded lower shoreface lithofacies overlain by the massive middle shoreface lithofacies in the McCourt Sandstone Tongue in measured section No. 8. The base of the McCourt Sandstone Tongue (arrow) is located near the lower right-hand corner of the photograph.

Figure 9. Thick, parallel beds of the middle shoreface lithofacies of the McCourt Sandstone Tongue in measured section No. 8. The middle shoreface lithofacies here is about 9 m thick.

Figure 8. Photograph of trace fossils in sandstone of the lower shoreface lithofacies of the McCourt Sandstone Tongue in SE¼SE¼sec.19,T.12N., R.107W. Traces include a) worm trails and b) crustacean living chambers. c) Light colored bands are crests of wave ripples.

Figure 10. Planar and small-scale trough crossbeds in the surf lithofacies of the McCourt Sandstone Tongue in measured section No. 8. [Scale 1 m] thickness of outcrop shown is about 2.0 m.

McCourt Sandstone Tongue, as shown in Figure 6. The end of deposition in the lagoon appears to correspond to the position of the upper surface of the Glades coal bed.

The sediments that filled the lagoon have distinctive upper and lower lithofacies that reflect fluctuating rates of sedimentation in the lagoon, changes in water salinities, and plant succession. The lower lithofacies was deposited by rapid sedimentation in a saltwater environment containing sparse vegetation. It is characterized by bay apron sandstone, brackish-water shale and siltstone, and a washover fan sandstone. The lithofacies called the bay apron occupied the landward part of the lagoon. It was

deposited by rapid infilling of the lagoon by sediments eroded from the subaerial parts of the older, abandoned shoreline, bench B, that was present along the west edge of the lagoon. The bay apron deposit weathers light gray and is composed mostly of thin, parallel, current-rippled, fine- to medium-grained sandstone and some very thin interbedded and interlaminated gray siltstone and gray silty shale (Fig. 13). The bay apron formed from small coalescing fans (fan deltas) at the mouths of streams that entered the lagoon from the west. The eastern part of the lagoon was occupied by an open body of brackish water on the bottom of which were deposited muds and silts. A washover fan composed

Figure 11. Thin, parallel, tabular sandstone in a forebeach lithofacies of the McCourt Sandstone Tongue in measured section No. 8. The pick in the upper center of the photograph is 43 cm long.

Figure 13. Thin, parallel, current-rippled sandstone and very thin interbedded and interlaminated siltstone and shale deposited as part of a bay apron lithofacies adjacent to the Glades coal bed in measured section No. 3. The pick in the right center of the photograph is 43 cm long.

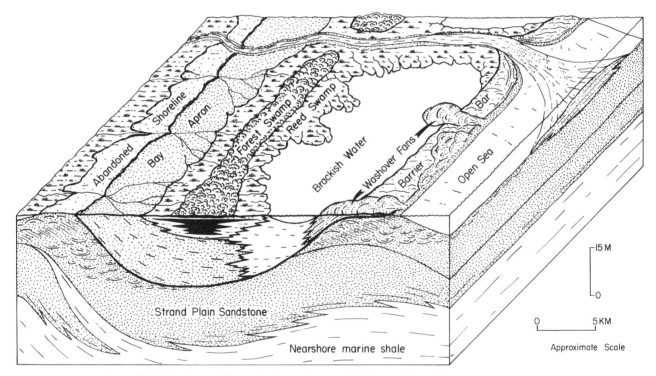

Figure 12. Block diagram illustrating the early stage of Glades coal deposition. The diagram has been constructed from the data shown in Figures 4 and 5.

of sand projected westward into the open waters of the bay from the back-barrier flat of bench C (Figs. 5, 6).

The upper lagoon lithofacies reflects a slow sedimentation rate, the freshening of the lagoon water, and the establishment of broad areas of swamps. A brackish-water reed swamp containing herbaceous, grasslike plants spread across the lagoon, covering the bay apron and the area formerly occupied by open brackish water. The sediments deposited in the reed swamp were mostly

carbonaceous muds. Later a freshwater forest swamp occupied the center of the lagoon, and soon enlarged to form a peat island. Eventually the peat island enlarged and the forest swamp expanded across the lagoon, replacing the reed swamp. The Glades peat (coal) bed is composed of organic debris that accumulated on the floor of the forest swamp. Dinoflagellate cysts have been identified in one of the coal samples collected from the Glades bed in measured section No. 8 (E. I. Robbins, written communi-

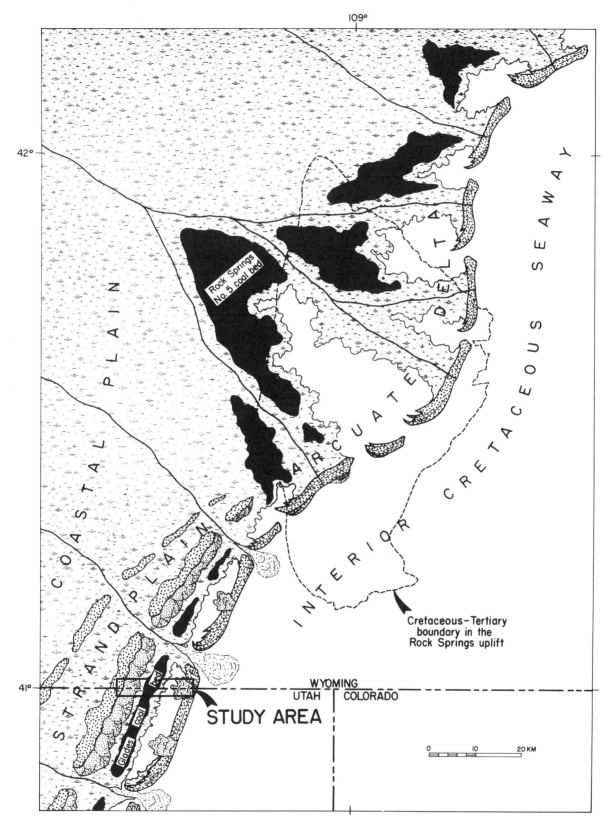

Figure 14. Idealized paleogeography of part of the western coastline of the interior Cretaceous seaway during deposition of the McCourt Sandstone Tongue and the Glades coal bed.

Figure 15. The upper part of the Glades coal bed exposed in a trench dug at measured section No. 8. Two of the tonsteins in the coal area identified by the letter "T." The lower tonstein is 65 mm thick.

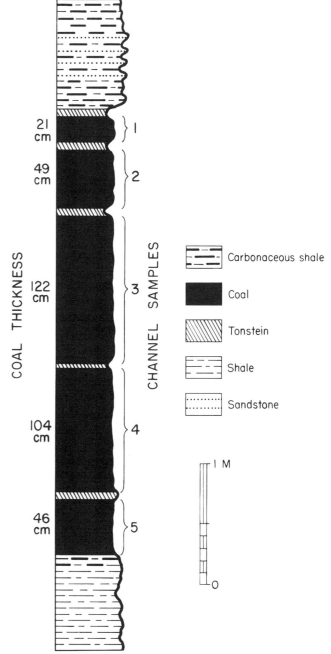

Figure 16. Columnar section of the Glades coal bed in measured section No. 8, located in SE¼sec.19,T.12N.,R.107W.

cation, 1984). The presence of this marine microfossil indicates 1) that tidal channels were present in the lagoon, 2) that the marine microfossils could have been carried inland through these channels by tidal flow, and 3) that the channels may have periodically overflowed their banks and flushed the marine microfossils into adjacent freshwater forest swamps.

The Gottsche Tongue of the Rock Springs Formation, which overlies the Glades coal bed, is composed of gray, fine- to medium-grained sandstone, gray siltstone and shale, gray and brown carbonaceous shale, and rare, thin beds of light-gray tuff and coal. These rocks are interpreted as fluvial channel and swamp deposits that were laid down on a coastal plain landward of the shoreline deposits of the McCourt Sandstone Tongue during the retreat of the Late Cretaceous interior sea from the study area.

A modern analog: Snuggedy Swamp, South Carolina. The McCourt Sandstone Tongue and the Glades coal bed were deposited in a setting that is analogous to the modern Snuggedy Swamp on the lower coastal plain of South Carolina. According to Staub and Cohen (1978), the peat beds in Snuggedy Swamp are as much as 450 cm thick and are situated between Pleistocene barrier islands several kilometers inland from presently active barrier-lagoon sedimentation. The Pleistocene barrier islands are composed of fine- to medium-grained quartz sand. They are undergoing erosion, and the eroded material interfingers with or overlies the Snuggedy peat beds. The Snuggedy peat beds are oriented parallel to the barrier islands. They have an undulatory basal contact with underlying sediments.

The peat beds in Snuggedy Swamp are composed of the remains of trees and grasses that grew in a freshwater environment. The peat beds are reddish brown and consist of well-preserved plant fragments in the upper part, but become dark brown to black and gel-like with depth. They contain thin layers of charcoal that were deposited as a result of the periodic burning of parts of the swamp.

Staub and Cohen (1979) believe that Snuggedy Swamp began as a lagoon composed of salt marshes and open-water bays. With time, freshwater vegetation encroached upon the salt marshes and formed islands of peat between tidal creeks. The peat islands eventually expanded and coalesced to form a blanket of peat that engulfed the swamp and lapped onto the adjacent barrier islands.

PALEOGEOGRAPHY

Figure 14 shows a segment of the western coastline of the Late Cretaceous interior seaway as it is interpreted to have looked during deposition of the McCourt Sandstone Tongue and the Glades coal bed. The strand-plain depositional environment in the study area had a straight, north-northeast-trending shoreline. Inland from these were the eroded remnants of older, abandoned shorelines that formed low sandstone ridges. The lateral spacing of these ridges varied from 5 to 12 km. The presence of the thick Glades coal bed above the McCourt Sandstone Tongue is anomalous. The Glades coal bed and associated rocks of lagoonal origin comprise the only important coal-forming depositional environment that has been identified between the offlapping shorelines of the McCourt Sandstone Tongue that cross the study area (Fig. 4).

Northeast of the study area and within the Rock Springs coal field, the McCourt strand-plain depositional environment merged with an arcuate delta-plain depositional environment. Landward of both the strand-plain and delta-plain environments a broad, swampy, coastal-plain depositional environment was present. The depositional environments and traces of the coastline southwest of the study area are unknown, because post-Laramide erosion along the Uinta Mountain uplift has removed all Cretaceous rocks.

The shapes of the Late Cretaceous shorelines undoubtedly were modified by the effects of longshore currents and tides. Sedimentary structures show that longshore currents moved uniformly southward along the western margins of the seaway, which caused a pronounced southward drift of sediments. The tidal ranges have not been determined, but diurnal tides of about 1 m are postulated for this period of deposition.

The Glades coal bed occupies the same stratigraphic position as the Rock Springs No. 5 coal bed along the west flank of the Rock Springs uplift (Fig. 14). Both beds have four thin tonstein partings within the coal and another thin tonstein at the top. The two coals were deposited in different depositional environments (strand plain vs. delta plain), but they appear to be chronostratigraphic equivalents.

COAL COMPOSITION AND RANK

The Glades coal bed was sampled for maceral and proximate and ultimate analyses in a trench that was dug at measured section No. 8, located in SE¼sec.19,T.12N., R.107W. (Figs. 3, 15). The bed at this location consists of 3.42 m of clean, bright coal, excluding four thin tonstein partings. Five channel samples were collected between the tonstein partings as indicated on a columnar section of the coal (Fig. 16). The tonsteins were not analyzed, but they appear to be composed of flesh-colored kaolinite of probable air-fall volcanic ash origin that weathers chalky white on outcrops.

The coal macerals (by volume) average 82 percent vitrinite, 4 percent exinite, and 14 percent inertinite (Table 1). The vitrinite is interpreted to have been derived from woody material (R. W. Stanton, written communication, 1983), a factor attesting to the forest swamp origin of the coal. The five samples from measured

TABLE 1. MACERALS IN THE GLADES COAL BED (VOL. PCT.) IN MEASURED SECTION NO. 8.

Channel sample number	Coal thickness (cm)	Vitrinite (woody material)	Exinite (resin, oil, wax, cuticle)	Inertinite (fusinite, macrinite)
1	21	86	4	10
2	49	75	4	21
3	122	82	4	14
4	104	83	3	14
5	46	86	4	10
Ave. vol. pct.		82	4	14

Note: The stratigraphic position and thickness of the sampled intervals are shown in Figure 16.

Source: Unpublished data of R.W. Stanton.

TABLE 2. PROXIMATE AND ULTIMATE ANALYSES OF WEATHERED CHANNEL SAMPLES OF THE GLADES COAL BED (AS RECEIVED; WT. PCT.) IN MEASURED SECTION NO. 8

Channel sample number	Proximate Analysis				Ultimate Analysis				
	Moisture	Ash	Volatile Matter	Fixed Carbon	Hydrogen	Carbon	Nitrogen	Sulfur	Oxygen
1	26.70	10.27	30.08	32.95	5.30	41.43	0.85	0.29	41.86
2	30.19	4.43	32.69	32.69	5.78	43.35	0.90	0.30	45.24
3	24.25	18.03	29.03	28.69	5.01	38.31	0.80	0.28	37.57
4	23.77	26.29	23.58	26.36	4.59	33.63	0.70	0.24	34.55
5	24.12	25.21	26.47	24.20	4.80	33.41	0.72	0.55	35.35
Ave. wt. (pct.)	25.81	16.85	28.37	28.98	5.10	38.03	0.79	0.33	38.91

Note: The stratigraphic position and thickness of the sampled intervals are shown in Figure 16.

H. W. Roehler

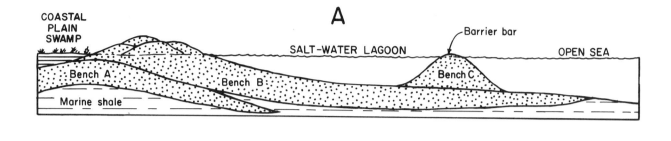

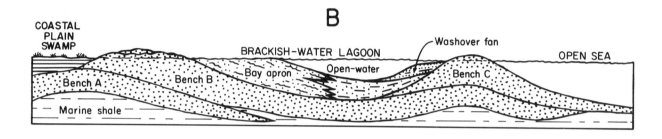

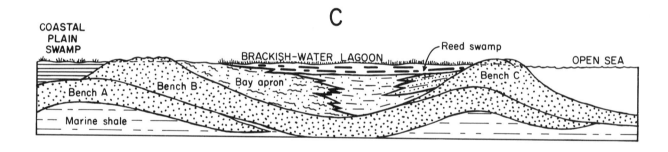

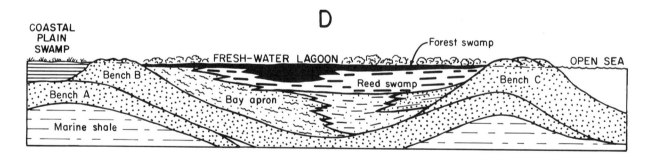

Figure 17. Cross sections depicting the depositional history of the McCourt Sandstone Tongue and Glades coal bed. Cross sections are not to scale. A) an early stage shows the development of a lagoon behind a barrier bar; B) a middle stage shows infilling of the lagoon by bay-apron and washover-fan deposits and laterally equivalent brackish water fine-grained sediments; C) shows the development of a brackish-water reed swamp; and D) a late stage during which a fresh-water forest swamp develops and gives rise to the Glades coal bed.

section No. 8 all contain 1 to 2 percent fusinite, which probably indicates that the swamp in which the peat (coal) was deposited was periodically damaged by fires.

The proximate and ultimate analyses of the coal samples from measured section No. 8 are shown in Table 2. These data compare to an overall average for coal in the Rock Springs Formation in the Rock Springs coal field of 13.2 percent moisture, 4.3 percent ash, 33.8 percent volatile matter, and 48.7 percent fixed carbon; 5.7 percent hydrogen, 63.6 percent carbon, 1.2 percent nitrogen, 0.9 percent sulfur, and 24.2 percent oxygen (Root and others, 1973). The higher moisture and oxygen, and lower volatile matter and carbon in the Glades bed, when compared to other lumped Rock Springs coals, can probably be [primarily] attributed to the surface weathering of the Glades outcrop samples. The higher ash of the Glades coal bed is probably due to depositional environment.

The average heating value for coal from the Rock Springs Formation in the Rock Springs coal field is 11,400 Btu/lb (Root and others, 1973). The average rank of the Rock Springs coal on the basis of this heating value is high-volatile C bituminous. The heating values for the analyzed samples of coal from the Glades bed in measured section No. 8 cannot be used to determine the rank of the coal, because the values are low (5,118-6,371 Btu/lb) due to the surface weathering. R. W. Stanton (written communication, 1983) has determined that the vitrinite reflectance of the coal in weathered samples from measured section No. 8 is 0.40 R_0. This reflectance indicates that the minimum rank of the coal is subbituminous.

The Glades coal bed, which has not been mined in the study area, occurs in strata that dip 25° to 45°. The area is remotely located, and the resources are small. These factors preclude mining of the coal in the foreseeable future.

CONCLUSIONS

The McCourt Sandstone Tongue and the Glades coal bed are products of a strand-plain, coal-forming depositional environment that was located along the western shore of the Late Cretaceous (Campanian) interior seaway of North America. The McCourt Sandstone Tongue is composed of several marine shoreline sandstones that offlapped southeastward across the study area in response to a regression of the interior seaway. The Glades coal bed was deposited in an elongate swamp that developed in a lagoon located between and parallel to two of the offlapping shoreline sandstones. The depositional history of the McCourt Sandstone Tongue and the Glades coal bed is depicted in Figure 17.

ACKNOWLEDGMENTS

I would like to thank E. I. Robbins, R. W. Stanton, and G. B. Schneider of the U.S. Geological Survey for analyzing samples I collected at measured section No. 8 (Fig. 2) and for providing valuable palynological, coal maceral, and petrographic data, respectively. S. T. Phillips assisted me in the field in 1979. Proximate and ultimate analyses of coal outcrop channel samples were done by Geochemical Testing, Somerset, Pa.

REFERENCES CITED

Hale, L. A., 1950, Stratigraphy of the upper Cretaceous Montana group in the Rock Springs Uplift, Sweetwater County, Wyoming: Wyoming 5th Annual Field Conference Guidebook, August 1950.
Kauffman, E. G., 1977, Geological and biological overview; Western Interior Cretaceous Basin: The Mountain Geologist, v. 14, nos. 3 and 4, p. 75–100.
Norris, G., Jarzen, D. M., and Awai-Thorne, B. U., 1975, Evolution of the Cretaceous Terrestial Palynoflora in western Canada: Geological Association of Canada Special Paper 13, p. 333–364.
Roehler, H. W., 1965, Summary of Pre-Laramide Late Cretaceous sedimentation in the Rock Springs uplift area: Wyoming Geological Association Guidebook 19th Annual Field Conference, Sedimentation of Late Cretaceous and Tertiary outcrops, Rock Springs uplift, 1965.
—— , 1983, Stratigraphy of Upper Cretaceous and Lower Tertiary outcrops in the Rock Springs uplift, Wyoming: U.S. Geological Survey Miscellaneous Investigations Series Map I-1500.
—— , 1984, Electric log correlations of the Upper Cretaceous Rock Springs and Blair Formations on the east and west flanks of the Rock Springs uplift, Wyoming: U.S. Geological Survey Miscellaneous Investigations Series Map MF-1785.
Roehler, H. W., and Phillips, S. T., 1980, Cross section of the Rock Springs and Blair Formations in measured sections in the Flaming Gorge-Minnies Gap-Clay Basin Area, Utah and Wyoming: U.S. Geological Survey Miscellaneous Field Investigations Map MF-1216.

Root, F. K., Glass, G. B., and Lane, D. W., 1973, Sweetwater County, Wyoming, Geologic map and atlas and summary of economic mineral resources: The Geological Survey of Wyoming, County Resource Series No. 2 (Coal).
Schultz, A. R., 1920, Oil possibilities in and around Baxter Basin, in the Rock Springs uplift, Sweetwater County, Wyoming: U.S. Geological Survey Bulletin 702, p. 32.
Smith, J. H., 1961, A summary of stratigraphy and paleontology, Upper Colorado and Montanan Groups, south-central Wyoming: Wyoming Geological Association Guidebook, 16th Annual Field Conference, Symposium on Late Cretaceous rocks, Wyoming and adjacent areas, Casper, Wyoming, p. 101–102.
—— , 1965, A summary of stratigraphy and paleontology, upper Colorado and Montana groups, southcentral Wyoming, northeastern Utah, and northwestern Colorado: Wyoming Geological Association Guidebook, 19th Annual Field Conference, Sedimentation of Late Cretaceous and Tertiary outcrops, Rock Springs uplift, 1965.
Staub, J. R., and Cohen, A. D., 1979, The Snuggedy Swamp of South Carolina; A Modern Back-Barrier Coal-Forming Environment: Journal of Sedimentary Petrology, v. 49, no. 1, p. 133–144.

MANUSCRIPT ACCEPTED BY THE SOCIETY APRIL 16, 1976

Discussion of paper by Henry W. Roehler. Responses by Roehler.

Robert Raymond (Los Alamos National Laboratory)
Question: Peat environments change radically before and after ash falls with respect to their organic constituents; that is, pioneer peat communities are very different from climax communities. Rather than comparing proximate analyses and maceral analyses for the entire coal section between tonstein layers, shouldn't you sample the coal sections to better represent the various plant communities?
Response: The Rock Springs No. 5 coal bed was sampled inch by inch by Norrie Robbins (USGS, Reston). Her data are not yet available, but she has apparently found that the palynomorphs indicate that fern-type vegetation was most abundant above the tonsteins, and that this vegetation grades upward into normal climax vegetation that formed most of the peats.

Joe Sarnecki (Exxon Coal Resources)
Question: What mechanism do you attest to the formation of the bay-apron sands at the base of the coals?
Response: Parallel streams along Bench "B" not only destroyed that bench but also brought terrestrial sands, etc., into the basin.

Paul C. Lyons
Question: Would you comment on whether other interpretations are valid for the origin of fusain or fusinite indicated in the Glades coal bed?
Response: I cannot answer this question because the maceral analyses of the Glades coal bed were done by Ronald W. Stanton (USGS, Reston). I favor the idea of swamp fires as the origin for the 1 to 2 percent fusinite in the coal.
Lyons: Teichmuller (in Stach's Textbook of Petrology) distinguished four different origins of fusain of fusinite. Degradation has to be considered as one alternative explanation for a pyrogenetic (fire) origin of fusain or fusinite.

Geological Society of America
Special Paper 210
1986

The non-transferability of a Cretaceous coal model in the San Juan Basin of New Mexico and Colorado

James E. Fassett
U.S. Geological Survey
903 National Center
Reston, Virginia 22092

ABSTRACT

The San Juan Basin of northwest New Mexico and southwest Colorado contains several Upper Cretaceous coal-bearing formations. The coals in these formations were deposited in environments associated with repeated transgressions and regressions of the Western Interior seaway in Late Cretaceous time. A detailed subsurface and surface study of the coal beds in one of these units, the Fruitland Formation, formed the basis for a coal-depositional model (Fassett and Hinds, 1971). This model basically shows that the thickest Fruitland coals formed landward of thickly stacked sandstone beds of the regressive-marine Pictured Cliffs Sandstone. Transferability of the Fruitland coal model was tested by comparing it to another San Juan Basin coal-bearing rock unit, the lower Menefee Formation. Lower Menefee coal deposits were formed in association with the Point Lookout Sandstone, an older regressive-marine unit. The purpose of this comparison was to see if thick lower Menefee coal beds were also concentrated adjacent to thick vertical shoreface-sandstone buildups. This comparison showed that even though thick sandstone buildups were found in the Point Lookout, no thick coal beds were found in the lower Menefee Formation adjacent to them. This test suggests that certain coal depositional models may have limited value as predictive tools and must be used with caution by coal explorationists. Even more importantly, potential coal-bearing areas should never be written off simply because they do not fit a previously described model.

INTRODUCTION

The San Juan Basin of northwest New Mexico and southwest Colorado (Fig. 1) contains large tonnages of coal in several Upper Cretaceous rock units. One of these units, the Fruitland Formation, was studied in considerable detail throughout the San Juan Basin by Fassett and Hinds (1971). That study showed that the distribution of the thickest total coal in the Fruitland seemed to be related spatially to the locations of large vertical buildups of the underlying regressive-marine Pictured Cliffs Sandstone. Because of this relationship, a model describing the occurrence of coal in the Fruitland Formation has been developed.

In this report, I have summarized the facts relating to the distribution of coal in the Fruitland and then compared the generalizations resulting from that study with the distribution of coal in another Upper Cretaceous coal-bearing unit, the basal part of the Menefee Formation. The basal Menefee was deposited

in the San Juan Basin about 8 to 10 million years before the Fruitland in a paleodepositional environment that was apparently remarkably similar to that of the Fruitland. I have concluded the paper with an assessment of the value of using models of coal occurrence in one formation to predict the occurrence of coal deposited in similar paleoenvironments in other formations.

GENERAL GEOLOGY

The central part of the San Juan Basin is outlined in Figure 1 by the outcrop of the Fruitland Formation. This outline is roughly circular in shape, except for the southwest part, which is linear and northwest-trending and the east side, which is linear and north-trending. The basin shape reflects both its tectonic

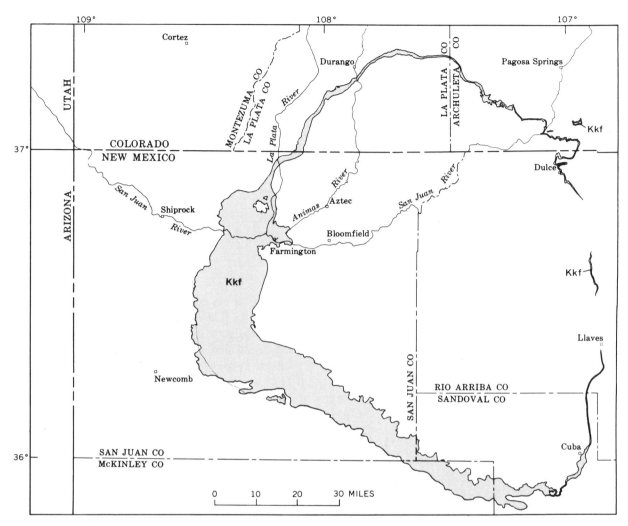

Figure 1. Index map showing the location of the San Juan Basin. Shaded area (kkf) outlining the basin is the Fruitland Formation outcrop. From Fassett and Hinds (1971).

origin and depositional history; the circular part to the northwest, north, and northeast and the linear east side reflect monoclinal uplifts that formed during late Paleocene, Eocene, and Oligocene time (Fassett, 1985). The northwest-trending southwest rim is not a structural feature; it reflects the physiographic grain of this part of the basin, which in turn reflects the northwest depositional strike of nearly all of the Upper Cretaceous rocks deposited in the San Juan Basin.

The basin structure is asymmetric (Fig. 2), with its northwest-trending axis located near and parallel to the northeast rim of the basin. Dips around the northwest, north, and east parts of the basin are on the order of 20–40 degrees, whereas dips on the west and south sides are quite gentle and average less than a degree. The diameter of the basin is about 161 km (100 mi) and its surface area is about 19,425 sq km (7,500 mi^2).

The San Juan Basin is a vast storehouse of gas, oil, and coal. In the United States the San Juan Basin gas field is second in size only to the Hugoton field of Oklahoma, Texas, and Kansas. Total cumulative gas production in the New Mexico part of the basin through 1982 was 12.8 trillion cubic feet of gas (CFG). Oil production, although not as impressive as the amount of gas production, is significant, with nearly 190 million barrels of oil produced through 1982. Including gas produced from oil wells and condensate produced from gas wells, the grand totals, through 1982 are 13.2 trillion CFG and 250 million barrels of oil. (Figures are from the New Mexico Department of Energy and Minerals as reported in Fassett, 1983a).

To produce all of this oil and gas, more than 16,000 oil and gas wells have been drilled in the San Juan Basin of New Mexico through 1982, most of them since the 1950s. Geophysical logs available for most of these wells have made it possible to do extremely detailed subsurface studies of the Upper Cretaceous rocks of the San Juan Basin. The excellent bedrock exposures in the basin have made it possible to correlate rock units from the subsurface directly to the outcrop to produce a total three-dimensional picture of the rocks of the basin.

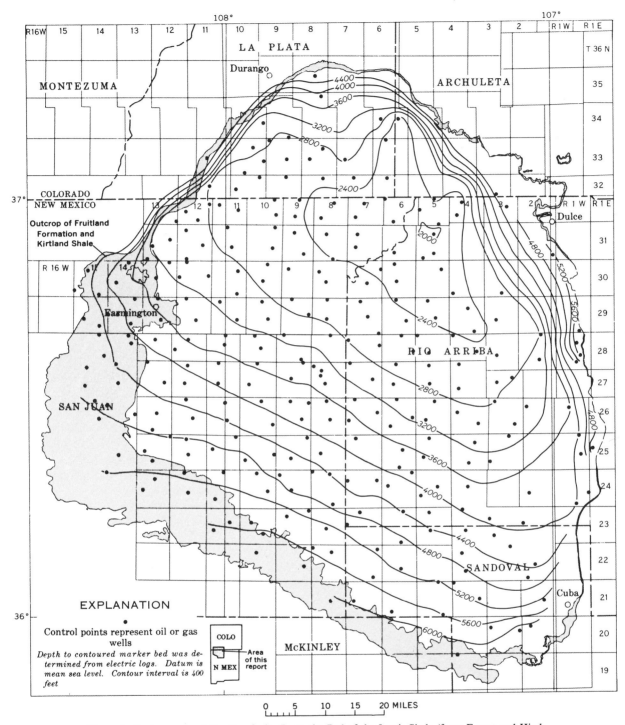

Figure 2. Contour map of the Huerfanito Bentonite Bed of the Lewis Shale (from Fassett and Hinds, 1971).

FRUITLAND FORMATION

Physical Characteristics

The stratigraphic relations of the Fruitland Formation to associated rocks are shown in Figure 3. Through most of the basin, the Fruitland is underlain by the Pictured Cliffs Sandstone; throughout the western two-thirds of the basin it is overlain conformably by the Kirtland Shale. In the eastern part of the basin the Fruitland Formation is unconformably overlain by the early, but not earliest, Tertiary Ojo Alamo Sandstone (Fassett and others, 1986). Figure 1 shows that the Fruitland is missing in two

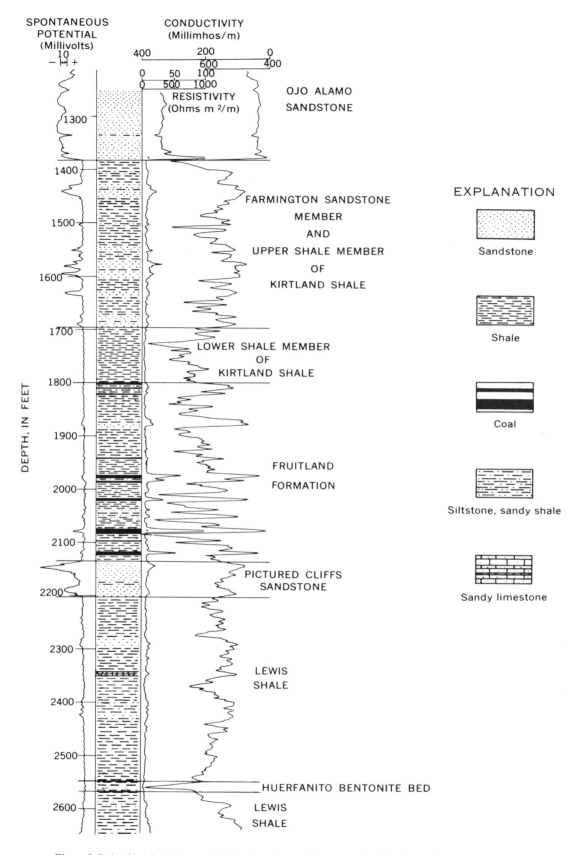

Figure 3. Induction-electric log and lithologic column of the type well of the Huerfanito Bentonite Bed of the Lewis Shale showing the interval from below the Huerfanito through the lower part of the Ojo Alamo Sandstone. Lithologies are based on an interpretation of the three curves shown (from Fassett and Hinds, 1971).

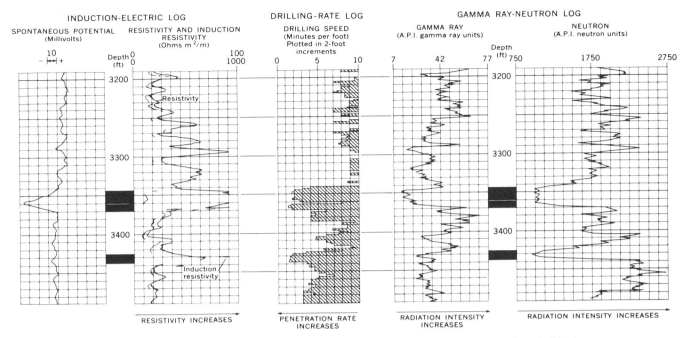

Figure 4. Induction-electric, drilling-rate, and radioactivity logs through the lower part of the Fruitland Formation, showing characteristic responses to coal (from Fassett and Hinds, 1971).

areas on the eastern edge of the basin where the formation has been removed by the pre-Ojo Alamo erosion cycle.

Where overlain by the Kirtland Shale, the Fruitland is 91 to 152 m (300–500 ft) thick, and generally thickens to the northeast. The contact between the Fruitland and Kirtland is gradational and often difficult to locate, both on the outcrop and on geophysical logs in the subsurface. As no apparent continuous lithologic break separates the two units basinwide, the contact is generally placed at the top of the highest coal or carbonaceous shale bed in the section (Fassett and Hinds, 1971). Even this criterion is fallible because thin carbonaceous shales or coaly beds are present in places in the lower part of the Kirtland.

Where overlain by the Ojo Alamo Sandstone in the eastern part of the basin, the upper contact of the Fruitland is an unconformity. The Fruitland thins eastward beneath the Ojo Alamo and is truncated along or near the east side of the basin. The relationship between the Fruitland Formation and the underlying Pictured Cliffs Sandstone is a key part of this report and is herein discussed at length.

Coal Beds

The Fruitland Formation is by far the most important coal-bearing unit of the San Juan Basin, containing more than 200 billion tons of coal (Fassett and Hinds, 1971). Fruitland coal beds range from thin stringers to beds more than 12 m (40 ft) thick. Coal zones may contain several coal beds that total as much as 24 m (80 ft) of coal. Heating values of the coal generally range from about 9,000 Btu to more than 13,000 Btu, on an as-received basis

(Hinds, 1964). These values are for pure coal exclusive of non-coal partings. Channel samples or core samples through an entire coal bed generally yield lower values, between 9,000 and 10,000 Btu, because of the ash content contributed by non-coal partings in most coal beds. Vitrinite reflectance studies (Rice, 1983) indicate that Fruitland coal rank ranges from subbituminous to medium- to low-volatile bituminous. Fruitland coal is non-coking.

Fruitland coal is generally high in ash content, even in samples free of macroscopic non-coal partings. Ash content for such samples generally ranges from slightly less than 8 percent to as high as 30 percent. There seems to be a general increase in ash content eastward across the basin. Moisture content of the coal averages from 2 to 5 percent. Sulfur content is low, averaging less than 1 percent, with a range of 0.5 to 2.5 percent. Amounts of fixed carbon and volatile elements vary across the basin, with a general increase in fixed carbon from around 50 percent in the southwestern half to more than 70 percent in the area of the present structural axis of the basin (Fassett and Hinds, 1971). This trend indicates that fixed carbon in Fruitland coals is generally related to the present depth of burial of the coal beds, although Rice (1983) points out that coal with the highest known vitrinite reflectance in the basin (1.45%) comes from a point north of the present structural axis of the basin.

The distribution of coal throughout the San Juan Basin has been determined, to a large extent, through the use of geophysical logs from oil or gas drill holes. Figure 4 shows how coal beds appear on electric, gamma ray–neutron, and drilling rate logs (data from Fassett and Hinds, 1971). More recently, density and sonic logs have been added to the files, which make the identification and measurement of coal beds in the subsurface easier but probably not much more accurate.

In conducting their subsurface coal evaluation study, Fassett and Hinds (1971) were able to confirm directly the presence and thickness of coal in the subsurface at 60 sites by being present on oil and gas drill rigs as holes were drilled through Fruitland Formation coal beds. Coal thicknesses were determined on the basis of coal cuttings that were discharged from the drill hole and, more accurately, on the basis of drilling-rate recorders on the drill rigs (see Fig. 4).

Later, when the logs (usually electric) for these wells became available, it was possible to directly compare the sample log and drilling-rate log with the electric log so as to make a direct comparison of the top and bottom of a coal bed with its log expression (Fig. 4). Having this suite of 60 carefully evaluated logs scattered across the basin made it possible to measure coal in intervening areas on the basis of logs alone with a high degree of confidence.

In hole GB-1 in the northeast part of the San Juan Basin, the Fruitland Formation was cored. A direct comparison of the coal depths and thicknesses measured from that core with a full suite of geophysical logs from the same hole further confirmed the accuracy of coal measurements based on geophysical logs. (See Fassett, 1968a, 1968b; Fassett and Hinds, 1971 for a description of the core and a depiction of some of the geophysical logs from hole GB-1.)

Figure 5 is an isopach map of Fruitland Formation total coal thicknesses throughout the San Juan Basin. Thicknesses shown at each control point represent the total of all coal beds .6 m (2 ft) or more in thickness at that point. Each thickness value may represent anywhere from one to as many as a dozen or more coal beds. A total of 324 control points (representing both subsurface and outcrop measurements) were used to construct the isopach map.

The coal distribution shown on Figure 5 reveals an interesting pattern consisting of a thick pod of coal in the southwest part of the basin; a swath of thin coal trending northwestward across the southwestern part of the basin; a band of thicker coal across the central basin area; and an area of thin coal in the northeasternmost part of the basin.

Figure 6 is an isopach map, constructed using the same control points as for Figure 5, but showing the thickest individual coal bed present at each control point. This map shows essentially the same pattern as Figure 5. What do these coal thickness patterns mean and what might they be telling us about the environments of coal deposition during Fruitland time? I will return to these questions following a short digression to discuss the formation immediately underlying the Fruitland Formation—the Pictured Cliffs Sandstone.

PICTURED CLIFFS SANDSTONE

The Pictured Cliffs Sandstone underlies the Fruitland For-

mation through most of the San Juan Basin. The Pictured Cliffs is a very fine- to fine-grained quartzose sandstone that, at most exposures, is made up of an upper part consisting of one or two ledges of massive sandstone and a lower part consisting of interbedded sandstones and shales. Sandstone beds in the lower part become thinner and finer grained downward in the section. The Pictured Cliffs was deposited during the final regression of the Late Cretaceous epeiric seaway from the San Juan Basin area; it was deposited as a strandline sandstone as the sea retreated northeastward out of the area. Figure 7 shows the paleogeography of North America during deposition of the Pictured Cliffs Sandstone.

The model for deposition of the Upper Cretaceous rocks of the San Juan Basin associated with transgressing and regressing shorelines over a period of some 25 million years was first described by Sears and others in 1941 in a classic, landmark paper. Their model, simply put, supposed a continuously subsiding trough (the seaway of Fig. 7) receiving sediment at a varying rate. A high rate of sediment influx resulted in outbuilding of the shoreline (regression), and a low rate of sediment influx resulted in landward advance of the shoreline (transgression). Thus, the Pictured Cliffs Sandstone strandline regressed from the southwest part to the northeast part of the San Juan Basin area in response to an increase in the amount of sediment being delivered to the shoreline by northeast-flowing streams. Figure 8 is an isopach map of the interval from the Huerfanito Bentonite Bed of the Lewis Shale to the top of the Pictured Cliffs Sandstone. The isopach lines are probably a fairly accurate portrayal of the positions of the Pictured Cliffs Sandstone shorelines throughout the time the sea was retreating across the basin area.

Figure 9 shows three stratigraphic cross sections oriented northeastward across the basin showing the relations of the Huerfanito Bentonite Bed, Pictured Cliffs Sandstone, Fruitland Formation, and overlying rocks. These sections show the time-transgressive nature of the Pictured Cliffs Sandstone, which becomes younger northeastward across the basin. These sections also show that the sea did not retreat steadily and evenly across the basin. For example, between wells 8 and 9 on cross section A-A′ and 10 and 11 on B-B′, there is a stratigraphic rise in the top of the Pictured Cliffs of about 61 m (200 ft). These rises indicate that, for a time, the shoreline in these areas ceased to regress northeastward and stayed in the same general geographic area, building the strandline sands into a thick vertical stack. Figure 8, the isopach map of the interval from the Huerfanito bed to the top of the Pictured Cliffs Sandstone also shows this large stratigraphic rise of the top of the Pictured Cliffs Sandstone along a northwest trend across the north-central part of the basin.

FRUITLAND COAL DEPOSITION MODEL

In 1941, Sears and others (p. 103) suggested that thick coal deposits should form shoreward of upbuilding beach-sand deposits. That suggestion was only theoretical at the time it was made because such an occurrence had not actually been documented.

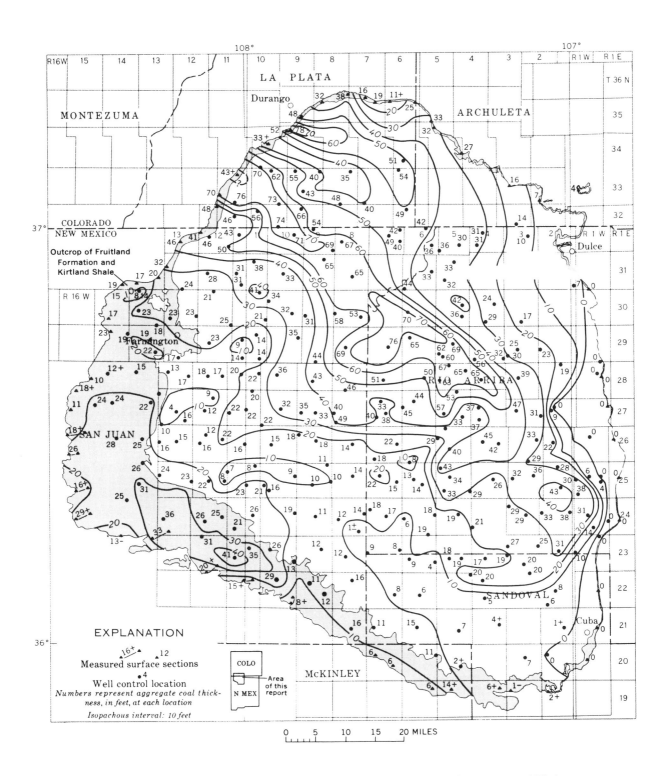

Figure 5. Isopach map of total thickness of coal in the Fruitland Formation (from Fassett and Hinds, 1971).

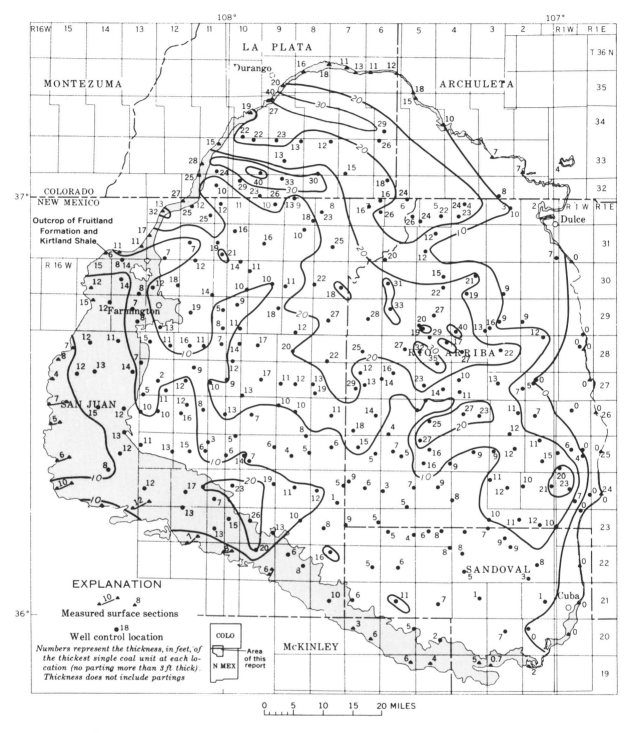

Figure 6. Isopach map of the thickest individual coal units (no parting more than .9 m [3 ft] thick) in the Fruitland Formation (from Fassett and Hinds, 1971).

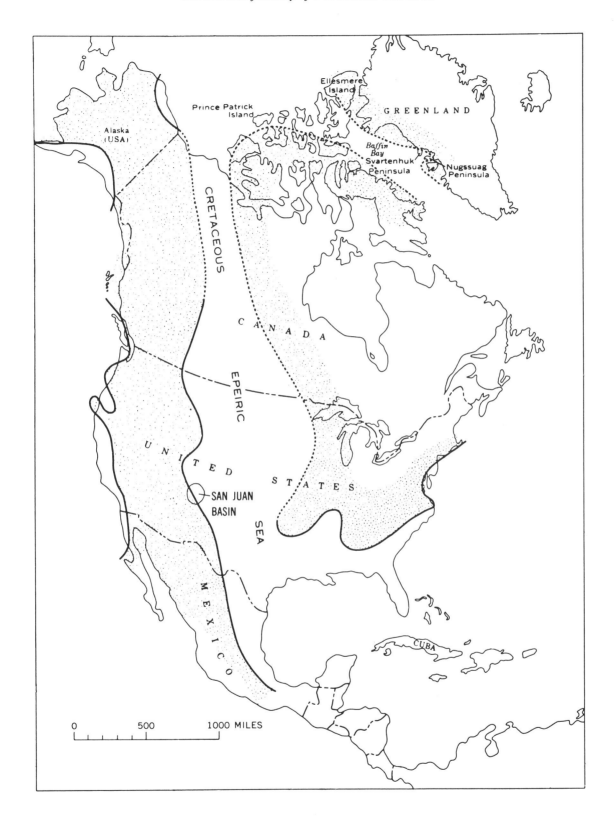

Figure 7. Probable configuration of the North American epeiric seaway at the time that the Upper Cretaceous rocks of the San Juan Basin were being deposited; from Fassett and Hinds (1971), after Gill and Cobban (1968, Fig. 15).

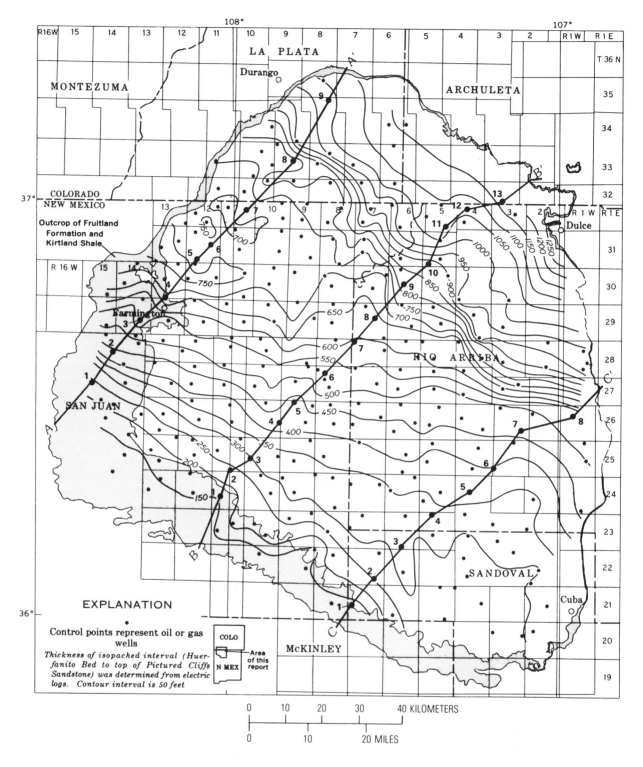

Figure 8. Isopach map of the interval between the Huerfanito Bentonite Bed of the Lewis Shale and the top of the Pictured Cliffs Sandstone. Lines of cross sections A–A′, B–B′, and C–C′ of Figure 9 are shown. Modified from Fassett and Hinds (1971).

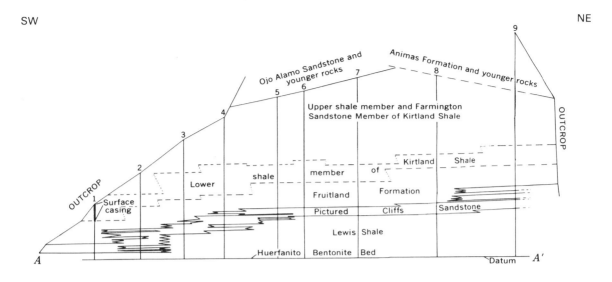

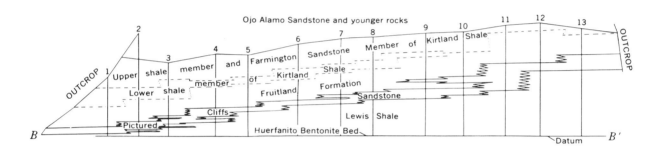

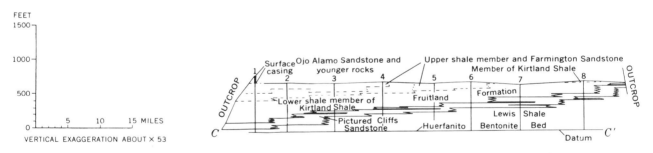

Figure 9. Northeast-trending stratigraphic cross sections showing the northeastward stratigraphic rise of the Pictured Cliffs Sandstone and associated rocks. Modified from Fassett and Hinds (1971).

Now, however, with the availability of almost unlimited subsurface control through the Fruitland Formation in the San Juan Basin, it has been possible to demonstrate (Fassett and Hinds, 1971) that the theoretical prediction of Sears and others (1941) is valid and that thick Fruitland coals were actually developed shoreward of upbuilding shoreface sands.

Figure 10 is a composite map of the Pictured Cliffs-Huerfanito isopach map (Fig. 8) and the total-Fruitland-coal isopach map (Fig. 6), showing that the thickest zone of Fruitland

coal is located southwest of the largest vertical buildup of the Pictured Cliffs Sandstone. The correspondence is not perfect, but considering the variability in natural systems, it is impressive. One of the problems with this depiction is that the total coal isopach map represents several coal beds in the Fruitland that occur through a stratigraphic interval as much as 91 m (300 ft) thick. A series of isopach maps of individual coal beds in the Fruitland would probably demonstrate more clearly the relationship of thick Fruitland coal beds to this large stratigraphic rise in the

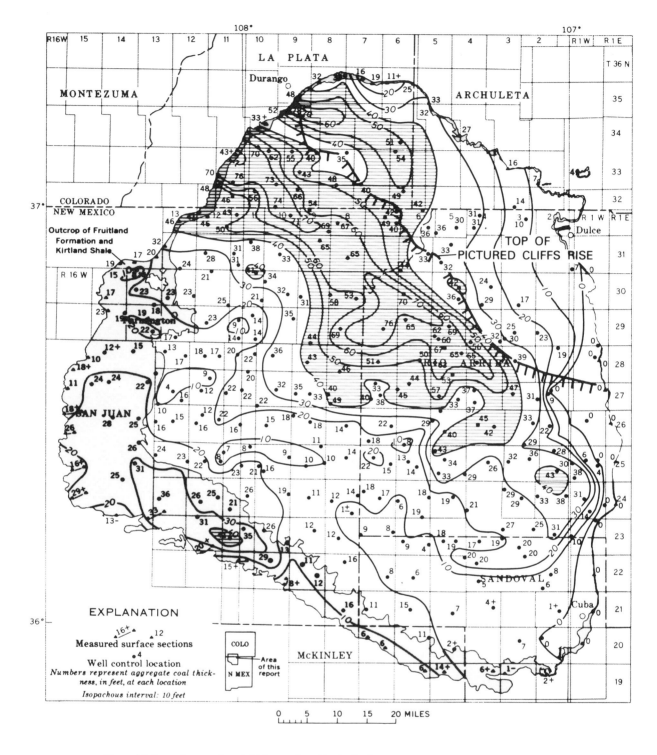

Figure 10. Isopach map of total thickness of coal in the Fruitland Formation. Areas where coal is more than 12 m (40 ft) thick are patterned. The top of the large stratigraphic rise of the Pictured Cliffs Sandstone in the north-central part of the San Juan Basin is shown; the area of thickest Fruitland coal is located southwest of this line. Modified from Fassett and Hinds (1971).

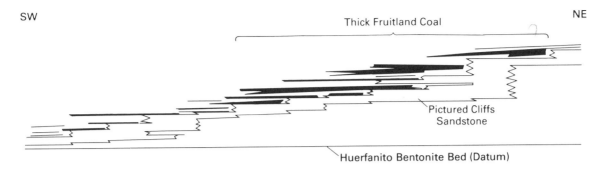

SW

Thick Fruitland Coal

NE

Pictured Cliffs
Sandstone

Huerfanito Bentonite Bed (Datum)

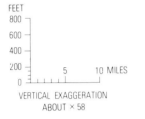

FEET
800
600
400
200
0

5   10 MILES

VERTICAL EXAGGERATION
ABOUT × 58

Figure 11. Northeast-trending stratigraphic cross section showing Fruit-land Formation coal beds and underlying Pictured Cliffs Sandstone. This cross section is modified from section B–B′ of Figure 9; coal bed thicknesses are from Fassett and Hinds (1971).

Pictured Cliffs Sandstone. Such a series of maps, however, is beyond the scope of this report.

Another way to portray the relations of thick Fruitland coals to stratigraphic rises in the Pictured Cliffs is in cross section. Figure 11 is a northeast-trending cross section showing the Fruitland Formation coal beds and the Pictured Cliffs Sandstone. The thickest Fruitland coals are clearly related to the largest stratigraphic rises of the Pictured Cliffs. Figure 12 is a diagrammatic portrayal of how thick coal beds were developed in the Fruitland Formation in association with vertical build-ups of strandline sandstones in the Pictured Cliffs Sandstone.

A TEST OF THE MODEL

Figure 13 is a northeast-trending cross section showing the Upper Cretaceous transgressive and regressive rock units of the San Juan Basin. Deposition of the Pictured Cliffs Sandstone took place during the final retreat of the Western Interior sea from the basin area. Examination of this cross section shows that the Point Lookout Sandstone also represents a northeastward strandline regression across the basin area with, remarkably, about the same amount of total stratigraphic rise as the Pictured Cliffs Sandstone. The Fruitland coal model indicates that the thickest coals lie adjacent to (landward of) the largest stratigraphic rises in the Pictured Cliffs Sandstone. A logical test of the general application of the Fruitland model would be to see if the thickest coal beds in the basal Menefee Formation, which overlies the Point Lookout Sandstone, are found adjacent to (landward of) the largest stratigraphic rises of the Point Lookout Sandstone.

The stratigraphic relations of the Menefee Formation to overlying and underlying rocks are shown on Figure 13. The lower part of the Menefee contains coal, and exposed Menefee coal beds have been mapped by many workers around the periphery of the San Juan Basin. On the outcrop, no thick coal zones

have been mapped in the basal Menefee; the thickest outcropping basal Menefee coal bed in the basin is 5 m (18 ft) thick, and this occurrence appears to be anomalous. In general, basal Menefee coals seldom reach 3 m (10 ft) in thickness. Menefee coals are usually lenticular and of limited lateral extent.

No detailed basin-wide studies of the Menefee coals comparable to the Fruitland coal study of Fassett and Hinds (1971) have been conducted; thus, it is not possible to portray lower Menefee coal thicknesses on an isopach map as was done for the Fruitland coals in Figure 10. A report by Whyte and Shomaker (1977) did evaluate Menefee coals in the southern part of the basin, but this study did not relate the lower Menefee coals to large stratigraphic rises in the Point Lookout Formation. The maximum total thickness of lower Menefee coal in the subsurface of the San Juan Basin cannot be determined specifically from the Whyte and Shomaker (1977) report because their isopachs treated coal throughout the entire Menefee and did not separate out the lower Menefee coal. It is clear, however, from the Whyte and Shomaker report (1977) that lower Menefee coals are relatively thin in the subsurface because total Menefee coal deposits average less than 3 m (10 ft).

Even though a detailed analysis of lower Menefee coals throughout the San Juan Basin is not available, there is a way to compare the relation of lower Menefee coal to Point Lookout stratigraphic rises with the Fruitland coal model. Figure 14 is a northeast-trending stratigraphic section showing the Point Lookout Sandstone and the coal beds present in the overlying lower Menefee Formation. This section shows that the coal beds of the lower Menefee are sparse and relatively thin. Furthermore, there is no buildup of thick coals landward of the big stratigraphic rise of the Point Lookout Sandstone in the middle part of the section.

Figure 14 also offers a direct comparison of the Fruitland Formation coal beds overlying the Pictured Cliffs Sandstone with the lower Menefee Formation coal beds overlying the Point

J. E. Fassett

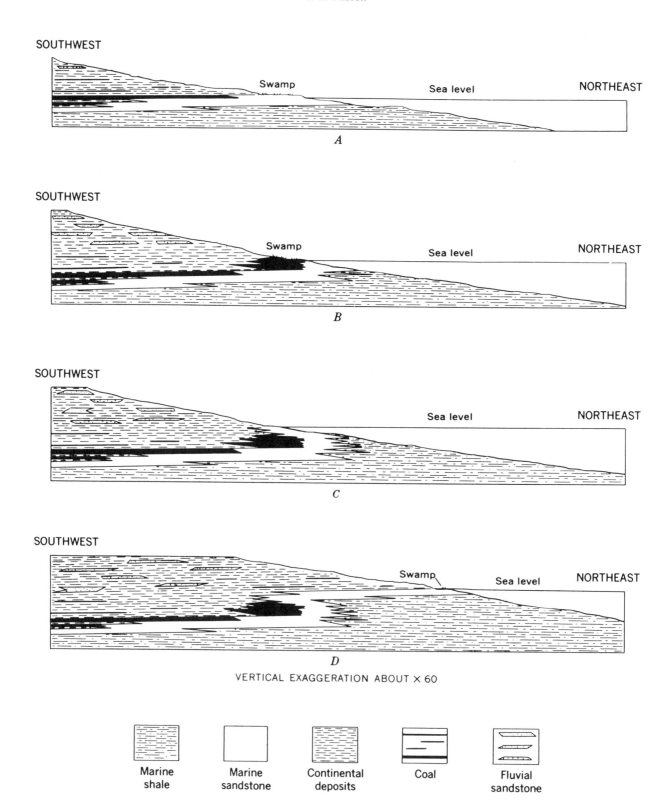

Figure 12. Diagrammatic cross sections showing the relations of the continental, beach, and marine deposits of Pictured Cliffs time after (A) shoreline regression, (B) shoreline stability, (C) shoreline transgression, and (D) shoreline regression. From Fassett and Hinds (1971).

SW   NE

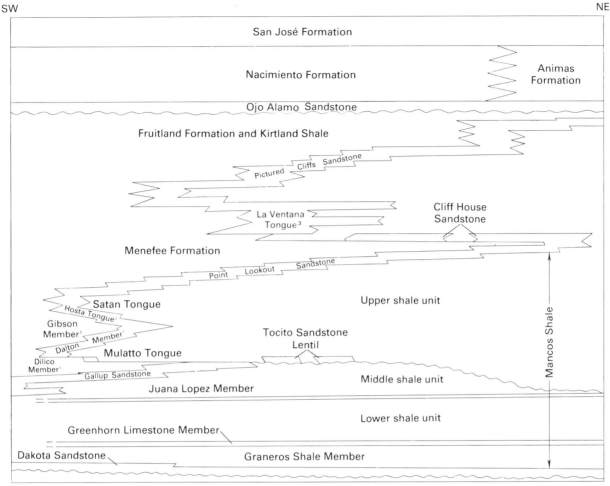

[1]Of Crevasse Canyon Formation
[2]Of Point Lookout Sandstone
[3]Of Cliff House Sandstone

Figure 13. Diagrammatic stratigraphic cross section of Cretaceous and Tertiary rocks of the San Juan Basin. Vertical exaggeration about X 150. Modified from Fassett (1974).

Lookout Sandstone. This comparison clearly shows that the Fruitland model of coal deposition does not work at all for the lower Menefee coal beds. Thus, a test of the Fruitland Formation coal model in the same basin and in rocks apparently deposited in a similar environment of deposition clearly fails. Why?

The reason for this failure is not apparent, although some speculations can be offered. Differences between coal deposition environments for these two formations may have included the following: climate, flora, swamp-water chemistry, or the location of distributary fluvial systems. The creation of coal requires a most delicate balance of physical conditions; we know a little bit about some of these conditions, but there is a lot more we do not know. Given this state of affairs, what value do coal models have as predictive tools?

VALUE OF COAL MODELS

From the comparison of coal occurrence in the Fruitland

with that in the Menefee, one conclusion is obvious: the Fruitland–Pictured Cliffs coal model has no value for predicting the location of thick coals in the lower Menefee-Point Lookout paleodepositional system. The result of this test does not totally condemn the Fruitland model as a predictive tool for the coal explorationist: There could be other coal fields where regressive-marine sandstones stacked up vertically and thick coals formed in associated back-shore swamps. The difficulty is that all of the other variables controlling coal deposition must have also been favorable for coal deposition for this model to work and, statistically, the odds are always going to be against applying any coal deposition model to another area because of all of those other variables. For this reason I would advise cautious pessimism on the part of the coal explorationist in using coal models as exploration tools.

In an earlier report (Fassett, 1983b), an evaluation was made of coal models developed in Utah for Upper Cretaceous

SW   NE

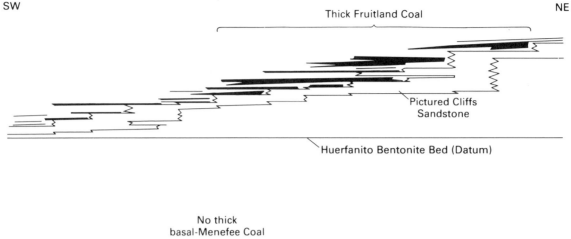

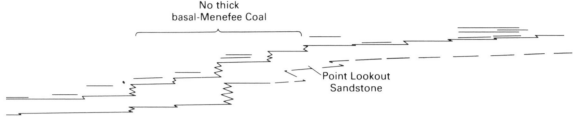

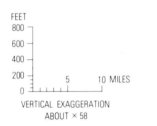

FEET
800
600
400
200
0
          5   10 MILES

VERTICAL EXAGGERATION
ABOUT × 58

Figure 14. Northeast-trending stratigraphic cross section showing the presence of thick coal landward of a large stratigraphic rise of the Pictured Cliffs Sandstone and little or no coal landward of large stratigraphic rises of the Point Lookout Sandstone. This figure is a modification of an electric-log section from Fassett (1979). The extent and thickness of coal beds shown is based on electric log interpretation. The transgressive Cliff House Sandstone, located stratigraphically between the Point Lookout and the Pictured Cliffs, is not shown on this cross section.

coal deposition: Those models were compared with the San Juan Basin Fruitland coal model. Like the Fruitland-Menefee comparison, the Utah–San Juan Basin comparison also showed little similarity between models. One of the greatest dangers in using coal models was summarized in the conclusion of that earlier report (Fassett, 1983b, p. 737): "Even though depositional models are valuable tools for predicting trends of coal occurrence, they can be misleading to the unwary explorationist looking only at model-predicted sites for thick coal deposits." In the San Juan Basin, for example, if the lower Menefee–Point Lookout system

had been the basis of a coal model first, would explorationists have written off the Fruitland potential on that basis (assuming of course that the Fruitland coals were not clearly exposed on the outcrop)? It may well turn out that most coal models will be unique to the area in which they were developed and, if so, they probably should not be called "models." However, as with most geologic studies, even though exact reproducibility seldom is possible, the experience gained from learning more about the many variables controlling coal deposition should give us at least a slight edge in locating nature's elusive economic mineral deposits.

REFERENCES CITED

Fassett, J. E., 1968a, Core description from GB-1 (Gasbuggy 1) in the northeastern part of the San Juan Basin, Rio Arriba County, New Mexico: U.S. Geological Survey Open-file report, 37 p.

——, 1968b, Summary of geologic data obtained from borehole GB-1, Project Gasbuggy, *in* San Juan-San Miguel-La Plata Region: New Mexico Geological Society 19th Field Conference Guidebook, p. 24–27.

——, 1974, Cretaceous and Tertiary rocks of the eastern San Juan Basin, New Mexico and Colorado, *in* Ghost Ranch: New Mexico Geological Society

25th Field Conference Guidebook, p. 225–230.

——, 1979, Geology of the Point Lookout, Cliff House, and Pictured Cliffs Sandstones of the San Juan Basin, New Mexico and Colorado, *in* San Juan Basin III: New Mexico Geological Society 28th Field Conference Guidebook, p. 193–197.

——, 1983a, Stratigraphy and oil and gas production of northwest New Mexico updated through 1983, *in* Fassett, J. E., ed., Oil and Gas Fields of the Four Corners area, v. III: Four Corners Geological Society, p. 849–863.

——— , 1983b, Comment on transgressive-regressive cycles and the occurrence of coal in some Upper Cretaceous strata of Utah: Geology, v. 11, no. 12, p. 736–738.

——— , 1985, Early Tertiary paleogeography and paleotectonics of the San Juan Basin area, New Mexico and Colorado, *in* Flores, R. M., and Kaplan, S. S., eds., Cenozoic paleogeography of the west-central United States: Rocky Mountain Section, Society of Economic Paleontologists and Mineralogists, p. 317–334.

Fassett, J. E., and Hinds, J. S., 1971, Geology and fuel resources of the Fruitland Formation and Kirtland Shale of the San Juan Basin, New Mexico and Colorado: U.S. Geological Survey Professional Paper 676, 76 p.

Fassett, J. E., Lucas, S. G., and O'Neill, F. M., 1986, Dinosaurs, pollen and spores, and the age of the Ojo Alamo Sandstone, San Juan Basin, New Mexico: *in* Geological Society of America Special Paper 209 (in press).

Gill, J. R., and Cobban, W. A., 1966, The Red Bird section of the Upper Cretaceous Pierre Shale in Wyoming: U.S. Geological Survey Professional Paper 393-A, 73 p.

Hinds, J. S., 1964, Btu values of Fruitland Formation coal deposits in Colorado and New Mexico, as determined from rotary-drill cuttings, *in* Geological Survey research 1964: U.S. Geological Survey Professional Paper 501-D, p. D90–D94 [1965].

Rice, D. D., 1983, Relation of natural gas composition to thermal maturity and source rock type in San Juan Basin, northwestern New Mexico and southwestern Colorado: American Association of Petroleum Geologists Bulletin, v. 67, no. 8, p. 1199–1218.

Sears, J. D., Hunt, C. B., and Hendricks, T. A., 1941, Transgressive and regressive Cretaceous deposits in southern San Juan Basin, New Mexico: U.S. Geological Survey Professional Paper 193-F, p. 101–121.

Whyte, M. R., and Shomaker, J. W., 1977, A geological appraisal of the deep coals of the Menefee Formation of the San Juan Basin, New Mexico, *in* Supplement to San Juan Basin III: New Mexico Geological Society 28th Field Conference Guidebook, p. 41–48.

MANUSCRIPT ACCEPTED BY THE SOCIETY APRIL 16, 1986

Discussion of paper by Fassett. Responses by Fassett.

Charles L. Rice

Question: Is it possible that different rates of sedimentation resulted in the differences in coal bed thickness between the older part of the model and the Fruitland sequences?

Response: As far as I can tell, average rates of deposition were about the same in Pictured Cliffs–Fruitland time and Point Lookout–Menefee time. The fluvial pattern was probably what contributed most to the differences in coal deposition in the Fruitland and lower Menefee.

Paul C. Lyons

Question: Would you care to comment on the relationship, if any, of your Fruitland model to PAC cycles such as advocated by Ryer in his recent *Geology* article?

Response: The Fruitland Formation coals developed landward of a regressing shoreline with the thickest coal developed behind (landward) of the largest stratigraphic rise of the Pictured Cliffs. Ryer's model for Utah predicts that thick coals will be found landward of shoreline turnarounds where transgressive and regressive strandline sandstones merge. Clearly, Ryer's model does not transfer to the San Juan Basin.

W. R. Sigleo (USGS, Reston)

Question: What is the relationship between coal quality and thickness of Fruitland coal across the basin?

Response: There is a correlation between coal thickness and coal quality in the San Juan Basin; both increase northeastward. However, the highest quality coal area (see USGS Prof. Paper 676) also now coincides with the present San Juan Basin axis indicating to me that depth of burial, rather than coal thickness, controlled coal quality.

R. L. Langenheim (Department of Geology, University Illinois, Urbana)

Comment: In considering reasons why the model derived from the upper sandstone did not apply to the lower, it appeared that the major transgression event responsible for the major coal deposit was not duplicated in the lower sandstone. The larger transgression recorded in the lower sandstone appeared to be a fairly closely spaced series of minor transgressions.

Response: The major transgressive event in the Pictured Cliffs regression is represented by a tongue of Pictured Cliffs sandstone within the Fruitland Formation. This transgression is associated with the thickest Fruitland coal build-up, but it probably resulted in less coal being formed. There appear to be no such transgressive events in the Point Lookout, although this could be the result of less intense study of the Point Lookout than of the Pictured Cliffs.

Printed in U.S.A

Geological Society of America
Special Paper 210
1986

Paleoenvironmental and tectonic controls in major coal basins of Alaska

Roy D. Merritt
Alaska Division of Mining and Geological Survey
794 University Avenue
Fairbanks, Alaska 99709

ABSTRACT

The general physiographic and geologic setting, lithostratigraphy, structural geology and regional tectonism, and depositional environments are summarized for six major coal basins in Alaska: the Susitna (Beluga and Yentna), Matanuska, Bering River, Nenana, Chignik Bay-Herendeen Bay, and Northern Alaska basins. Alaska's Cretaceous and Tertiary subbituminous to bituminous coals are found in most physiographic regions of the state and may underlie as much as 9.0 percent of its land area. Continental Tertiary deposits are widely distributed and contain most of the subbituminous coals. Cretaceous formations contain most of the bituminous coals and usually have been influenced by marine environments during their deposition.

Constraints related to paleodepositional environments affecting coal formation and character are expected to play an important role in future mine planning and pre-development site investigations in the Susitna, Nenana, Chignik Bay-Herendeen Bay, and Northern Alaska coal basins. Paleodepositional modeling will probably not greatly assist future mine planning in the Matanuska or Bering River coal basins because of complex geologic structure. Ultimately, other limiting factors such as location with respect to tidewater and potential export markets, coal quality considerations, resource base, permafrost distribution, infrastructure and port development, technological advances, and economics may determine the minability of Alaska's vast coal resources.

INTRODUCTION

Coal is found in most physiographic regions of Alaska, and geologic formations containing coal deposits may underlie as much as 9.0 percent of Alaska's land area (Fig. 1). Alaska's total hypothetical coal resources are estimated to range from 2.0 to more than 5.5 trillion short tons and may constitute the most important resource in Alaska's energy future. These deposits could ultimately prove to constitute half of the United States' coal resource base and as much as 15 percent of the world's coal resource base. Alaska's hypothetical coal resources are equivalent to 7–20 trillion barrels of oil, which would equate to 700–2000 Prudhoe Bays (original recoverable reserves of about 10 billion barrels). Because of the present scarcity of data and relatively low inventory of Alaska's coal resources, identified coal resource figures, however, are low compared to hypothetical total coal resources. Total indicated and inferred coal resources amount to nearly 170 billion short tons (Schaff and Merritt, 1984). The coal resources of the six major Alaska coal basins to be discussed in this paper are summarized in Table 1, and outcrop photographs of representative coal beds are shown in Figure 2.

The majority of Alaska's coals are of subbituminous and bituminous ranks; in general, 57 percent of Alaska's coal is bituminous and 42 percent is subbituminous. Anthracite, which is found locally in the Bering River and Matanuska fields, and lignite together comprise about 1 percent (McGee and Emmel, 1979). The coals exhibit variable moisture and ash contents and very low sulfur contents (Table 2). Organic sulfur is commonly the most abundant form in Alaskan coals, with minor pyritic and sulfate sulfur.

GENERAL DEPOSITIONAL REGIME

Most of the coal basins of Alaska formed during the Cre-

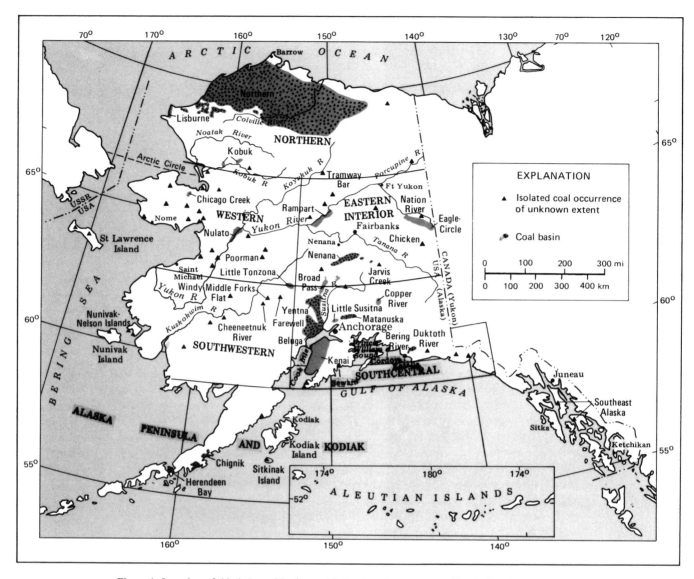

Figure 1. Location of Alaska's coal basins and isolated coal occurrences. The basins discussed in this paper are stippled.

TABLE 1.   SUMMARY OF THE COAL RESOURCES OF MAJOR COAL BASINS
            IN ALASKA (IN MILLIONS OF SHORT TONS)

Major Coal Basin	Measured Resources	Indicated & Inferred Resources	Hypothetical Resources
Susitna lowland (Beluga and Yentna fields)	2,500	10,000	30,000
Matanuska Valley	50	120	500
Bering River basin	60	100	3,500
Nenana basin	4,000	8,000	20,000
Chignik Bay-Herendeen Bay basins	20	200	3,000
Northern Alaska basins	250	150,000	4,000,000

Modified from McGee and Emmel (1979) and McConkey and others (1977).

A. 'Brown Seam', Tyonek Formation, upper Chuitna
River, Beluga Field.

B. Wishbone Hill coal beds, Chickaloon Formation,
Matanuska Field.

C. Queen Vein, Kushtaka Formation, Bering River Field.

D. Sheep — Moose Creeks coal bed, Suntrana Formation,
Nenana Field.

E. Mine Harbor coal beds, Chignik Formation, Herendeen
Bay Field.

F. Kukpowruk River coal bed, Corwin Formation.

Figure 2. Coal-bed exposures in major Alaskan coal basins.

TABLE 2.   RANGE IN ANALYSES OF COALS FROM MAJOR ALASKA COAL BASINS ON AN AS-RECEIVED
BASIS (COMPILED FROM VARIOUS SOURCES)

Major Coal Basin (Geologic Unit)	Moisture (%)	Volatile Matter (%)	Fixed Carbon (%)	Ash (%)	Sulfur (%)	Heating Value (Btu/lb)	Apparent Rank[*]
Susitna lowland (Kenai Group)	10-30	28-40	25-45	3-30	0.1-0.7	6200-9500	subC
Matanuska Valley (Chickaloon Formation)							
Wishbone Hill	3-9	32-45	38-51	4-22	0.2-1.0	10400-13200	hvBb
Chickaloon	1-5	14-24	60-72	5-20	0.4-0.7	11960-14400	lvb
Anthracite Ridge	3-9	7-11	65-81	7-20	0.2-0.7	10720-14000	sa
Bering River basin (Kushtaka Formation)	1-8	13-17	65-91	2-30	0.1-1.0	11000-15000	lvb
Nenana basin (Coal-bearing group)	10-31	21-43	24-25	3-30	0.2-1.2	6200-9800	subC
Chignik Bay-Herendeen Bay (Chignik Formation)	7-9	32-45	45-51	7-30	0.3-2.8	10000-11800	hvBb
Northern Fields (Nanushuk Group)							
Foothills	2-10	31-36	53-58	4-15	0.1-0.3	10000-13500	hvCb
Coastal Plain	8-20	30-36	38-50	3-20	0.2-0.8	7700-10700	subB

[*]sa = semianthracite; lvb = low-volatile bituminous; hvBb = high-volatile
B bituminous; hvCb = high-volatile C bituminous; subB = subbituminous B; subC =
subbituminous C.

taceous and Tertiary periods with the exception of the Lisburne or Point Hope field (Fig. 1) in northwestern Arctic Alaska, which is Mississippian in age. Figure 3 indicates the major coal-bearing formations of Alaska and their geologic ages and correlations. Correlations of most of the Cretaceous and Tertiary units are only tentative, and the exact stratigraphic relationships of many of the nearly coeval units are presently unknown. Table 3 lists coal-bearing formations of Alaska with their associated general depositional regime.

SUSITNA LOWLAND

Physiographic and Geologic Setting

The entire Cook Inlet-Susitna lowland Tertiary province is about 515 km long by 130 km wide (Fig. 4). The Susitna lowland part of the province encompasses about 13,000 km², and is bounded by the Alaska Range on the north and west, the Talkeetna Mountains on the east, and Cook Inlet on the south. Surface altitudes of the lowlands range from sea level at Cook Inlet to about 300 m northward; uplands of intrusives and pre-Tertiary rocks rise to 1,200 m above the surrounding lowlands.

The Susitna lowland is a northwestern extension of the Cook Inlet Tertiary basin. Barnes (1966) referred to this area as the Beluga-Yentna region. The Castle Mountain fault, a major northeast-trending discontinuity, separates upper Cook Inlet and the Susitna lowland (Fig. 4). Most stratigraphic, petroleum-oriented studies of Cook Inlet terminate at the fault. Important coal deposits in the Beluga area, however, lie on both sides of the fault.

Lithostratigraphy of the Kenai Group

The current stratigraphic nomenclature for the Tertiary coal-bearing strata of the Susitna lowland was first proposed by Calderwood and Fackler (1972) for the Cook Inlet basin (Fig. 5). They changed the "Kenai Formation," originally named by Dall and Harris (1892), to the Kenai Group, consisting of five formations: West Foreland, Hemlock Conglomerate, Tyonek, Beluga, and Sterling Formations. The Tyonek Formation is the most important coal-bearing unit of the Kenai Group and contains most of the minable coal resources of the Susitna lowland. Coal beds 1.5 to 15 m thick are characteristic of the formation.

The Kenai Group consists of clastic fore-arc basin deposits that display many characteristics of a continental fluvial system. Only local lacustrine deltas exist, and they appear to be products of a sinuously meandering fluvial regime, particularly those of the Tyonek Formation. Fining-upward sequences and rapid lateral and vertical changes in lithology are common. Channel-fill deposits are characteristically coarse-grained; interfluve sediments are fine-grained rooted siltstones, shales, and thin coals. Levee deposits are typically fine-grained sandstone and siltstone. Sedimentary structures, other than cross-stratification in coarser-grained units, are rare.

Sediments of the Kenai Group in the Susitna lowland were predominantly derived from plutonic and metamorphic sources in the tectonically active Alaska Range and Talkeetna Mountains. The model is that of a broad intermontane trough confined by borderlands of low to moderate relief with warm to temperate climatic conditions. Kirschner and Lyon (1973) divide the deposition of the Kenai Group of the Cook Inlet basin into three

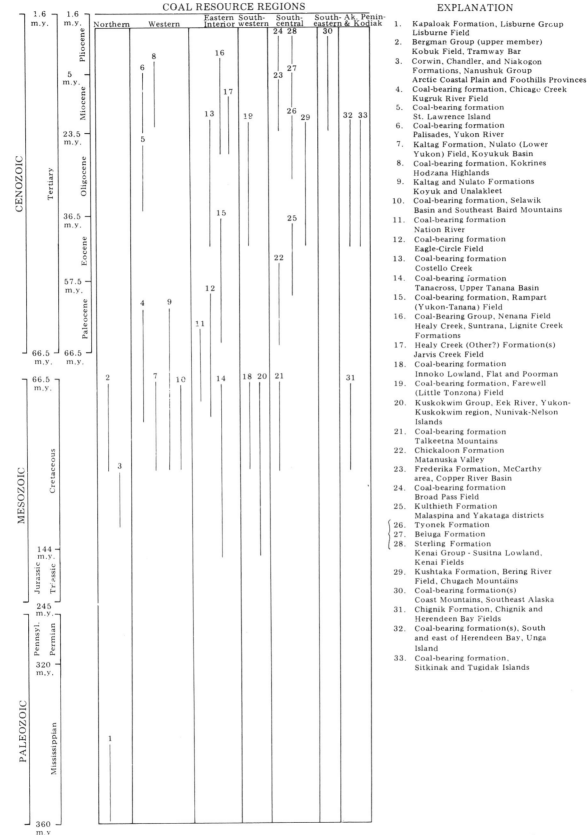

Figure 3. Generalized geologic age and correlation diagram for the major coal-bearing formations of Alaska.

TABLE 3. DEPOSITIONAL REGIME OF ALASKA'S MAJOR COAL-BEARING FORMATIONS

Group, Formation, Unit	Coal Field or Area	Coal Resource Region	Age	Lithology	Depositional Regime
Bergman Group (upper member)	Kobuk coal field	Northern	Late Cretaceous	Sandstone, conglomerate, sub-bituminous to bituminous coal	Continental
Bergman (upper member)	Tramway Bar--Middle Fork of Koyukuk River	Northern	Late Cretaceous	Sandstone, conglomerate, and bituminous coal	Continental
Kapaloak Formation of Lisburne Group	Lisburne coal field	Northern	Mississippian	Mudstone, sandstone, limestone, minor conglomerate, and coal	Transitional--marine and non-marine
Nanushuk Group	Northern coal fields	Northern	Cretaceous	Sandstone, claystone, silty claystone, siltstone, carbonaceous shale and coal beds	Prograding deltaic depositional system in swampy coastal lowland
Coal-bearing	Chicago Creek--Kugruk River coal field	Western	Late Cretaceous-Early Tertiary	Poor- to well-consolidated conglomerate, sandstone, siltstone, carbonaceous shale, and lignite	Continental
Kaltag Formation	Nulato and Kateel Rivers area, Koyukuk basin, Yukon River--Blackburn to Nulato	Western	Late Cretaceous	Siltstone, dark-gray and olive-gray shale, lesser sandstone, and bituminous to subbituminous coal beds	Continental
Coal-bearing	Palisades--Yukon River	Western	Miocene	Grayish-white granule conglomerate and sandstone, reddish-brown claystone, and lignite	Continental
Kaltag and Nulato Formations	Koyuk, Unalakleet	Western	Late Cretaceous-Tertiary	Graywacke, mudstone, sandstone, conglomerate, and coal	Terrigenous--shallow marine
Coal-bearing	St. Lawrence Island	Western	Oligocene	Poorly consolidated sandstone, fine to coarse conglomerate, carbonaceous mudstone, ashy tuff, volcanic breccia, and pods of lignite to 0.6 m.	Continental
Coal-bearing	Selawik Basin and southeastern Baird Mountains	Western, Northern	Late Cretaceous	Conglomerate, sandstone, mudstone, and bituminous coal	Continental
Coal-bearing	Costello Creek	Eastern Interior	Tertiary	Sandstone, siltstone, mudstone, conglomerate, and subbituminous coal	Continental
Coal-bearing	Eagle coal field	Eastern Interior	Late Cretaceous-Tertiary	Sandstone, mudstone, shale, conglomerate, and sub-bituminous coal to lignite	Continental
Coal-bearing	Rampart coal field	Eastern Interior	Early Tertiary	Claystone, sandstone, conglomerate, and subbituminous coal to lignite	Continental
Coal-bearing	Tanacross (upper Tanana basin)	Eastern Interior	Cretaceous	Conglomerate, sandstone, shale, siltstone, tuff, tuffaceous sandstone and shale, lignite, and chert	Continental
Coal-bearing group: Healy Creek, Suntrana, and Lignite Creek Formations	Nenana coal field	Eastern Interior	Tertiary	Sandstone, conglomerate, claystone, and subbituminous coal	Continental
Healy Creek Formation	Jarvis Creek coal field	Eastern Interior	Tertiary	Sandstone, claystone, siltstone, and coal	Continental
Coal-bearing	Nation River	Eastern Interior	Late Cretaceous-Paleocene(?)	Sandstone, conglomerate, shale, and bituminous coal	Continental
Coal-bearing	Farewell coal field--Little Tonzona, Deepbank Creek, Windy Fork of Kuskokwim River	Southwestern	Tertiary	Sandstone, siltstone, coal, burn, and bentonite	Continental

TABLE 3. (CONTINUED)

Group, Formation, Unit	Coal Field or Area	Coal Resource Region	Age	Lithology	Depositional Regime
Coal-bearing	Yukon-Kuskokwim delta region--Nunivak-Nelson Islands	South-western	Late Cretaceous	Graywacke, siltstone, pebble conglomerate, and coal	Littoral marine
Kuskokwim Group	Eek River	South-western	Cretaceous	Black carbonaceous shale, graywacke, conglomerate, siltstone, and coal	Shallow marine to nonmarine
Chickaloon Formation	Matanuska coal field	South-central	Paleocene-Eocene	Claystone, siltstone, sandstone, conglomerate, and coal	Fluvial braided to meandering (lower part) and fluvial meandering to paludal (upper part)
Coal-bearing	Broad Pass coal field	South-central	Late Tertiary	Lignite, conglomerate, sandstone, claystone, carbonaceous claystone	Continental
Frederika Formation	McCarthy area, Copper River basin	South-central	Miocene	Conglomerate, sandstone, silt-stone, shale, impure limestone and lignite	Continental
Kenai Group: Beluga, Tyonek, and Sterling Formations	Susitna lowland-Kenai lowland	South-central	Tertiary	Sandstone, conglomerate, clay-stone, siltstone, and sub-bituminous coal to lignite	Continental
Kulthieth Formation	Malaspina district; Robinson Mountains, Yakataga district	South-central	Paleocene(?)-Eocene	Sandstone, siltstone, and num-erous thin beds of high-rank coal	Transitional--continental and marine
Kushtaka Formation	Bering River coal field	South-central	Tertiary	Graywacke, feldspathic sandstone, siltstone, shale and bituminous to anthracite coal beds	Continental
Coal-bearing	Kootznahoo Inlet coal field, Admiralty Island	South-eastern	Tertiary	Coarse sandstone, conglomerate, shale, and bituminous coal beds	Continental
Chignik Formation	Chignik Bay and Herendeen Bay coal fields	Alaska Peninsula and Kodiak	Late Cretaceous	Sandstone, pebble-cobble conglomerate, siltstone, shale, and bituminous coal beds	Cyclic near-shore marine and nonmarine
Bear Lake Formation, Unga Conglo-merate Mbr.	South and east of Herendeen Bay, Unga Island	Alaska Peninsula and Kodiak	Tertiary	Sandstone, conglomerate, clay-stone, and subbituminous coal	Transitional--marine and nonmarine
Sitkinak Formation	Trinity Islands	Alaska Peninsula and Kodiak	Tertiary	Sandstone, shale, conglomerate, and subbituminous coal	Continental

phases based on the lithologic and mineralogic character of the sediments: 1) an Oligocene-Miocene transgressive phase, 2) a brief late Miocene stillstand, and 3) a Pliocene regressive phase. The West Foreland Formation, Hemlock Conglomerate, and the lower part of the Tyonek Formation were deposited during the transgressive phase. The late Miocene stillstand was characterized by a transitional period of low-energy sedimentation during which siltstone, carbonaceous shale, and coal accumulated in the upper part of the Tyonek Formation and lower part of the Beluga Formation. The upper part of the Beluga Formation and the Sterling Formation were deposited during the Pliocene regressive phase.

Structural Geology and Regional Tectonism

Cenozoic structures of the Cook Inlet basin have been super-

imposed on the five major Mesozoic tectonic elements of south-central Alaska first recognized by Payne (1955; Fig. 4). The Susitna lowland is separated from the Cook Inlet basin by a partially buried ridge of granitic rocks (Kelly, 1963). The major synclinal axis of the Cook Inlet basin bifurcates northward with one arm extending into the Yentna region and the other extend-ing northeastward into Matanuska Valley. The continental depos-its that fill the basins of the Cook Inlet region contain a large number of discontinuous coal beds.

According to Hackett (1976), the Tertiary coal-bearing ba-sins of the upper Cook Inlet region represent a system of tilted horsts and grabens produced by extensional fragmentation of a pre-Tertiary basement. Hackett (1976, p. 13) postulated substan-tial translational and rotational block movements in south-central Alaska during Late Cretaceous and Early Tertiary times, caused

180   *R. D. Merritt*

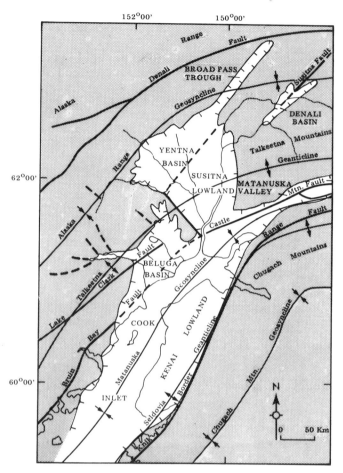

Figure 4. General location and physiographic setting for the Susitna lowland. Mesozoic and Cenozoic tectonic elements, major faults, basins, and highland exposures of Pre-Tertiary basement rocks (shaded) in the Cook Inlet region are also shown (modified from Payne, 1955; and Hackett, 1977).

SYSTEM	SERIES	GROUP	FORMATION	DESCRIPTION
	QUATER-NARY		Alluvium and glacial deposits	
CENOZOIC	TERTIARY	KENAI GROUP	Sterling Formation	Massive sandstone and conglomerate with occasional thin lignite beds
			Beluga Formation	Claystone, siltstone, and thin sandstone beds; thin subbituminous coal beds
			Tyonek Formation	Sandstone, claystone, and siltstone interbeds and thick subbituminous coal beds
			Hemlock Conglomerate	Sandstone and conglomerate
			West Foreland Formation	Tuffaceous siltstone and claystone; scattered sandstone and conglomerate beds
			Older Tertiary, Cretaceous, and Jurassic rocks	

Figure 5. Generalized stratigraphic nomenclature for the Tertiary Kenai Group of southcentral Alaska (after Calderwood and Fackler, 1972).

have shared a similar tectonic and sedimentologic history. However, each contains a variable number and thickness of coal beds.

Depositional Environments of the Kenai Group

Source areas adjacent to the basins of the Susitna lowland were rejuvenated during Late Cretaceous and Early Tertiary times. Periodic or gradual uplift converted areas of the basinal flood plains into widespread coal-forming environments during late Oligocene to middle Miocene time when the Tyonek Formation was deposited (Fig. 6). Gradual subsidence with periodic stillstands resulted in the formation of coal swamps in paleotopographic lows protected from floods. At any given time, peat formed in relatively small areas of the region, as illustrated by the lack of extensive lateral continuity of the beds. Clastic partings in coal beds also show the nonuniformity of conditions over the lowland, and indicate lateral shifting of subenvironments with time.

Most of the stratigraphic successions within the Tyonek Formation of the Kenai Group display fining-upward features. Some sequences show cycles of sedimentation that include (from bottom to top) conglomerate, often immature; pebbly, very

by a change from normal to oblique subduction between major plate boundaries. Continued oblique rifting during the Middle and Late Tertiary further accentuated these coal-bearing basins.

Major structural discontinuities divide the Susitna lowland into a southeastern segment of thicker Kenai Group strata (as much as 3000 m thick) and a northwestern segment of thinner rocks (less than 600 m thick; Hartman and others, 1972). The major high-angle reverse faults and small-scale high-angle block faults within the Susitna lowland offset coal-bearing sections. The effects of this faulted structure on future coal exploration and development are not fully known. Downthrown blocks commonly have localized channeling, which resulted in the erosion of coal seams. However, the faulting has also served to isolate blocks favorable for coal mining, as in the Chuitna River area of the Beluga field.

The major faults of the Cook Inlet region have acted to control the development and general configuration of basinal depocenters. The Susitna lowland contains several basins that coarse-grained sandstone; medium- to coarse-grained sandstone; fine-grained sandstone; fine-grained sandstone interbedded with shale and siltstone; underclay, carbonaceous shale, or siltstone; and coal. A complete cycle is rare because of syndepositional erosion and truncation. These cycles resulted from shifts of channels and sediment deposition across an alluvial plain. Cyclic deposition suggests alternating periods during the Tertiary when areas of the basinal flood plains were coal-forming swamps and periods of uplift in source regions that were associated with the influx of clastics and relative rapid basin subsidence. These cycles resulted in discontinuous accumulation and preservation of peat. Paleoenvironmental conditions were most favorable for the accumulation and preservation of thick peat beds in the late Oligocene to middle Miocene when the Tyonek Formation was deposited.

MATANUSKA VALLEY

Physiographic and Geologic Setting

The Matanuska coal field lies in the valley of the Matanuska River at the head of Cook Inlet between the Talkeetna and Chugach mountain ranges of southcentral Alaska (Figs. 1 and 7). The coal field varies from 9.5 to 13 km in width and is more than 60 km long, with an area more than 500 km^2. The valley generally trends N.70°E and lies 40 to 95 km northeast of tidewater. The lower Matanuska Valley (west of Chickaloon) is about 160 km north of Seward (where Alaska's first deep water coal export facility has been built). The Matanuska coal field is accessible by rail from either Seward or Anchorage and by the Glenn Highway.

The Matanuska coal field can be subdivided into five smaller fields: Eska-Moose, Young Creek, Castle Mountain, Chickaloon, and Anthracite Ridge (Merritt and Belowich, 1984; Fig. 7). In general, the Eska-Moose field, which includes the Wishbone Hill region of the lower Matanuska Valley, and the Chickaloon field contain an estimated two-thirds of the potentially minable coal resources of the region. Coal beds of the Chickaloon Formation range from 0.5 to 11.5 m in thickness.

Lithostratigraphy of the Chickaloon Formation

The main Tertiary rock units of the Matanuska Valley are the Chickaloon, Wishbone, and Tsadaka Formations, volcanic beds, and intrusive rocks (Table 4). The coal-bearing Chickaloon Formation is Paleocene to earliest Eocene in age, forms the base of the Tertiary sequence, and is overlain unconformably by the Wishbone Formation.

The Chickaloon Formation is at least 1500 m thick and contains as many as 30 coal beds in the upper 450 m of the unit (Clardy, 1978; Conwell and others, 1982). All known coal deposits in the Matanuska Valley are found in the Chickaloon Formation. This formation is older than the Tertiary Kenai Group and also differs in lithology, structure, presence of asso-

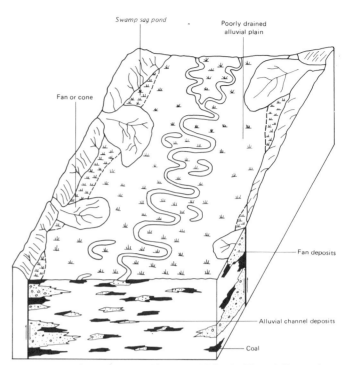

Figure 6. Idealized paleodepositional model for the Tyonek Formation, Kenai Group, Cook Inlet, Alaska (after Hite, 1976).

ciated intrusives, and the character and rank of the coal beds (Paige and Knopf, 1907). The general stratigraphic relationships of the Chickaloon Formation to older rocks is complex. The Chickaloon Formation appears to have undergone deformation similar to that in the underlying Cretaceous rocks, and has been considerably folded and faulted. Correlations within the Chickaloon Formation are difficult due to the numerous faults and the lenticularity and relative similarity in many of the beds.

The Chickaloon Formation consists of sequences of shale, sandstone, coal, and thin conglomerate lenses. Shales are dominant in the formation, sandstone is more abundant in the lower part of the unit. The numerous coal beds occur mainly in series of three or more beds (Barnes and Payne, 1956). Coal, sandstone, and shale vary laterally in thickness and lithologic character within short distances. Thickness changes of these units may have resulted largely from differential compaction. Shale is typically sandy, gray to dark bluish gray, feldspathic, and in some areas contains thin coaly streaks and abundant organic matter. Interstratified sandstone is gray, hard, moderately consolidated, lenticular, arkosic (with disseminated muscovite, shale, and other rock fragments), and is thick-bedded in the lower part of the formation. Concretionary iron carbonate in nodules and thin lenses is common throughout the Chickaloon Formation. The coal-bearing strata somewhat resemble units in the Paleozoic coal measures of the Appalachian region (Paige and Knopf, 1907).

The coal beds of the Chickaloon Formation range from subbituminous to anthracite rank. Generally, most coals of the lower Matanuska Valley are bituminous while those of the upper

182   R. D. Merritt

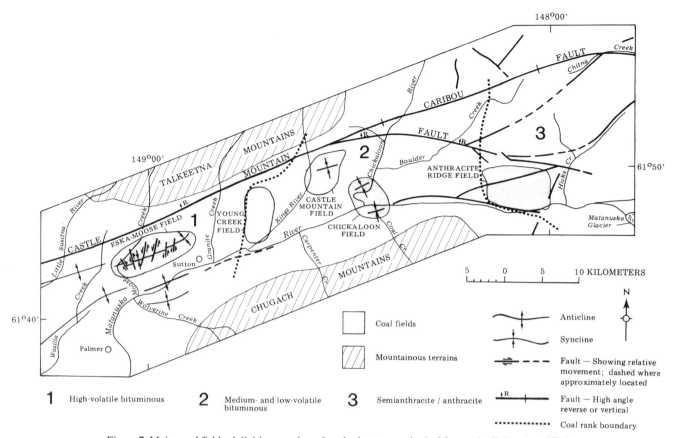

Figure 7. Major coal field subdivisions, rank, and geologic structure in the Matanuska Valley (modified from Merritt and Belowich, 1984).

TABLE 4. SUMMARY OF CHIEF CHARACTERISTICS OF TERTIARY AND CRETACEOUS SEDIMENTARY
ROCK FORMATIONS OF THE MATANUSKA VALLEY

Formation	Age	Thickness	Lithology	Stratigraphic relationship	Depositional environment
Tsadaka	Oligocene; time equivalent of lowest beds of Kenai Group	More than 150 m in Tsadaka Canyon	Crudely stratified massive conglomerate; marginal conglomeratic facies of Kenai Group	Overlies Wishbone and Chickaloon Formations with distinct angular unconformity in lower Matanuska Valley	Sheet-flood debris deposited on alluvial fan
Wishbone	Eocene	550-600 m	Well-lithified conglomerate, sandstone and siltstones	Overlies Chickaloon Formation unconformably in Matanuska Valley	Fluvial environment; alluvial fans and associated braided streams, perhaps meandering stream deposits in part
Chickaloon	Paleocene	At least 1,500 m	Well-indurated claystone, siltstone, sandstone, conglomerate, coal	Conformable with overlying Wishbone Formation south of Willow Creek in southwestern Talkeetna Mountains	Fluvial meandering to paludal environment in upper part; and fluvial braided to meandering stream environment in lower part
Arkose Ridge	Paleocene	Unknown	Coarse-grained clastics --arkosic conglomerate, minor shale	Nonconformably overlies plutonic rocks along south flank of Talkeetna Mountains	Local source, fanglomerate deposit
Matanuska	Early to Late Cretaceous (Albian to Maestrichtian)	More than 1,200 m at type section	Siltstone, sandstone, and cobble conglomerate	Underlies Tertiary rocks with local disconformity	Marine; sublittoral to outer bathyal or abyssal deposition by density currents or submarine slumps

Compiled from Clardy, 1978

Matanuska Valley are semianthracite to anthracite rank. The coals of the Anthracite Ridge district were raised to a higher rank by means of igneous intrusive activity and contact metamorphism accompanying regional deformation.

Structural Geology and Regional Tectonism

The Matanuska Valley occupies a portion of the Mesozoic structural trough named the Matanuska geosyncline by Payne (1955). This trough is bounded by the Talkeetna and Seldovia geanticlines on the north and south, respectively. The geologic history of the Matanuska geosyncline as a marine depositional trough ended by orogeny in Paleocene and Eocene time when an extensive continental sedimentary basin developed (Grantz, 1964). By the end of the Eocene and the cessation of peat accumulation, the surrounding region was uplifted and thick gravels and sands were deposited in the lower reaches of the basin. A major period of uplift in the adjacent Chugach Mountains took place during the Miocene and Pliocene epochs (Kirschner and Lyon, 1973). Extensive faulting in the Neogene was accompanied by intrusions of igneous rocks in the Pliocene. The Matanuska River cut its present valley after extensive excavation by repeated glacial advances and retreats during the Pleistocene.

The Matanuska Valley is an extension of the Cook Inlet Tertiary basin, and falls within the fore-arc terrane of the Alaska-Aleutian volcanic arc. Faulting in the region has resulted from complex intraplate strain caused by subduction of the Pacific plate beneath the convergent margin of the North American plate (Bruhn and Pavlis, 1981). The Matanuska basin is 8 to 16 km wide and about 80 km long, and narrows markedly towards the northeast where the coal-bearing Chickaloon Formation has undergone the greatest amount of compression.

The coal-bearing sedimentary rocks of the region are bounded on the north by the large-scale, high-angle Castle Mountain fault system (Barnes and Payne, 1956) and on the south by another major fault system. The Castle Mountain fault system separates the Matanuska Valley proper from the plutonic and metamorphic terrane of the Talkeetna Mountains to the north, and the fault system on the south separates the valley from Jurassic to Upper Cretaceous sedimentary, metasedimentary, and volcanic rocks of the Chugach Mountains (Fig. 7). In general, right-lateral separation has taken place along the Castle Mountain fault throughout Mesozoic and Early Tertiary time and vertical separation since Oligocene time (Grantz, 1964).

Chickaloon Formation rocks are generally moderately to strongly folded with predominantly open but locally sharp and overturned folds. Steep dips and complex structures are present throughout much of the Matanuska Valley. However, some areas in the lower Matanuska Valley show a uniform dip for considerable distances. The strike of rocks in general is parallel to the easterly trend of Matanuska Valley. Many minor faults cut fold axes.

The dominant structural features of the lower Matanuska Valley is the Wishbone Hill syncline, a canoe-shaped open fold

that extends the length of the district and is cut by several transverse faults (Barnes and Payne, 1956). These north-trending faults may represent secondary shears related to deformation along the Castle Mountain fault system (Bruhn and Pavlis, 1981). The syncline strikes south 55 to 80° west, and plunges southwest 10 to 25°. Coal beds of the Jonesville, Premier, Eska, and Burning Bed coal series crop out around the margins of the syncline, and extend to considerable depths beneath Wishbone Hill. Past coal mining has been largely restricted to the moderately dipping north limb of the syncline.

In general, areas around Wishbone Hill of the lower Matanuska Valley, and Castle Mountain and Chickaloon of the central Matanuska Valley are less structurally disturbed than those around Anthracite Ridge (Fig. 7), where the coal-bearing strata are folded east to west into a broad synclinal basin. Structure in the Chickaloon district is somewhat more complex than that farther west, with faulting and igneous intrusives more prevalent.

Depositional Environments of the Chickaloon Formation

An extensive freshwater basin of deposition developed in the Matanuska Valley region in Paleocene and early Eocene time. Based on the widespread megafossil flora (predominantly ferns, fan palms, cycads, conifers, and various broad-leaf genera) in the Chickaloon Formation, a warm temperate to subtropical climate is inferred during this period (Wolfe and others, 1966). The basin formed on a surface of considerable relief. As the area of sedimentation broadened in the basin, successively younger beds of the formation were more extensively deposited. Marshy conditions resulted in the formation of coal beds of moderate extent. Alternating periods of weak to strong orogenic movements provided structural control (Capps, 1927).

The deposits of the Chickaloon Formation include conglomerate, sandstone, siltstone, silty claystone, coal, bone, and coaly claystone. The environments of deposition include channel-fill, floodplain, stagnant lake and swamp. In general, the Chickaloon Formation represents a fluvial, braided to meandering stream environment in the lower part, and a fluvial, meandering to paludal environment in the upper part (Table 4). Second-order sedimentary cycles developed in the coal measures; each period of uplift in source regions initiated a new cycle of fairly rapid deposition. The first-order cycle was dominated by fluvial sedimentation forming a fining-upward succession of sand and gravel grading into finer clastic materials containing a few peat beds. Sustained regional swamp and stagnant-lake conditions developed subsequently during periods of quiescence with formation of alternating beds of thick coal, bone, claystone, and other strata (Payne, 1945; Clardy, 1978).

BERING RIVER BASIN

Physiographic and Geologic Setting

The Bering River coal basin is located in the Katalla district of the Controller Bay region and Gulf of Alaska Tertiary province, southeastern Alaska (Fig. 1). Scattered coal-bearing outcrops occur in about 180 km^2 of east-central Cordova and west-central Bering Glacier quadrangles. The center of the coal field lies about 95 km southeast of Cordova on Prince William Sound and 19 km northeast of Katalla. The wedge-shaped field extends about 32 km east to west in an area north and northeast of Bering River and 3 to 10 km wide, increasing in width toward the east. It is bounded on the north by the Martin River and Bering Glaciers of the Chugach Mountains, by the Stellar and Bering Glaciers on the east, by the Gulf of Alaska on the south, and by Bering Lake and the Copper River delta to the west. The coal field occupies a part of the foothill zone between the Chugach Mountains and the coast (Fisher and Calvert, 1914; Barnes, 1951; Sanders, 1976).

Regional topographic relief ranges from sea level to about 1070 m, with most mountain ridges being about 600 m above sea level. The area is characterized by irregular, mostly northeast-trending, densely forested, rugged hills of moderate elevation and by featureless lowlands with numerous small streams or arms of glaciers (Fisher and Calvert, 1914). The U-shaped valley of Shepherd Creek, a major stream on the west side of the field, drains Lake Charlotte, a morainal lake. Carbon Creek and its tributaries are steep-sided V-shaped canyons that indicate rapid post-glacial origin and erosion. Many streams are fault-controlled; waterfalls as much as 30 m high are common (Fisher and Calvert, 1914; Sanders, 1976).

Lithostratigraphy of the Kushtaka Formation

The Bering River coal field is delineated in general by the outcrop extent of the coal-bearing Kushtaka Formation (Fig. 8). The stratigraphy of the Kushtaka Formation and other Tertiary units of the eastern Gulf of Alaska are poorly understood. Sanders (1976), who has done the most recent and extensive coal resource evaluation of the area, was unable to find a complete stratigraphic section in the Kushtaka Formation because of the extreme structural complexity. The entire Tertiary sequence includes at least 6100 m of marine and continental sediments in this area. There are at least three formations of Early to Middle Tertiary age that comprise this apparently conformable sequence—the Kushtaka, Tokun, and Katalla Formations (Table 5). The Stillwater Formation is placed at the base of the Tertiary sequence but may be at least partly coeval with the Kushtaka Formation. The predominantly marine beds of the Stillwater Formation interfinger with and grade eastward into the predominantly nonmarine older strata of the Kushtaka Formation (Miller, 1961).

Units of Early Tertiary age include the Kushtaka and lower Tokun Formations, which are composed of well-indurated and complexly deformed rocks containing abundant Eocene macrofossil plant remains. The Middle Tertiary (Oligocene to early Miocene) units include the upper Tokun(?) and Katalla Formations, which contain as much as 2,740 m of poorly indurated and

deformed rocks in the Katalla district. The Tokun Formation is composed of gray to dark gray mudstone, siltstone, and claystone, and gray to brownish-gray, fine-grained, thinly-banded sandstone. Although the exact thickness of the coal-bearing Kushtaka Formation is unknown, its total thickness is probably more than 1000 m (Fisher and Calvert, 1914; Miller, 1961; Plafker, 1971; and Wheelabrator Coal Services Company, 1983).

The Kushtaka Formation consists of alternating coarse, pebbly, feldspathic to arkosic graywacke and intertonguing, commonly calcareous sandstone, siltstone, shale, claystone, and coal. Sandstones are micaceous and poorly sorted, with crushed quartz and corroded feldspar grains. The coal-bearing strata are intruded by diabase and basalt dikes and sills (Fisher and Calvert, 1914).

Coal beds of the Katalla district occur throughout the Kushtaka Formation (Barnes, 1951). Fisher and Calvert (1914) cited the occurrence of at least 22 coal beds more than 0.9 m in thickness, but they also recognized possible repetition by folding and faulting. The coal beds of the Kushtaka Formation seem to occur in three indefinite series—a lower series of 8 moderately thick beds 30 to 250 m apart; a middle series of 9 beds in 120 m of strata; and an upper series of 5 beds, more widely spaced than those in the middle series.

The coal beds of the Kushtaka Formation lack persistence due both to structural deformation (squeezing, faulting, and truncation) and to stratigraphic thinning (Fisher and Calvert, 1914). In addition to the structural complexity, correlation is extremely difficult because of the lack of diagnostic key beds. The coal beds can be thick locally, commonly found in large pods or lenses from 1.8 to 9 m thick and rarely to 18 m thick. The coals have been greatly devolatilized because of low-grade regional metamorphism associated with Late Tertiary deformation, and range in rank from high-volatile bituminous in the western part of the district, to low-volatile bituminous in the middle part, and to semi-anthracite and anthracite east of Canyon Creek (Fig. 8). The low-volatile bituminous and anthracitic coals are mostly noncoking (Sanders, 1976).

Structural Geology and Regional Tectonism

The structure of the Bering River coal basin is complex and poorly understood. The intensity of folding, reflecting compressive stresses, increases progressively northeastward. The magnitude of displacement of the numerous faults also appears to increase northward. The folding and faulting in the region is complicated by the local emplacement of stocks, dikes, and sills and thermal metamorphism of sedimentary rocks.

The Katalla area of the eastern Gulf of Alaska is located at the boundary of Pacific and North American lithospheric plates, and hence has been subjected to intense dynamic stresses. Convergent plate motion is accommodated by underthrusting of the Pacific plate beneath the North American plate along the northeastward-dipping Aleutian subduction zone. This underthrusting results in compression of the overlying crust, causing the

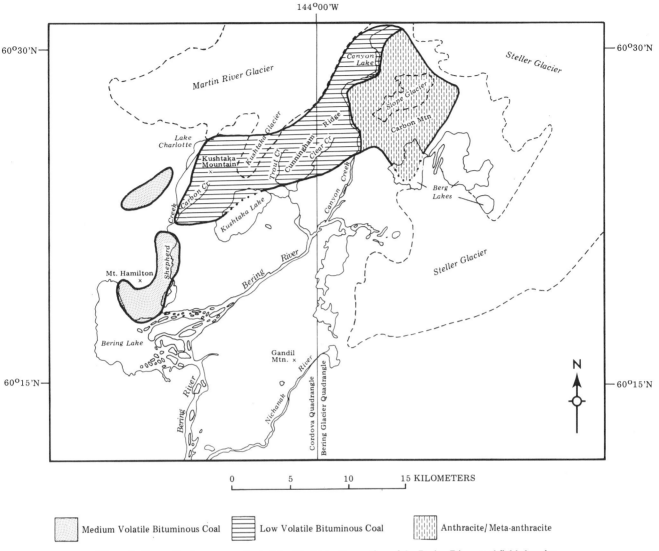

Figure 8. Generalized outcrop extent of the Kushtaka Formation of the Bering River coal field showing the northeastward to eastward increase in coal rank.

folds, high-angle reverse faults and thrust faults in the Bering River coal basin (Wheelabrator Coal Services Company, 1983).

Tertiary rocks have been intensely folded and cut by many faults caused by uplift and compressive forces normal to the Chugach Mountain front. The Katalla area was subjected to east-west compressive stresses during an Early Tertiary (Paleogene) orogeny. Neogene tectonic activity involved folding and faulting of bedrock, associated metamorphism with local igneous intrusions, and subsequent regional uplift in Quaternary time (Miller, 1951; Plafker, 1971).

The Bering River basin has been divided into two structural provinces east and west of Canyon Creek. The western province is characterized by open, fairly regular folds and at least two major and several minor synclines that strike northeast and dip northwest. The eastern district is more complex, with overturned

folds, a complicated system of overthrust faults, and numerous igneous dikes and sills. Although the strata exhibit relatively uniform northwest dips from 20 to 80° and averaging 40°, the structure is actually characterized by closely-spaced overturned folding. The axes of many of the individual folds are cut by faults with resulting further repetition of beds (Barnes, 1951).

Tectonic deformation has progressively elevated the rank of the coal eastward with the increased heat-attending compression. Shearing, crushing, and small-scale faulting may have affected the overall character of the coal more than the major folding and faulting effects. Slickensides are prevalent in the more competent strata, whereas crushing is extensive along bedding planes in less competent strata. Crushing was most common in coal beds with highly developed shearing planes. Shearing has also caused the introduction of additional mineral matter into the coal. The com-

TABLE 5.   GENERALIZED SECTION OF ROCKS IN THE
BERING RIVER COAL FIELD

Age	Formation/Unit	Character of rocks	Thickness (meters)
Quaternary	Unconsolidated sediments	Stream deposits, lake sediments, morainal deposits, marine silt and clay	0 — 180m
Tertiary or later	Igneous rocks	Diabase and basalt dikes and sills	— — —
Tertiary	Katalla	Conglomerate, sandstone, and shale Sandstone Shale, concretionary Sandstone Shale	6100+
	Tokun	Sandstone Shale	
	Kushtaka	Arkose with many coal beds	1000±
	Stillwater	Shale and sandstone	
Pre-Tertiary	Basement rocks	Graywacke, slate, and igneous rocks	— — —

Modified from Barnes, 1951.

plex structure of the Bering River coal basin is the most important factor critical to the economic value of the coal deposits, and ultimately must be better understood in order to determine the true future potential of the large aggregate coal resource of the region (Barnes, 1951).

Depositional Environments of the Kushtaka Formation

Detailed modeling of the depositional environments of the Kushtaka and other Tertiary formations of the eastern Gulf coast of Alaska has not been developed mainly because of complexities of structure and stratigraphic relationships. The shallow marine to continental sedimentary rocks of the Kushtaka Formation contain abundant coal in the eastern Katalla district and an abundant Eocene plant fossil macroflora indicative of a subtropical to temperate environment. The thick carbonaceous deposits of the Kushtaka Formation formed in peat swamps of near-marine, coastal plain, or alluvial environments 50 million years ago.

NENANA BASIN

General Physiographic and Geologic Setting

The Nenana basin of interior Alaska lies in the Alaska Range physiographic province and encompasses an area of more than 6500 km^2 (Fig. 1; Wahrhaftig, 1965). Outcrops of the Tertiary coal-bearing group are restricted to an area less than 2500 km^2. The coal-bearing rocks extend for about 225 km along the north-central flank of the Alaska Range in a belt as much as 50

km wide. The center of the deposits lies 95 km southwest of Fairbanks and 320 km north of Anchorage. The trend of these coal-bearing rocks continues 240 to 320 km southwest of the Nenana basin proper and includes deposits of the Farewell (Little Tonzona) field (Fig. 1).

Lignite Creek and Healy Creek are the most important of the structurally similar series of separate, relatively shallow basins (Fig. 9). The others include, from west to east, the western Nenana (Teklanika), Rex Creek, Tatlanika Creek, Mystic Creek, Wood River, West Delta, East Delta, and Jarvis Creek basins.

The Nenana basin is a region of diverse physiographic features. The outer ridges of the foothills belt descend downward to the Tanana Flats, which is a lowland of slight relief with a width of about 50 km. The northward extent of the coal belt beneath the Tanana Flats is unknown.

Lithostratigraphy of the Coal-Bearing Group

The Tertiary coal-bearing group of the Nenana basin is less than 900 m thick and was subdivided by Wahrhaftig and others (1969) into five formations (in ascending order): the Healy Creek, Sanctuary, Suntrana, Lignite Creek, and Grubstake Formations (Fig. 10). The folded and locally faulted strata are slightly to moderately consolidated and deeply incised by present drainages. Locally thick and nearly complete stratigraphic sections are exposed along Healy and Lignite Creeks. These stratigraphic sections consist of cross-bedded sandstone, siltstone, claystone, slightly-cemented conglomerate, gravel, whitish quartzose grit and numerous coal beds. The Healy Creek, Suntrana, and Lignite

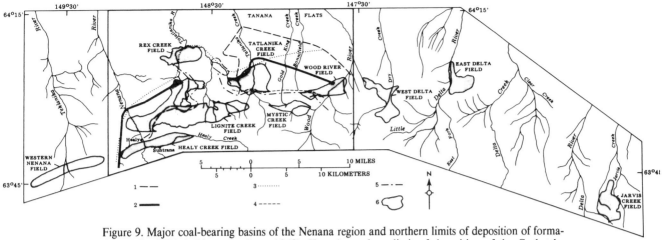

Figure 9. Major coal-bearing basins of the Nenana region and northern limits of deposition of formations (after Wahrhaftig and others, 1969). Key: 1. northern limit of deposition of the Grubstake Formation; 2. approximate zone of interfingering of the coal-bearing and noncoal-bearing facies of the Lignite Creek Formation; 3. northern limit of deposition of the Suntrana Formation; 4. northern limit of deposition of the Sanctuary Formation; 5. northern limit of deposition of the Healy Creek Formation; and 6. coal field.

Creek Formations contain significant coal resources. The Suntrana Formation holds most of the minable deposits including the thicker (commonly 3 to 18 m thick) and laterally more continuous beds.

The coal-bearing units are characterized by rapid lateral facies and thickness changes. Volcanic ash partings or tonsteins occur at several horizons and crop out locally throughout the Nenana coal field. Coal and coaly shale occur in sandstones as wavy stringers and lenses. Coalified and permineralized tree trunks and other abundant plant remains are present (Wahrhaftig, 1958).

Locally, coal-bearing sections contain a basal conglomerate with pebbles of schist, angular quartz, quartzite, and chert. Sandstone is commonly composed of quartz and black chert with local 'salt-and-pepper' texture. Cross-bedding is common. Mica is abundant and was derived from older schists. Differential erosion in softer portions of sandstone beds and some coals results in mushroom-shaped rock bodies and castellated forms. Differentially-cemented calcium carbonate concretions to five feet in diameter occur in some sections (Wahrhaftig, 1958).

Dickson (1981) suggests that two lithologic changes during the deposition of parts of the coal-bearing group indicate a general climatic cooling and a decrease in chemical weathering from older to younger formations: 1) transition from dominantly kaolinitic clays of the Healy Creek Formation to montmorillonitic clays in the Suntrana Formation and younger beds and 2) pebble clasts in the Healy Creek and Suntrana Formations, which are more resistant than those of the underlying Lignite Creek Formation.

Structural Geology and Regional Tectonism

The coal-bearing group strata of the Nenana region occur within structurally-similar isolated basins along the northern flank of the Alaska Range. These basins began to form on the highly eroded surface of Precambrian-Paleozoic metamorphic rocks in Middle Tertiary (late Oligocene) time. Erosion of this basement surface resulted in a major unconformity at the base of the coal-bearing group. Low to moderate highlands in the general vicinity of the western Yukon-Tanana Upland may have served as a clastic source for most of the coal-bearing group (Wahrhaftig, 1958; Dickson, 1981). Late Tertiary uplifts in the Alaska Range resulted in elevation and tilting of some structural blocks and locally in the erosion of the coal-bearing sequence. By Pliocene time, when the Nenana Gravel was deposited, the source of clastic materials had shifted from the north to the south following rejuvenations in the Alaska Range.

On the basis of gravity and magnetic surveys and structural evidence, Hackett and Gilbert (1983, personal communication) have outlined several major tectonic blocks across the north-central portion of the Alaska Range. Their data show a broad Bouguer gravity low greater than 12 milligals near Healy and that large density contrasts exist between Tertiary coal-bearing sediments of the Healy Creek and Lignite Creek basins and underlying Precambrian-Paleozoic basement rocks. The down-dropped tectonic blocks of Tertiary sediments that rest on the underlying denser Paleozoic or older basement result in a low gravity anomaly along the trend of the synclinal axes of the Nenana basin to the east.

Both the Healy Creek and Lignite Creek coal deposits occur in synclinal structures. A high-angle fault separates the two basins. The coal-bearing strata on the north side are displaced upward about 1500 m, so that the coal beds there are locally shallow and amenable to surface mining.

The Healy Creek coal-bearing stratigraphic section occurs in

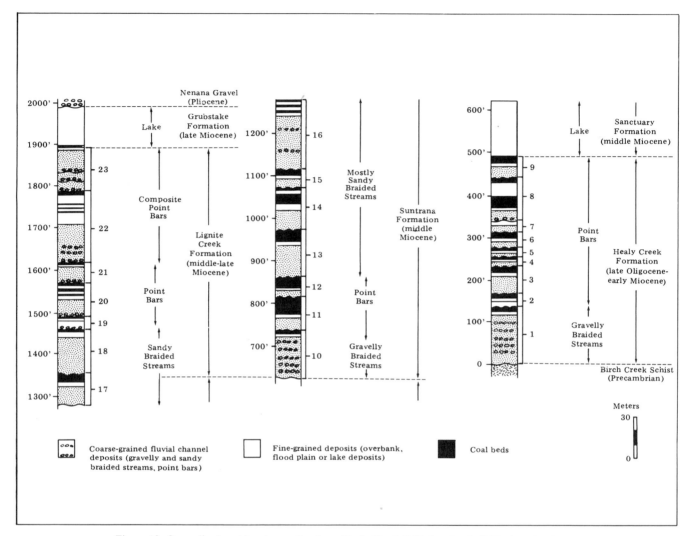

Figure 10. Generalized coal-bearing section from Healy Creek field showing individual cycles (numbered) and their respective paleodepositional types. Associated current stratigraphic nomenclature of the respective coal-bearing formations of the Nenana basin is also shown (after Buffler and Triplehorn, 1976; and Wolfe and others, 1980).

an asymmetric syncline that plunges westward and has bedding that dips from 30 to 90°. Mining on Healy Creek has been limited to the south limb of the structure where dips are 45°. Near the east end of the Healy Creek basin and the axis of the syncline, beds are very steep to overturned, and drag folds are locally present (Wahrhaftig and Freedman, 1945; Conwell, 1972). The geologic structure of the Lignite Creek basin is dominated by several synclines and anticlines with lower dips of about 20°, but with broader flexures in places (Wahrhaftig and Birman, 1954). The hornblende dacite intrusion of Jumbo Dome has greatly affected the section adjacent to the flanks of the dome, and has caused significant structural adjustments and attitude changes within the Tertiary coal-bearing group. However, the intrusion does not appear to have significantly increased the rank of the coal in the area.

Depositional Environments of the Coal-Bearing Group

The coal-bearing deposits of the Nenana basin formed in late Oligocene and Miocene times (Wolfe and others, 1980), and all have a similar sedimentologic and structural character. They are products of terrestrial sedimentation, including fluvial, lacustrine, and swamp deposits. They accumulated on an irregular, deeply weathered, and eroded land surface (Precambrian and Paleozoic metamorphic rocks) that was elevated in Cretaceous time (Wahrhaftig and others, 1969).

Coal developed at different times along what is now the north-central flank of the Alaska Range on a subsiding alluvial plain crossed by laterally-shifting streams. Resultant units have little lateral continuity and their correlation is uncertain. Buffler and Triplehorn (1976) cite evidence for at least 23 fining-upward cycles of continental sedimentation in coal-bearing group strata in the Healy Creek basin. They believe that these cycles reflect both uplift and subsidence and lateral shifting of stream channels. Figure 10 illustrates the cycles and respective interpretations of depositional environments related to them.

The Healy Creek Formation is a fluvial sequence deposited in late Oligocene and early Miocene time (Wahrhaftig, 1958; Fig. 11A). The weathered schist basement on which it was deposited was a highly irregular surface with as much as several hundred meters of relief. Coal swamps developed in nearly isotopographic lows on this irregular surface. Swamps, ponds, stream channels, levees, and crevasse splays occurred on this lowland plain, which was surrounded by forested uplands of moderate relief. Clastics carried by meandering streams across the swampy plains were derived mainly from weathered schist and quartz veins of nearby hills, as well as by a diversity of other source rocks. At intervals, the forests were either destroyed by fires (as indicated by fusain bands in the coal) or the hills laid barren, resulting in erosion and large landslides. Clastic sediments washing into the peat swamps terminated each coal-forming episode. Deposits are preserved in several basins in a region about 225 km long and 50 km wide. Variations in local conditions of deposition have resulted in lenticular and intertonguing beds in the Healy Creek Formation. Discontinuous sand sheets often occur as splits in coal seams. Although coal beds of the Healy Creek Formation are locally thick, they have little lateral continuity.

The Sanctuary Formation is a shale unit that ranges to over 100 m thick. It was deposited in shallow lakes in the early to middle Miocene (Fig. 11B). Clastic sources for the formation were different than those that contributed to the Healy Creek Formation, possibly from basic igneous rocks in a fairly distant region. Prominent lacustrine deltas composed of sand and silt formed locally in these shallow lakes. The formation thickens to the south and southeast. Parts of the lakes became sufficiently shallow and restricted so that small coal swamps formed during deposition of the uppermost Sanctuary Formation strata. The very little coal that has been preserved lies near the top of the formation.

The Suntrana Formation formed on a subsiding plain and contains scattered, fairly extensive swamp deposits of middle Miocene age (Fig. 11C and 11D). Periods in which streams deposited sheets of sand and gravel from northern source areas during times of source uplift and basin subsidence (Fig. 11C) alternated with periods in which most of the plain was a coal-forming swamp (Fig. 11D). Paleoenvironments included channels, levees, crevasse splays, forested plains, and alluvial fans. Subsidence was greatest to the south, and the formation gradually thickens in this direction. Chert pebbles in the formation suggest that the source was the Livengood Chert, which occurs near the western margin of the Yukon-Tanana Upland (Dickson, 1981). Paleocurrent directions from sandstones are also southerly. Coal beds in the Suntrana Formation are relatively more laterally continuous than those of the Healy Creek Formation. Several depocenters with thick coal developed toward the southern margin of the basin

where subsidence was greatest. Following a period of diminishing erosion, silts and clays of the uppermost part of the formation were deposited.

Sediments of the Lignite Creek Formation were deposited in the same basin(s) as the Suntrana Formation in middle Miocene time (Figs. 11E and 11F). The pattern of deposition was similar to that of the Suntrana Formation. No significant break in deposition occurred between the Suntrana and Lignite Creek Formations, and the subsiding basin was filled with sediments derived from northern sources at an increased rate (Fig. 11E). Since pebble clasts of the Lignite Creek Formation are less resistant than those in the Suntrana Formation, they may have been derived from different sources or represent second-cycle weathering due to rejuvenation of the source area. Large alluvial fans developed between the subsiding basin and highland source areas. The peat-forming swamps that developed at this time were often inundated by flood waters, which deposited silts, sands, and gravel (Fig. 11F). Coal seams of the Lignite Creek Formation are very lenticular and laterally discontinuous. Splits in the coal seams appear to increase in number and thickness toward clastic source areas. The highlands to the north were eventually eroded away and shallow lakes formed locally in the basin into which silts and clays were deposited.

The Grubstake Formation consists mainly of claystone, sandstone, and fine conglomerate and was deposited during a transition period in the late Miocene that separated the derivation of clastic materials from northerly source areas (Suntrana and Lignite Creek Formations) from later southerly source areas (Nenana Gravel, Fig. 11G). The Grubstake Formation was deposited on an unconformity and depositional environments alternated between large shallow lakes and broad alluvial plains. New highlands began to rise to the south. Local uplifts closed off drainage and resulted in the formation of shallow lakes. Lacustrine deltas formed locally. The absence of coal and the occurrence of interbedded finer-grained sediments with sandstones and conglomerates in the Grubstake Formation indicate unstable tectonic conditions in the depositional basin. The Nenana Gravel was derived from southerly source areas during the Pliocene and covered areas of the coal-bearing group with a thick layer of coarse to very coarse gravel (Fig. 11H).

CHIGNIK AND HERENDEEN BAY BASINS

Physiographic and Geologic Setting

Rocks of the Coal Valley Member of the Chignik Formation (Upper Cretaceous) are exposed in a long, narrow belt on the Alaska Peninsula between Pavlof Bay and Wide Bay (Fig. 12). The two main coal fields of the region, the Chignik Bay and Herendeen Bay fields are about 160 km apart. Rock outcrops in the coal fields include clastic volcanic and marine to nonmarine sediments of Jurassic and Cretaceous age that are intruded by Tertiary and Quaternary dikes and sills and also large, intermediate composition multiphase intrusive bodies (Burk, 1965;

R. D. Merritt

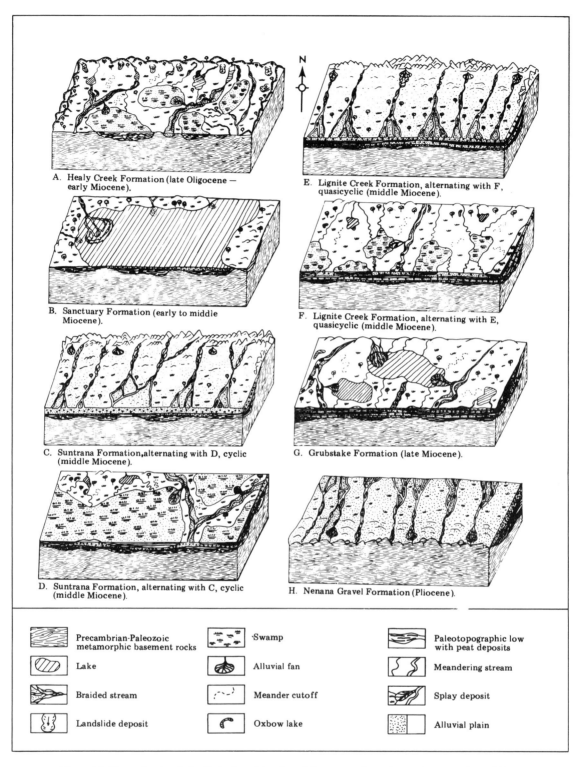

A. Healy Creek Formation (late Oligocene — early Miocene).

B. Sanctuary Formation (early to middle Miocene).

C. Suntrana Formation, alternating with D, cyclic (middle Miocene).

D. Suntrana Formation, alternating with C, cyclic (middle Miocene).

E. Lignite Creek Formation, alternating with F, quasicyclic (middle Miocene).

F. Lignite Creek Formation, alternating with E, quasicyclic (middle Miocene).

G. Grubstake Formation (late Miocene).

H. Nenana Gravel Formation (Pliocene).

Precambrian-Paleozoic metamorphic basement rocks

Lake

Braided stream

Landslide deposit

Swamp

Alluvial fan

Meander cutoff

Oxbow lake

Paleotopographic low with peat deposits

Meandering stream

Splay deposit

Alluvial plain

Figure 11. Generalized and simplistic depositional models representing paleoenvironmental conditions during the formation of the Tertiary coal-bearing rocks of the Nenana basin. Refer to text for discussion. No particular scale or specific area is implied. The ancestral mountains (C and E) represent potential clastic source areas near the northern part of the present Tanana Flats or western end of the Yukon-Tanana Upland. The ancestral mountains to the south (H) represent uplifts in the Alaska Range.

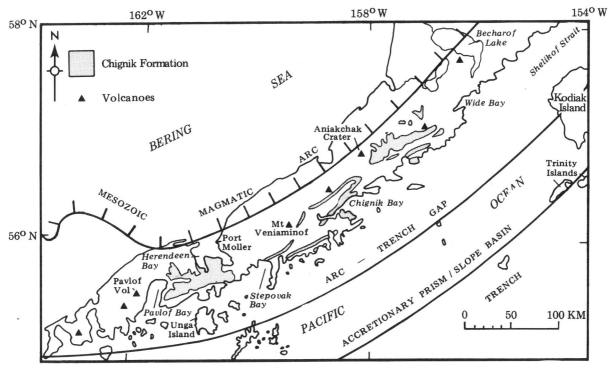

Figure 12. Distribution of Chignik Formation coal-bearing rocks on the Alaska Peninsula, and the general configurations of the Late Cretaceous tectonic framework and subduction complex (modified from Burk, 1965; and Mancini and others, 1978).

McGee, 1979). The Coal Valley Member contains all the significant and potentially commercial coal deposits in the Upper Cretaceous rocks of the Alaska Peninsula. Coal beds are typically less than 2.5 m thick.

The Herendeen Bay field, south of Herendeen Bay, is about 560 km southwest of Kodiak. In this area the Alaska Peninsula is nearly severed by deep indentations of the coast line; Herendeen Bay forms the only deep embayment in the Bering Sea side of the Alaska Peninsula. The chain of mountains that forms the backbone of the Alaska Peninsula is the dominant physiographic feature of the region. The highest of the sharp and rugged peaks is 900 m in elevation. The Cretaceous coal-bearing strata here cover at least 100 km^2 (Resource Associates of Alaska, Inc., 1980).

The Chignik Bay coal field, about 400 km southwest of Kodiak, comprises about 100 km^2 of coal-bearing strata. It forms a northeast-trending belt about 40 km long and 1.5 to 5 km wide on the northwest shore of Chignik Bay (Martin, 1925).

Lithostratigraphy of the Chignik Formation and Associated Rocks

Five Jurassic to Cretaceous sedimentary rock formations are exposed in the Herendeen Bay coal field; four of the same five formations occur in the Chignik Bay coal field. These include the Naknek and Staniukovich Formations, Herendeen Limestone in the Herendeen Bay area, the Chignik Formation (including the Coal Valley Member), and the Hoodoo Formation (Fig. 13). The

formations exhibit gradational, interfingering contacts with units above and below. These relationships have resulted from transgressional-regressional cycles operating in phase with uplift and subsidence caused by pulsating crustal plate convergence. The interfingering between formations also results from deposition of clastic debris in different but coeval environments ranging from subaerial to outer continental shelf marine (Vorobik and others, 1981).

The Upper Cretaceous (Campanian to Maestrichtian) sedimentary rock succession consists of the Chignik Formation and the overlying black siltstones and shales of the Hoodoo Formation (Fig. 13). Younger Tertiary and Quaternary sediments cover large areas of the Cretaceous belt where the Coal Valley Member is probably present in the subsurface (McGee, 1979; Mancini, 1977).

Sandstone of the Chignik Formation is composed primarily of subangular to subrounded grains of feldspar and quartz, which suggests a plutonic source terrane. Some of the clasts in the Chignik Formation conglomerates appear to be derived from Naknek Formation argillites; thus, erosion of the Naknek and adjacent formations probably provided some debris for the Chignik and Hoodoo Formations. The source area for the clastic materials comprising the Chignik and Hoodoo Formations that best fits the available petrographic and paleocurrent data is to the north and northwest (Burk, 1965; Mancini and others, 1978; McGee, 1979).

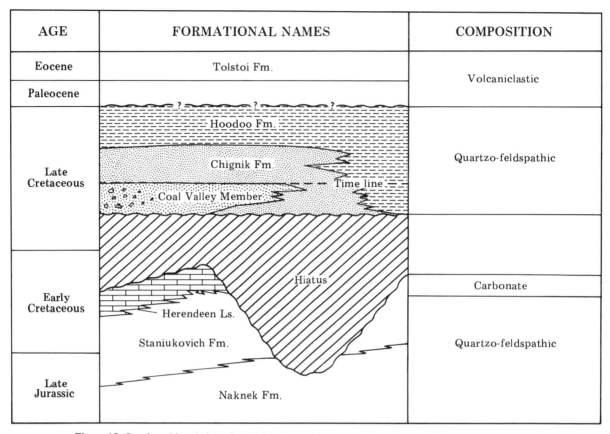

AGE	FORMATIONAL NAMES	COMPOSITION
Eocene	Tolstoi Fm.	Volcaniclastic
Paleocene		
Late Cretaceous	Hoodoo Fm. / Chignik Fm. / Time line / Coal Valley Member	Quartzo-feldspathic
Early Cretaceous	Hiatus / Herendeen Ls. / Staniukovich Fm.	Carbonate / Quartzo-feldspathic
Late Jurassic	Naknek Fm.	

Figure 13. Stratigraphic relationships of the Upper Jurassic and Cretaceous sedimentary rocks of the Alaska Peninsula (modified from Burk, 1965; Moore, 1974; and Mancini and others, 1978).

The Chignik Formation is a Late Cretaceous neritic to sub-aerial depositional sequence that includes shallow marine sand-stone, siltstone, and claystone units in its upper and lower parts, separated by the deltaic sandstone and coal of the Coal Valley Member. Chignik Formation sandstone composition varies from quartz arenite to arkosic subgraywacke. The sandstones are greenish gray, gray, pink, and tan, and commonly exhibit cross-bedding, ripple lamination, and bioturbation. *Inoceramus,* cepha-lopods and gastropods, and carbonaceous root, log, and other plant remains including pollen, spores, and phytoplankton indi-cate continental shelf deposition (Mancini and others, 1978; McGee, 1979; Vorobik and others, 1981).

Detterman (1978) reported three 'complete cycles' and a part of a fourth represented in marginal marine to nonmarine rocks of a Chignik Formation section on the northwest shore of Chignik Lagoon. The Chignik Formation in the vicinity of Port Moller is about 750 m thick, massively bedded, homogeneous, fine- to medium-grained sandstone interbedded with siltstone. The Chignik Formation section measured by Burk (1965) near Staniukovich Mountain is about 500 m thick. The upper 120 m consists of gray to tan friable sandstone and siltstone commonly containing pelecypods and carbonaceous plant remains. The lower 380 m is the type section of the Coal Valley Member, which

includes, downsection, 1) 120 m of medium gray to tan and brown conglomerate containing volcanic and chert clasts; 2) 150 m of gray-green sandstone and siltstone, locally very clayey and carbonaceous with rare thin (0.2–1.5 m) and lenticular beds of coal; and 3) 110 m of sandstone, siltstone, claystone, and thin (less 1.5 m) coal beds. The clastics of the basal section are pre-dominantly light gray and tan, weathered to a mottled light brown, reddish brown, and tan. The sandstones are predomi-nantly fine-grained and easily friable. No marine fossils were noted in the Staniukovich Mountain section of Chignik Forma-tion but numerous beds contain abundant carbonaceous plant fragments (McGee, 1979; Mancini and others, 1978).

Coal Valley Member sediments are relatively well-sorted and stratified and contain abundant organic matter. The con-glomerates of the Coal Valley Member contain subrounded pebbles and cobbles in a clayey sand matrix and beds 3 to 30 m thick. The quartzo-feldspathic sandstone beds are 1 to 3 m thick. Channeling and trough cross-bedding are common features in the basal part of the sandstone, whereas ripple and convolute lamina-tions typify the upper part. The grain size also decreases upward in some sandstone beds. Siltstone beds average 2 m thick and are carbonaceous. The coal horizons are interbedded with carbon-aceous claystone and sandstone, and individual coal beds vary in

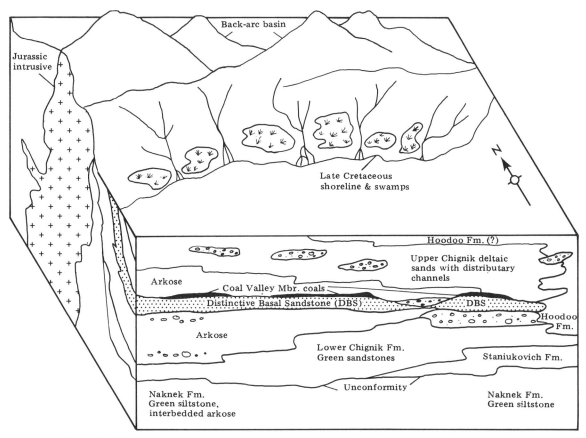

Figure 14. Schematic block diagram of the Late Cretaceous paleogeography in the Chignik area. The subduction zone-trench complex was offshore to the southwest (from Vorobik and others, 1981).

thickness from 0.3 to 2.5 m thick. Correlations between individual coal beds are difficult and it is necessary to correlate carbonaceous coaly intervals (Mancini and others, 1978; McGee, 1979).

At the base of the Coal Valley Member, a 6 to 12 m thick distinctive arkosic to quartzose 'platform' sandstone rests conformably on the lower Chignik green sandstones and conglomerates at Chignik Bay (DBS of Figure 14). The thickest carbonaceous siltstones and coals were deposited on this 'platform' sandstone and were succeeded by quartzose and locally calcareous sand and thin coal horizons. The Coal Valley Member appears to represent the only instance when there was sufficient stability in the depositional system for 'platform' development (Vorobik and others, 1981).

Structural Geology and Regional Tectonism

The structure of the Chignik Bay and Herendeen Bay coal fields has been dominated by convergent plate tectonics and arc-trench development, which have resulted in continuous uplift and erosion of plutonic rocks and subsequent deposition of marine and nonmarine arkose, claystone, and sandstone. Arc-building was initiated on the Aleutian margin by the emergence of an Early Jurassic magmatic arc along the northern edge of the pres-

ent Alaska Peninsula (Fig. 14). Moore and Connelly (1977) identified three periods of magmatic arc and subduction complex activity and infer that plates were mobile from Late Triassic to Late Jurassic, Early to Middle Cretaceous, and Late Cretaceous to Paleocene time. Although Burk (1965) and Moore and Connelly (1977) have slightly differing views on the time of onset of convergence in the Alaska Peninsula region, the result of tectonism from Jurassic time onward is well recorded in the stratigraphic sections in the Chignik Bay and Herendeen Bay areas (Vorobik and others, 1981).

The general structure of the Chignik district is that of an intensely shattered rock mass in which the structural constituents consist of relatively small, gently tilted blocks separated by faults or zones of shattering. The dominant trend of faults and major folds is subparallel to the long axis of the Alaska Peninsula, that is, generally slightly north of east (Martin, 1925; Resource Associates of Alaska, Inc., 1980).

The first of three major periods of deformation of Upper Cretaceous Chignik Formation rocks in the Chignik Bay area involved penecontemporaneous small-scale, low-amplitude folding in the lower but not the upper part of the Chignik Formation. The second deformational period subjected most of the Jurassic and Cretaceous age sediments to intense compressional foreshortening. The most conspicuous structural feature of this period in the Chignik area is the Chignik anticline and overthrust complex. Moderately to highly deformed Naknek Formation rocks have been anticlinally arched and thrust southeastward over Cretaceous Chignik and Hoodoo Formations. The strike of the Chignik thrust and anticline is subparallel to the dominant structural trend throughout the Chignik area. The third deformational event involved local, high-angle normal transverse faults. These faults evidently resulted from late tensional adjustment within the Chignik rocks that post-dates the anticlinal arching and is probably a brittle response to a shift in the compressional vector of the convergent plate motion (Vorobik and others, 1981).

The Chignik Formation and underlying older sedimentary rocks of an area in the Herendeen Bay coal field are folded into a syncline with the axes approximately paralleling the valley of Mine Creek but displaced slightly north in the eastern part of the drainage. The plunge of this structure is gentle and where measured is less than 7°. The syncline is asymmetrical with the dips of the north limb ranging from 10 to 18° and from 20 to 37° on the south limb. The south limb is broken into blocks by at least three major strike-slip faults, which strike almost due north. On one of these faults, a coal bed has been displaced 75 m along the strike of the fault. Numerous minor faults paralleling the major fault systems have displacements as much as several meters. Most of the coal potential in this area lies on the north limb of this synclinal structure (Gates, 1944; McGee, 1979).

Depositional Environments of the Chignik Formation and Associated Rocks

The general environment of deposition of Chignik and coeval Hoodoo Formations of the Alaska Peninsula is that of a fore-arc basin landward of the trench-slope break. The Coal Valley Member of the Chignik Formation and the Hoodoo Formation are composed mainly of plutonic rock fragments, feldspar, and quartz, which suggest derivation from the eroding Late Cretaceous arc front (Mancini, 1977).

Burk (1965) suggested that deposition of nonmarine sands of the Coal Valley Member, nearshore sediments of the Chignik Formation, and the deep-water marine Hoodoo Formation represents a marine transgression. Mancini (1977) interpreted these units as approximately coeval facies deposited in different environments. He cited examples of proximity to source in alluvial-fan, braided-stream, and flood-plain depositional environments for the conglomerate, quartzo-feldspathic sandstone, and coal of the Coal Valley Member; examples of inner-neritic continental shelf (upper and lower shoreface) environments for the sandstone and siltstone of the Chignik Formation; and finally outer-neritic continental shelf to bathyal continental slope environments for the predominantly fine argillaceous sediments of the Hoodoo Formation. Both Burk (1965) and Mancini and others (1978) interpret the conglomerate and coarse sandstone incorporated in the Hoodoo Formation siltstone as turbidite deposits. McGee (1979) finds that this general facies model concept is

supported in areas where nonmarine beds of the Coal Valley Member locally grade laterally into marine beds very similar to the upper part of the Chignik Formation.

The depositional environments of the lower part of the Coal Valley Member include valley flat (floodplain cut by meandering distributary levees), paludal, and lacustrine (shallow lake) environments. The increase in conglomerate in the upper part of the Coal Valley Member indicates that either distance to source areas had decreased or that the source areas were tectonically more active. The conglomerate is interpreted to have been deposited in coalescing alluvial fans in a piedmont environment (McGee, 1979).

Most of the coals in the Coal Valley Member were developed as the result of preservation of swamps developed on flat and gently sloping areas. Although the swamps were numerous, they were not laterally extensive. Most were probably fresh-water swamps, but marine waters may have influenced swamp development at or near the littoral zone separating the Coal Valley Member from the marine upper Chignik Formation. There is little evidence to suggest that conditions were favorable for coal accumulation during the onlap of upper Chignik Formation sediments. The presence of rare thin coal beds characteristic of estuarine, delta, or salt marsh environments in the upper Chignik Formation indicates intervals of further clastic deposition during which peat areas were preserved by deeper burial or that peat-forming conditions were relatively brief so that thick peats did not accumulate. These discontinuous swamps developed in lagoons behind beach barriers or in restricted basins between interdistributary levees (McGee, 1979).

NORTHERN ALASKA BASIN

General Physiographic and Geologic Setting

The major coal deposits of northern Alaska are delineated mainly by the outcrop belt of Nanushuk Group rocks, which extend nearly continuously from the sea cliffs of Corwin Bluff on the west some 650 km eastward to the Sagavanirktok River of the eastern Arctic Slope (Fig. 15). Nanushuk Group exposures are typically better on the western Arctic Slope where stream channels have locally incised through 500 m of section. The coal deposits mainly occur in two major physiographic provinces: 1) the Arctic Foothills belt, in the northern part of which Nanushuk Group rocks are largely exposed, is located north of the Brooks Range; and 2) the Arctic Coastal Plain, which spans the remaining terrain to the Arctic Ocean. The Arctic Foothills province is characterized by treeless rolling hills, ridges, and valleys generally aligned east to west parallel to the mountain front, and cut by numerous north-flowing streams and rivers. It is made up of a Southern Foothills section and a Northern Foothills section. The Southern Foothills section averages about 1200 m altitude. The relief of the Northern Foothills section ranges from 60 to 300 m and altitudes average 180 m. The Arctic Coastal Plain is an extensive, nearly featureless tundra plain with numerous lakes

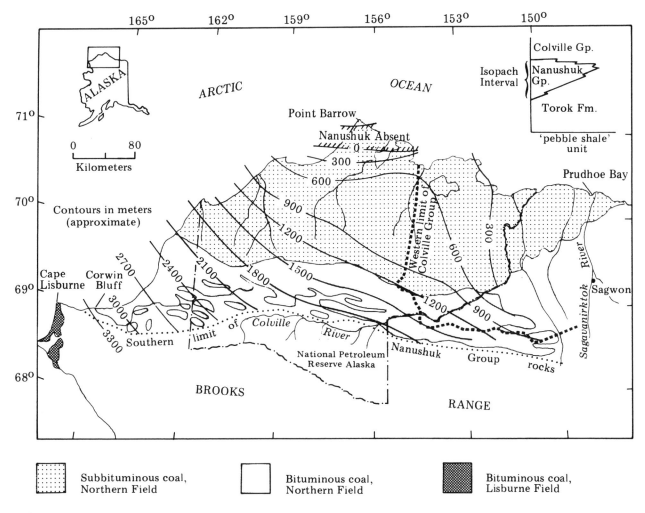

Figure 15. Distribution and extent of coal-bearing rocks of northern Alaska showing coal rank and thickness of the Nanushuk Group (modified from Bird and Andrews, 1979).

and marshes and poorly developed streams (Martin and Callahan, 1978; Mull, 1979).

Lithostratigraphy of the Nanushuk Group and Associated Rocks

The coals of the Northern Alaska fields occur in three major sedimentary rock sequences: the Nanushuk Group (early Albian to Cenomanian), which contains the best quality coals; the Colville Group (Late Cretaceous; Figure 16), and the Sagavanirktok Formation (Paleocene and Eocene). The lower part of the Cretaceous succession is composed predominantly of marine shales, which grade upward to the marginal-marine and nonmarine coal-bearing rocks of the Nanushuk Group, the intertonguing marine and nonmarine coal-bearing rocks of the Colville Group, and the dominantly nonmarine rocks of the Sagavanirktok Formation. The Nanushuk Group has been subdivided into formations based mainly on the marine and nonmarine character of the rocks. They

have been successfully correlated by use of spore, pollen, and plant megafossil zonations in nonmarine facies and of dinoflagellate, foraminiferal, and limited megafaunal zonations in marine and marginal marine facies. In the western part of the Foothills belt and Coastal Plain, the Kukpowruk Formation comprises the lower marginal-marine facies of the Nanushuk Group and the Corwin Formation comprises the upper nonmarine facies. The type section for the Corwin Formation is at Corwin Bluff (Sable, 1956; Smiley, 1969). This unit contains most of the coal resources of the Nanushuk Group. Coal beds less 1.5 m thick are characteristic but beds 4.5 to 7 m thick are not uncommon. In addition to the numerous coal beds, the unit also contains fine- to coarse-grained sandstone, siltstone, claystone, carbonaceous shale, and minor limestone.

The Nanushuk Group essentially forms a wedge-shaped rock unit in which the coarsest nonmarine sediments and the trend of greatest thickness occurs in the proximal portion of the deltaic clastic wedge. Available evidence suggests at least two

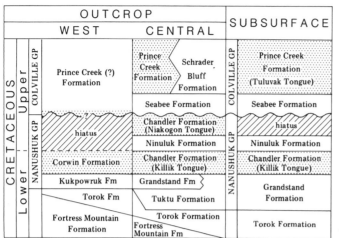

Figure 16. General stratigraphic nomenclature and correlation diagram for the coal-bearing Nanushuk and Colville Groups (from Ahlbrandt and others, 1979). The dominantly nonmarine units are stippled.

sources for the clastic materials of the Nanushuk Group: 1) from the Brooks Range to the south and 2) from a northwest-trending uplift in the area of Cape Lisburne and its offshore extension beneath the Chukchi Sea (Mull, 1979).

Only reconnaissance data on the distribution and extent of coal beds of the Nanushuk Group are available. The Nanushuk Group forms a continuous subcrop beneath Pleistocene and Holocene deposits in the Coastal Plain. In the Foothills, however, the outcrop area of nonmarine rocks is discontinuous and coal beds are exposed only in the cutbanks of the larger streams and along sea cliffs at Corwin Bluff (Callahan and Martin, 1981).

The sedimentary rock sequence of Cretaceous age is more than 4600 m thick in the southern part of the National Petroleum Reserve in Alaska (NPRA) but thins northward to about 900 m near Barrow. The thickness of the Nanushuk Group alone decreases from southwest to northeast from more than 3300 m at Corwin Bluff to zero in eastern NPRA. The Corwin Formation comprises the entire thickness of the Nanushuk Group measured at Corwin Bluff but decreases to about 1200 m thick in west-central NPRA. Most stratigraphic sections represent only the lower part of the original thickness of the Corwin Formation. The Nanushuk Group in eastern NPRA is as much as 1500 m thick; the nonmarine units range from zero to about 600 m thick. The Colville Group unconformably overlies the Nanushuk Group in eastern NRPA and reaches a maximum thickness of about 900 m (Brosge and Tailleur, 1971; Callahan and Martin, 1981).

Most of the coal resources of the Northern Alaska fields are contained in the nonmarine facies of the Nanushuk Group, primarily in the central part of the clastic wedge, stratigraphically in the upper half of the sequence, and widely separated from the underlying marginal-marine facies, indicating deposition considerably inland (several tens of km or more) from the sea. This contrasts significantly with the pattern found in other deltaic and paralic sequences in the western United States where they are generally found in the first 30 m of nonmarine section above the marine facies. The thicker coal seams are in the upper part of the Corwin Formation; the coals of the lower part of the Corwin Formation are relatively thin. Although coals of the Corwin Formation are, overall, low in sulfur (generally less 1 percent), the sulfur content of the latter coals seems to be generally higher and more erratic than coals stratigraphically higher in the Corwin Formation. Coals of the Colville Group in the eastern NPRA appear to be of poorer quality, and are less abundant than coals in the Nanushuk Group (Weimer, 1977; Martin and Callahan, 1978; Callahan and Martin, 1981).

In the eastern section of the Foothills and Coastal Plain (eastern NPRA), Nanushuk Group nonmarine units are the coal-bearing Chandler and Niakogon Formations, which intertongue with marginal marine facies of the Tuktu, Grandstand, and Niuluk Formations and the marine Torok Formation. Source areas include Corwin delta sources and sources in the central Brooks Range to the south.

The Sagavanirktok Formation (Paleocene and Eocene) is a sequence of poorly consolidated siltstone, sandstone, conglomerate, and lignite that forms an important eastern extension of the Northern Alaska coal fields (Detterman and others, 1975). The formation ranges from 1150 to 1800 m thick and has been subdivided into three units (in ascending order), the Sagwon, Franklin Bluffs, and Nuwok Members. The Sagwon Member contains numerous coaly beds composed mainly of lignite and carbonaceous shale. Individual lignite beds are as much as 6 m thick with abundant shale partings. At its type section in bluffs along the west side of the Sagavanirktok River about 3 km northwest of Sagwon, the coal-bearing member is over 140 m thick but locally increases to about 365 m thick elsewhere in the region. Shallow-water to deltaic type crossbedding in sandstone and conglomerate units indicates a source to the southwest. The Kogosukruk Tongue of the Prince Creek Formation (Upper Cretaceous) underlies the Sagwon Member and contains coal beds of slightly higher quality.

Structural Geology and Regional Tectonism

The structure of the Cretaceous coal-bearing and associated rocks of the Northern Alaska fields is characterized by folding and faulting along roughly east-trending axes generally parallel to the Brooks Range. The intensity of the deformation decreases northward from the mountains; very gentle open folding and little faulting characterizes the Coastal Plain, whereas greater structural complexity and steeper dips are found in the Foothills. The Nanushuk Group strata exhibit a gentle homoclinal dip to the south in the Coastal Plain. The Corwin Formation in the Foothills occupies the central parts of the numerous broad but relatively simple synclinal basins separated by tightly folded, east-trending anticlines. Most of these anticlines are complicated by high-angle reverse faults or north-directed thrust faulting (Martin and Callahan, 1978; Callahan and Martin, 1981).

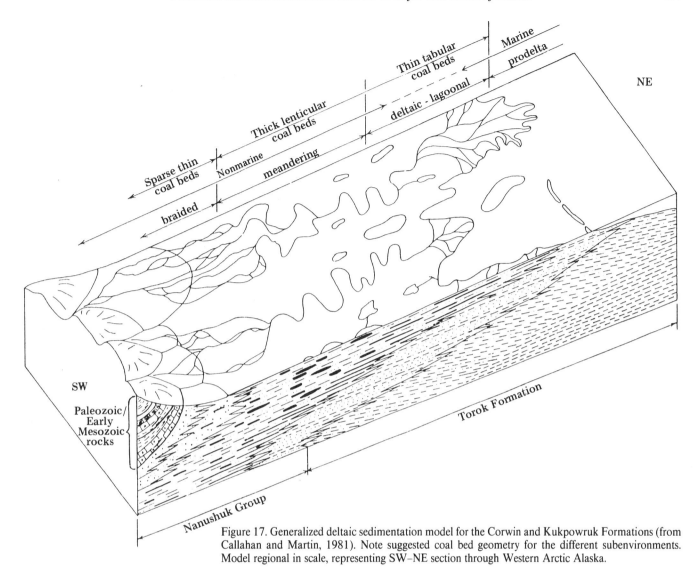

Figure 17. Generalized deltaic sedimentation model for the Corwin and Kukpowruk Formations (from Callahan and Martin, 1981). Note suggested coal bed geometry for the different subenvironments. Model regional in scale, representing SW–NE section through Western Arctic Alaska.

Lower Cretaceous sedimentation on the North Slope reflects the uplift of the Brooks Range orogenic belt and attendant deposition in a marine basin along the north flank of this range. The Lower Cretaceous rocks of the western and central Brooks Range record an abrupt shift from dominant northern sources to southern and southwestern sources. The Brooks Range orogenic belt consists of multiple allochthonous sheets or major thrust sequences of mafic igneous and sedimentary rock from which the Corwin delta sediments of the Nanushuk Group were derived. The allochthons formed by underthrusting as a result of a counterclockwise rotation of the Arctic Alaska plate that moved relatively southward and was obducted by oceanic crust at a south-dipping subduction zone (Mull, 1979).

Downwarping and sedimentation appear to have taken place concurrently with, and probably as a result of the thrust faulting accompanying the uplift of the mountain range to the south. The thermal maturity of the rocks suggests a greater depth of burial, uplift, and erosion in the Foothills than in the Coastal Plain. Parts of the Nanushuk Group rocks have been removed by erosion, especially in the Foothills belt and the eastern Arctic Slope. Thus, regional tectonism has greatly affected the ultimate distribution and rank of coal beds between the Foothills and Coastal Plain on the Arctic Slope of northern Alaska (Carter and others, 1977; Martin and Callahan, 1978; and Ahlbrandt, 1979).

Depositional Environments of the Nanushuk Group

Ahlbrandt and others (1979) developed a deltaic sedimentation model, later refined by Callahan and Martin (1981; Fig. 17), to reconstruct depositional environments and facies represented by the Kukpowruk and Corwin Formations. The Nanushuk Group clastic wedge prograded to the north and northeast becoming thinner and increasingly more marine in character away from its sources. Nanushuk Group rocks in the Corwin Bluff area are the oldest and thickest, contain the coarsest material, and have the most nonmarine assemblage of any rocks on the western North Slope. The Torok, Kukpowruk, and coal-bearing Corwin Formations are interpreted as having formed in prodelta, delta-front and delta-plain environments respectively (Ahlbrandt, 1979; Ahlbrandt and others, 1979; Stricker and Roehler, 1981).

Because of the preliminary nature of this deltaic sedimentation model (Fig. 17), interpretations that have been drawn from it should be regarded as tentative and subject to change as further data become available. According to model hypotheses, coals stratigraphically higher in the Corwin Formation may have formed in backswamp areas between stream channels in an upper-delta-plain or floodplain environment, where thick peat accumulations were possible because of the greater channel stability and more prolific plant growth. The relatively lower sulfur content of these coals might suggest isolation from brackish water influences. These stratigraphically higher and thicker coals (up to 7 m thick) tend to thin and split over short distances. Post-depositional tectonism and erosion evidently removed intervals of the upper-delta-plain and alluvial deposits. Numerous coal beds of intermediate thickness (2 to 3 m thick) and continuity (to 10 km) in the middle part of the Corwin Formation may have developed on platforms underlain by abandoned channels and splay deposits in the middle-delta-plain environment. Coals of this transition zone may ultimately prove to have the best commercial potential. The relatively higher sulfur content of the thinner and more discontinuous coals of the lower part of the Corwin Formation may indicate peat deposition in interdistributary bays in the lower (more seaward) part of the delta system that were subjected to periodic exposure to salt and brackish water (Callahan and Martin, 1981; Stricker and Roehler, 1981).

RELATIONSHIP OF PALEOENVIRONMENTAL AND TECTONIC CONTROLS TO ULTIMATE COAL-RESOURCE DEVELOPMENT POTENTIAL

Limited depositional modeling in the Susitna lowland (Beluga and Yentna basins) has resulted in a general improved understanding of the nature of continental fluvial coal deposits of the Tertiary Kenai Group. Constraints related to depositional environments affecting coal formation and character are expected to play an important role in future mine planning and pre-development site investigations. Although structural problems may locally complicate mining, they are not expected to be significant compared to other basins in Alaska. In general, world-class coal mines are possible in the Susitna lowland. Large-scale surface mines (up to 15 million short tons per year production) are planned, and even larger mines are feasible. The coal resource base of this region is not a limiting factor. Because of its strategic location relative to tidewater, it is envisioned that coal fields of the Susitna lowland will serve as a major future source of steam coal for countries in the Far East.

Overall, it is not believed that depositional modeling of the fluvial meandering to paludal deposits of the upper part of the

Tertiary Chickaloon Formation will significantly assist initial future mine planning in the Matanuska Valley. Unraveling the fairly complex geologic structure will be more beneficial in the long term. The geologic structure and limited resource base will severely restrict the size of coal mines in this region. Large-scale operations (more than 1 million short tons per year as used here) are not practical in the Matanuska coal field. The deposits are important, however, because they contain the only known bituminous coals within Alaska that are accessible by railroad.

The chief limiting factor to coal development in the Bering River coal field is the complex geologic structure. A better understanding of the depositional environments of the Tertiary Kushtaka Formation might assist in an improved knowledge of coal character but would probably not greatly support exploration and developmental planning. The complex geologic structure in the field will also severely constrain the size of future mine operations. It is believed that the coal deposits will serve as a source for high quality specialty or metallurgical coal or low-ash carbon raw material.

Improved depositional modeling of the Tertiary continental-fluvial coal-bearing group strata in the Nenana basin should be important for future mine planning in this region. Structure again may be a local complicating factor but, in general, is not expected to be a severe limiting constraint to mine development. The resource base of the Nenana basin will not be a limiting factor to further coal development, although it is not likely that future mine size will exceed 5 million short tons per year. The coal fields of this region will serve as an increasingly important source of steam coal both for Alaska and Pacific-rim nations. Export of coal from the Usibelli Coal Mine, Inc. to South Korea began in December 1984.

The Chignik Bay and Herendeen Bay basins contain many thin (less 2.5 m thick) seams of coal in cyclic nearshore marine and nonmarine deposits of the Upper Cretaceous Chignik Formation that have been mined in previous years. It is believed that both coal bed geometry and resource base may be limiting factors to future development. Coal character and bed thickness in these areas indicate that thick coals with large lateral extent will probably not be encountered in the Cretaceous coal-bearing strata anywhere on the Alaska Peninsula. Thick coal accumulations cannot be expected to occur in inter-outcrop areas if Cretaceous depositional environments were the same everywhere. However, this should not preclude the possibility of developing small mines. Potentially commerical coal in the two areas are found in the interval from the base of the Coal Valley Member of the Chignik Formation upwards to the base of the first massive conglomerate.

The development of a deltaic sedimentation model for the coal-bearing Cretaceous Nanushuk Group rocks of the Northern Alaska fields will eventually lead to a greater understanding of coal character and ultimate development potential for the different facies of the unit. A very tentative interpretation is that coals of intermediate thickness and continuity in the transition zone between upper and lower delta plain deposits may prove to have the best future commercial potential. Thicker coal beds of the upper-delta-plain deposits preliminarily appear to exhibit poor lateral continuity, and coal beds of the lower delta-plain environment seem to be relatively high in sulfur and generally too thin to mine. The coal resource base of the Northern Alaska fields is definitely not a limiting factor to future development. Indeed, they comprise one of the largest coal deposits in the world. The problem of mining in permafrost, reclamation, and transportation will, however, likely be formidable challenges to coal mine development in the Northern Alaska coal fields.

ACKNOWLEDGMENTS

I thank Ross G. Schaff, former State Geologist, Alaska Division of Geological and Geophysical Surveys (DGGS), Anchorage, for his encouragement in producing this paper. Edward G. Sable and Gary D. Stricker of the U.S. Geological Survey, Denver, reviewed the original manuscript and corrected many misinterpretations, oversights and errors of fact. Gary Anderson of NERCO Minerals Company, Fairbanks, allowed the use of proprietary information from unpublished reports on the Chignik Bay and Herendeen Bay coal fields, and Don L. McGee of DGGS permitted the use of an unpublished paper on the same regions. James E. Callahan and Robert B. Sanders, Anchorage consulting geologists, loaned photographs (Fig. 2C and 2F respectively). Michael A. Belowich drafted certain text figures and Karen Pearson gave cartographic assistance.

REFERENCES CITED

Ahlbrandt, T. S., 1979, Introduction to geologic studies of the Nanushuk Group, North Slope, Alaska, *in* Ahlbrandt, T. S., ed., Preliminary geologic, petrologic, and paleontologic results of the study of Nanushuk Group rocks, North Slope, Alaska: U.S. Geological Survey Circular 794, p. 1–4.

Ahlbrandt, T. S., Huffman, A. C., Jr., Fox, J. E., and Pasternak, Ira, 1979, Depositional framework and reservoir-quality studies of selected Nanushuk Group outcrops, North Slope, Alaska, *in* Ahlbrandt, T. S., ed., Preliminary geologic, petrologic, and paleontologic results of the study of Nanushuk Group rocks, North Slope, Alaska: U.S. Geological Survey Circular 794, p. 14–31.

Barnes, F. F., 1951, A review of the geology and coal resources of the Bering River coal field, Alaska: U.S. Geological Survey Circular 146, 11 p.

—— , 1966, Geology and coal resources of the Beluga-Yentna region, Alaska: U.S. Geological Survey Bulletin 1202-C, p. C1-C54, scale 1:250,000, and 1:63,360, 7 sheets.

Barnes, F. F., and Payne, T. G., 1956, The Wishbone Hill district, Matanuska coal field, Alaska: U.S. Geological Survey Bulletin 1016, 88 p.

Bird, K. J., and Andrews, Jack, 1979, Subsurface studies of the Nanushuk Group, North Slope, Alaska, *in* Ahlbrandt, T. S., ed., Preliminary geologic, petrologic, and paleontologic results of the study of Nanushuk Group rocks, North Slope, Alaska: U.S. Geological Survey Circular 794, p. 32–41.

Brosge, W. P., and Tailleur, I. L., 1971, Northern Alaska petroleum province, *in* Cram, I. H., ed., Future petroleum provinces of the United States—Their geology and potential: American Association of Petroleum Geologists Memoir 15, v. 1, p. 68–99.

Bruhn, R. L., and Pavlis, T. L., 1981, Late Cenozoic deformation in the Matanuska Valley, Alaska; three-dimensional strain in a forearc region: Geological Society of America Bulletin, v. 92, no. 5, p. 282–293.

Buffler, R. T., and Triplehorn, D. M., 1976, Depositional environments of continental Tertiary deposits, central Alaska, *in* Miller, T. P., ed., Recent and ancient sedimentary environments in Alaska: Anchorage, Alaska Geological Society, p. H1–H10.

Burk, C. A., 1965, Geology of the Alaska Peninsula—Island arc and continental margin: Geological Society of America Memoir 99, 250 p.

Calderwood, K. W., and Fackler, W. C., 1972, Proposed stratigraphic nomenclature for Kenai Group, Cook Inlet basin, Alaska: American Association of Petroleum Geologists Bulletin, v. 56, no. 4, p. 739–754.

Callahan, J. E., and Martin, G. C., 1981, Coal occurrences of the Nanushuk Group, western Arctic Alaska—An update, *in* Rao, P. D., and Wolff, E. N., Focus on Alaska's coal '80, Alaska Coal Conference, 2nd, Fairbanks, October 21-23, 1980, Proceedings: University of Alaska Mineral Industry Research Laboratory Report 50, p. 32–50.

Capps, S. R., 1927, Geology of the upper Matanuska Valley, Alaska: U.S. Geological Survey Bulletin 791, 88 p.

Carter, R. D., Mull, C. G., Bird, K. J., and Powers, R. B., 1977, The petroleum geology and hydrocarbon potential of Naval Petroleum Reserve No. 4, North Slope, Alaska: U.S. Geological Survey Open-file Report 77-475, 61 p.

Clardy, B. I., 1978, Stratigraphy of the Matanuska-Susitna area, northeastern Cook Inlet basin, Alaska: Louisiana Land and Exploration Company, Western Division, Denver, unpublished industry report, 15 p.

Conwell, C. N., 1972, Alaskan coals: Society of Mining Engineers, American Institute of Mining Engineers Transactions, v. 252, no. 3, p. 279–282.

Conwell, C. N., Triplehorn, D. M., and Ferrell, V. M., 1982, Coals of the Anchorage Quadrangle, Alaska: Alaska Division of Geological and Geophysical Surveys Special Report 17, 8 p., scale 1:250,000, 4 sheets.

Dall, W. H., and Harris, G. D., 1892, Correlation papers—Neocene: U.S. Geological Survey Bulletin 84, p. 232–268.

Detterman, R. L., 1978, Interpretation of depositional environments in the Chignik Formation, Alaska Peninsula, *in* Johnson, K. M., ed., The United States Geological Survey in Alaska, accomplishments during 1977: U.S. Geological Survey Circular 772-B, p. B62–B65.

Detterman, R. L., Reiser, H. N., Brosgé, W. P., and Dutro, J. T., Jr., 1975, Post-Carboniferous stratigraphy, northeastern Alaska: U.S. Geological Survey Professional Paper 886, p. 37–39.

Dickson, R. K., 1981, Uranium mineralization in the Nenana coal field, Alaska, *in* Short notes on Alaskan geology: Alaska Division of Geological and Geophysical Surveys Geologic Report 73, p. 37–42.

Fisher, C. A., and Calvert, W. R., 1914, Geology of the Bering River field and its relations to coal mining conditions, *in* Report on coal in Alaska for use in the United States Navy: 63rd Congress, 2nd Session, House of Representatives Document 876, p. 29–50.

Gates, G. O., 1944, Part of Herendeen Bay coal field, Alaska: U.S. Geological Survey Open-file Report 2, 5 p.

Grantz, Arthur, 1964, Stratigraphic reconnaissance of the Matanuska Formation in the Matanuska Valley, Alaska: U.S. Geological Survey Bulletin 1181-I, 33 p.

Hackett, S. W., 1976, Speculative tectonic evolution of the Cenozoic Shelikof trough, southcentral Alaska, *in* Short notes on Alaskan geology—1976: Alaska Division of Geological and Geophysical Surveys Geologic Report 51, p. 13–17.

—— , 1977, Gravity survey of Beluga basin and adjacent area, Cook Inlet region, southcentral Alaska: Alaska Division of Geological and Geophysical Surveys Geologic Report 49, 26 p.

Hartman, D. C., Pessel, G. H., and McGee, D. L., 1972, Preliminary report on the stratigraphy of the Kenai Group, upper Cook Inlet, Alaska: Alaska Division of Geological and Geophysical Surveys Special Report 5, 11 plates.

Hite, D. M., 1976, Some sedimentary aspects of the Kenai Group, Cook Inlet, Alaska, *in* Miller, T. P., ed., Recent and ancient sedimentary environments in

Alaska: Anchorage, Alaska Geological Society, p. 11–123.

Kelly, T. E., 1963, Geology and hydrocarbons in Cook Inlet basin, Alaska, *in* Childs, O. E., and Beebe, B. W., eds., Backbone of the Americas—A symposium: American Association of Petroleum Geologists Memoir 2, p. 278–296.

Kirschner, C. E., and Lyon, C. A., 1973, Stratigraphic and tectonic development of Cook Inlet petroleum province, *in* Pitcher, M. G., ed., Arctic geology: American Association of Petroleum Geologists Memoir 19, p. 396–407.

Mancini, E. A., 1977, Alaska Peninsula late Cretaceous fore-arc deposition: American Association of Petroleum Geologists Bulletin, v. 61, no. 5, p. 811.

Mancini, E. A., Deeter, T. M., and Wingate, F. H., 1978, Upper Cretaceous arc-trench gap sedimentation on the Alaska Peninsula: Geology, v. 6, no. 7, p. 437–439.

Martin, G. C., 1925, The outlook for petroleum near Chignik, *in* Brooks, A. H., and others, eds., Mineral resources of Alaska, report on progress of investigations in 1923: U.S. Geological Survey Bulletin 773, p. 209–213.

Martin, G. C., and Callahan, J. E., 1978, Preliminary report on the coal resources of the National Petroleum Reserve in Alaska: U.S. Geological Survey Open-file Report 78-1033, 23 p.

McConkey, W., Lane, D., Quinlan, C., Rahm, M., and Rutledge, G., 1977, Alaska's energy resources; final report, phase 1, v. 2, Inventory of oil, gas, coal, hydroelectric and uranium resources: Alaska Division of Energy and Power Development, Anchorage, p. 133–216.

McGee, D. L., 1979, Depositional environments and resource potential of Cretaceous coal-bearing strata at Chignik Bay and Herendeen Bay, Alaska Peninsula: Alaska Division of Geological and Geophysical Surveys unpublished report, 41 p.

McGee, D. L., and Emmel, K. S., 1979, Alaska coal resources: Alaska Division of Geological and Geophysical Surveys unpublished report, 26 p.

Merritt, R. D., and Belowich, M. A., 1984, Coal geology and resources of the Matanuska Valley, Alaska: Alaska Division of Geological and Geophysical Surveys Report of Investigations 84-24, 64 p., scale 1:100,000, 3 plates.

Miller, D. J., 1951, Preliminary report on the geology and oil possibilities of the Katalla district, Alaska: U.S. Geological Survey Open-file Report 50, 66 p.

——, 1961, Geology of the Katalla district, Gulf of Alaska Tertiary province, Alaska: U.S. Geological Survey Open-file Report 206, scale 1:96,000, 2 sheets.

Moore, J. C., 1974, The ancient continental margin of Alaska, *in* Burk, C. A., and Drake, C. L., eds., The geology of continental margins: New York, Springer-Verlag, p. 811–815.

Moore, J. C., and Connelly, William, 1977, Mesozoic tectonics of the southern Alaska margin, *in* Talwani, Manik, and Pitman, W. C., eds., Island arcs, deep sea trenches, and back arc basins: American Geophysical Union, Maurice Ewing Series, v. 1, p. 71–82.

Mull, C. G., 1979, Nanushuk Group deposition and the late Mesozoic structural evolution of the central and western Brooks Range and Arctic Slope, *in* Ahlbrandt, T. S., ed., Preliminary geologic, petrologic, and paleontologic results of the study of Nanushuk Group rocks, North Slope, Alaska: U.S. Geological Survey Circular 794, p. 5–13.

Paige, Sidney, and Knopf, Adolph, 1907, Reconnaissance in the Matanuska and Talkeetna basins, *in* Brooks, A. H. and others, eds., Mineral resources of Alaska, report on progress of investigations in 1906: U.S. Geological Survey Bulletin 314, p. 104–115.

Payne, T. G., 1945, Stratigraphic and structural features, lower Matanuska Valley coal field, Alaska [abs.]: Economic Geology, v. 40, no. 1, p. 93.

——, 1955, Mesozoic and Cenozoic tectonic elements of Alaska: U.S. Geological Survey Miscellaneous Geologic Investigations Map I-84, scale 1:5,000,000.

Plafker, George, 1971, Possible future petroleum resources of Pacific-margin Tertiary basin, Alaska, *in* Cram, I. H., ed., Future petroleum provinces of United States—Their geology and potential: American Association of Petroleum Geologists Memoir 19, v. 1, p. 120–135.

Resource Associates of Alaska, Inc., 1980, Literature review and status of Chignik and Herendeen Bay coal fields, southern Alaska Peninsula: Unpublished industry report, 15 p.

Sable, E. G., 1956, New and redefined Cretaceous formations in western part of northern Alaska: American Association of Petroleum Geologists, v. 40, no. 11, p. 2635–2643.

Sanders, R. B., 1976, Geology and coal resources of the Bering River field, *in* Rao, P. D., and Wolff, E. N., eds., Focus on Alaska's coal '75: Alaska Coal Conference, 1st, Fairbanks, October 15-17, 1975, Proceedings: Fairbanks, University of Alaska Mineral Industry Research Laboratory Report 37, p. 54–58.

Schaff, R. G., and Merritt, R. D., 1984, Coal resources of Alaska: Alaska Division of Geological and Geophysical Surveys Information Circular 17, 9 p.

Smiley, C. J., 1969, Floral zones and correlations of Cretaceous Kukpowruk and Corwin Formations, northwestern Alaska: American Association of Petroleum Geologists Bulletin, v. 53, p. 2079–2093.

Stricker, G. D., and Roehler, H. W., 1981, Deltaic coals and sediments of the Cretaceous Torok, Kukpowruk, and Corwin Formations in the Kokolik-Utukok region, National Petroleum Reserve in Alaska, *in* Rao, P. D., and Wolff, E. N., Focus on Alaska's coal '80, Alaska Coal Conference, 2nd, Fairbanks, October 21-23, 1980, Proceedings: University of Alaska Mineral Industry Research Laboratory Report 50, p. 61.

Vorobik, J. L., Farnstrom, H. E., Cantrell, C. L., Jaworski, M. J., and Beeson, D. C., 1981, Exploration and evaluation of the coal potential of Bristol Bay Native Corporation lands in the Chignik area, Alaska: Resource Associates of Alaska, Inc., unpublished industry report, 5 v.

Wahrhaftig, Clyde, 1958, Lithology and conditions of deposition of the formations of the coal-bearing group in the Nenana coal field: U.S. Geological Survey unpublished report, 93 p.

——, 1965, Physiographic divisions of Alaska: U.S. Geological Survey Professional Paper 482, 52 p.

Wahrhaftig, Clyde, and Birman, J. H., 1954, Stripping-coal deposits on lower Lignite Creek, Nenana coal field, Alaska: U.S. Geological Survey Circular 310, 11 p.

Wahrhaftig, Clyde, and Freedman, Jacob, 1945, Coal deposits in the valley of the Healy River, Alaska: U.S. Geological Survey War Minerals Report, 8 p.

Wahrhaftig, Clyde, Wolfe, J. A., Leopold, E. B., and Lanphere, M. A., 1969, The coal-bearing group in the Nenana coal field, Alaska: U.S. Geological Survey Bulletin 1274-D, p. D1–D30.

Weimer, R. J., 1977, Stratigraphy and tectonics of western coals, *in* Murray, K. D., ed., Geology of Rocky Mountain coal, Proceedings of the 1976 symposium, Golden, Colorado: Colorado Geological Survey Department of Natural Resources, Resource Series No. 1, p. 9–27.

Wheelabrator Coal Services Company, 1983, Assessment of the feasibility and implementation of port and transportation system alternatives for the Bering River coal field; phase 1: Unpublished report prepared for the City of Cordova, Alaska, p. 5.4–5.17.

Wolfe, J. A., Hopkins, D. M., and Leopold, E. B., 1966, Tertiary stratigraphy and paleobotany of the Cook Inlet region, Alaska: U.S. Geological Survey Professional Paper 398-A, 29 p.

Wolfe, J. A., Hopkins, D. M., Leopold, E. B., and Tanai, Toshimasa, 1980, The Miocene Seldovia Point flora from the Kenai Group, Alaska: U.S. Geological Survey Professional Paper 1105, 52 p.

MANUSCRIPT ACCEPTED BY THE SOCIETY APRIL 16, 1986

Typeset by WESType Publishing Services, Inc., Boulder, Colorado
Printed in U.S.A. by Malloy Lithographing, Inc., Ann Arbor, Michigan